# FISHERY SCIENCE
## Its Methods and Applications

## LAST OF THE SALT-BANKERS

The stirring era of the sailing schooners and dory fishermen on the Grand Banks, romantically depicted in Kipling's *Captains Courageous*, has ended for New England fishermen. This shows the last fishermen's race off Boston in 1938. The winning schooner *Bluenose* of Lunenberg, Nova Scotia (right), and the *Gertrude L. Thebaud* of Gloucester, Massachusetts, were the last vessels in the fleet depending wholly on sail. This shows the climax of the race when the two nearly collide as the *Bluenose* crowds to windward of the *Thebaud*.

# FISHERY SCIENCE

## Its Methods and Applications

**GEORGE A. ROUNSEFELL, Ph.D.**

SENIOR RESEARCH BIOLOGIST, BRANCH OF FISHERY
BIOLOGY, FISH AND WILDLIFE SERVICE, UNITED STATES
DEPARTMENT OF THE INTERIOR

**W. HARRY EVERHART, Ph.D.**

ASSISTANT PROFESSOR OF ZOOLOGY, UNIVERSITY OF
MAINE; HEAD, FISHERY RESEARCH AND MANAGE-
MENT DIVISION, MAINE DEPARTMENT OF INLAND
FISHERIES AND GAME

**JOHN WILEY & SONS, INC., NEW YORK**

**LONDON**

Library of Congress Catalog Card Number: 53–7496

# FOREWORD

The past two decades have witnessed unprecedented advances in various fields of applied biology, especially in conservation. Research and management have made great strides in each of the fields of fisheries, wildlife, forestry, and soil conservation. These activities so overlap that widespread improvement in one is often reflected by improved conditions in another. Scientific advances in one may find important application in another. Contrariwise the lack of sound conservation in one branch often affects others adversely. The relations between forest cover and run-off, soil erosion and floods, impoundments and regulated stream flow, certainly have a marked bearing on the fishery resources of a stream. While coastal marshes may be managed specifically for waterfowl and muskrats, the type of management cannot help but profoundly affect oysters, crabs, clams, the young of many species of fishes seeking food and protection in the marshes, and the nursery grounds for shrimp in their younger stages. The type and management practices of agriculture certainly limit the kinds and extent of wildlife dependent upon the specific environment of the farm, and also affect the numbers and kinds of fish in the farm pond and adjoining streams.

One of our greatest needs is the development of a realization that successful conservation is a unity and that each of the specialized fields relating to it represents but a facet of a much larger problem. Marine and freshwater fishery management have developed more or less independently of each other. However, the authors of this book, skillfully blending the great mass of accumulated knowledge, have shown the basic similarity of freshwater and marine fisheries. Combining their rich and varied experiences in these two fields, they have integrated for the first time the most successful and specialized methods employed in the research, conservation, and management of fishery resources regardless of where the fish occur.

Because of the impossibility of estimating most populations of fish by direct enumeration, scientists in this field have developed actuarial techniques that are highly recommended to all students of population dynamics. The authors carefully explain these techniques, showing their application and the necessity of using accurate quantitative methods rather than basing conclusions upon ephemeral and variable data from casual observations, which usually cannot be replicated. This phase of the book should be of great help to administrators, technicians, and scientists in the varied allied fields of biological management—agriculture, wildlife conservation, forestry, or soil conservation. Obviously, the student interested in any phase of aquatic biology—fishery biology, limnology, or oceanography—will find this book indispensable. Biologists, sportsmen, or commercial fishermen interested in fish or wildlife conservation will derive great benefit from the vast fund of information and from the authors' philosophy of scientific management. This splendid pioneering book is not a mere compilation and reference text, but a very readable and realistic summary of the better methods and procedures for solving the problems affecting marine and freshwater fisheries.

CLARENCE COTTAM,
Assistant Director,
Fish and Wildlife Service,
Department of the Interior,
Washington 25, D. C.

*February 20, 1953*

# PREFACE

Fishery management is the application of scientific knowledge concerning fish populations to the problems of obtaining the maximum production of fishery products, whether stated in tons of factory material or in hours of angling pleasure. This knowledge concerns the dynamics of fish populations, their environment, and their responses to variations in their environment, including exploitation by man. This text is not a guide to ichthyology; it is not an account of the biology of fishes, nor is it written to show the application of statistics to biological data. The real purpose is to present the problems that confront the administrator, the research worker, and the student, and to show how to go about solving them.

Modern fishery science had it roots in the work of the pioneer oceanographers such as Sir John Murray and Michael Sars, the work of many famous ichthyologists such as David Starr Jordan, and the works of innumerable marine biologists. An indication of its establishment can be found in the works of T. Wemyss Fulton and C. G. Joh. Petersen in the 1890's in Europe, and in the work of Spencer F. Baird, G. Brown Goode, and Charles G. Atkins of the old U. S. Fish Commission in the 1880's. Perhaps the most conspicuous milestone, and the first extensive work of modern character, was the monumental volume entitled, *Fluctuations in the Great Fisheries of Northern Europe* by Johan Hjort in 1914. In the United States pioneers of modern fishery management were Charles H. Gilbert, George C. Embody, James G. Needham, John O. Snyder, and William C. Kendall. In the United States and Canada an increasing number of colleges and universities are offering courses in fishery management. Many more include limnology, ichthyology, and other subjects related to fisheries. Numerous marine and freshwater laboratories on both coasts, the Great Lakes, and minor lakes are maintained by federal and state governments, state and endowed universities, and private foundations. They extend from St. Johns, Newfoundland, to Miami, Florida, and westward to Texas; from Ketchikan, Alaska, south to La Jolla, California. Hundreds of new multiple-purpose reservoirs and hundreds of thousands of farm ponds have created a great need for fishery management throughout the interior states and provinces. Despite the great and growing need there is no adequate textbook. There are textbooks in many allied sciences—limnology, oceanography, ichthyology—but not in fisheries.

The authors offer no apologies for omissions. The very diversity of the field and the number of sciences employed have doubtless been contributing factors to the present lack of any complete textbook, and they preclude any deviation from the main theme. The senior author has been engaged in research and administration on marine and anadromous fishes of both coasts since 1924. The junior author has specialized in research on freshwater fishes and has also established university courses in fishery management. It is hoped that this book will prove of service to the administrator, who seldom has the time, training, or facilities to obtain guidance from scattered research papers; that it will aid the research worker in defining and solving his problems; and that it will be of value to the student of fisheries in grasping the real problems of fishery management.

We wish to express our gratitude to the colleagues who have aided us in various ways. Carl L. Hubbs has made a critical review of the entire manuscript. Scott H. Bair made many helpful suggestions on fishways and fish screens. Boris Knake reviewed the chapter on fishing gear. Paul S. Galtsoff read several chapters, especially those on limiting factors and pollution. Theodore Widrig checked the material on population estimates. Other chapters were read by Herbert W. Graham, Leslie W. Scattergood, Howard A. Schuck, John Glude, Victor L. Loosanoff and Clyde C. Taylor. Jennie Boynton and Velma Rounsefell gave generously of their time in preparation of the manuscript. Nan Everhart and Robert Rupp were particularly helpful in the construction of the index.

We would like to thank the Department of Inland Fisheries and Game of the State of Maine for permission to use the colored plates between pages 212 and 213, which first appeared in *The Fishes of Maine,* published by the Department in 1950.

GEORGE A. ROUNSEFELL
W. HARRY EVERHART

*Orono, Maine*
*February 1, 1953*

# CONTENTS

# INTRODUCTION

The desirability of maintaining good fishing is attested by millions of enthusiastic anglers and hundreds of thousands of commercial fishermen. They know what they want, and it isn't necessary to recite from the *Compleat Angler* of Izaak Walton or Victor Hugo's *Toilers of the Sea* to convince them. Fishermen are considered by some to be prone to exaggeration, but, despite these imputations of some psychological maladjustment, fishermen know what they have seen.

Within the span of one lifetime they have watched watercourses dry up from deforestation and soil erosion. Huge dams have halted the hordes of shad and salmon. Millions of gallons of untreated sewage have closed miles of clam flats and oyster reefs. Industrial wastes have suffocated stream fishes and blanketed their spawning beds. Only by constant improvement of gear and vessels, and longer and longer voyages, have the seas continued to yield a livelihood.

In this book we have not endeavored to recite these evils. They are self-evident. Rather an attempt has been made to discuss the causes of low abundance, how environmental factors (including man) affect the aquatic resources, and how one solves the problems of restoration and maintenance of good fishing.

The first chapter clarifies the sometimes hazy thinking concerning research. Research is a mental process designed to produce knowledge; it is most successful when conducted along orderly lines.

Each population of fishes at any given stage of its life history occupies a particular ecological niche. Many populations must have taken a long time in adapting themselves to the niches they now occupy. It should be emphasized that living things are plastic. Different populations of the same species have become adapted to different ecological niches. An excellent illustration is furnished by the sockeye salmon of the Fraser River. The salmon that must swim upriver to the headwaters in northern British Columbia enter the river early and well provided with fat to furnish the necessary energy. Those that enter the lower tributaries run later and do not contain fat in the quantities that would be essential for the longer journey. Those that

1

spawn in the Pitt River are much larger than the average (Ricker 1950). Smaller fish would find it very difficult to dig out spawning redds in the coarse rubble and small boulders of the Pitt. The young of those that spawn in the main stream below Harrison rapids go immediately to sea without the customary sojourn in a lake. The eggs of this population are very large, presumably to furnish the large fry necessary for the more strenuous conditions to which they are

FIG. 1   Fly fishing for sea-run Atlantic salmon (*Salmo salar*) on the Narraguagus River in Maine. (Credit: Robert Elliot, Maine Development Commission)

subjected. Without a grasp of the significance of habitat adaptations the student may fail to realize the complexity of the problems of maintaining a fishery.

Part II deals with fish populations. The student of fishery science should have knowledge of what fish populations are—how they wax and wane in abundance—how one goes about determining their size and their reaction to exploitation—before he delves into the particular. This approach is by analysis rather than synthesis, in keeping with the best traditions of fishery science which has developed largely in the field, not in the laboratory. A fish population—like a swarm of bees—is as much a biological entity as the individuals that compose it. In beginning with populations one comes to realize the need for, and use of, much of the more detailed material that follows. The age of fish for example is of great value in making accurate estimates of population size.

From the outset it is apparent that one cannot evaluate without the use of quantitative measures continuous population changes. Indeed, the theme that is emphasized throughout is the quantitative nature of fishery science. In applying statistical methods to biological problems one must never lose sight of the need for common sense. Statistics are a very useful tool, but a gardener does not display his tools. He sharpens them, uses them, then puts them out of sight. When necessary to explain how a problem can be solved through the use of statistics, the method is shown, but with no attempt to delve into statistical theory which is adequately covered in numerous texts.

Fish ponds are furnishing an ever-increasing amount of sport and fresh protein. A pondful of fish is just as valuable as a deep freeze stocked with meat. Acre for acre a pond produces more fish than land produces beef. Although over a million fish ponds have been constructed within the past few years, this number will increase for a long time. The growing of fish crops is entirely feasible, but there are many problems, especially those of maintaining balanced populations.

One of the chief means of management is through modification of the means, times, places, and efficiency of catching fish. A very essential part of the equipment of the biologist, the administrator, or the fisherman is a thorough knowledge of the characteristics of each type of fishing gear.

Many types of gear are adapted to fishing for only one or two species. Some fish only in certain situations. A few, like the otter trawl and purse seine, are adapted to a wide range of conditions. Some take all sizes of fish; others are highly selective. All of these characteristics are important in the management of fisheries.

Fish are subjected to many manmade hazards, including dams, power and irrigation diversions, and pollution. As our civilization advances in complexity these hazards tend to increase. The protection of migrating fish against dams and water diversions has assumed increasing importance as more dams are built for flood control, power, and irrigation. The use and proper design of fishways and screens have been little understood. This lack of knowledge has resulted in the waste of millions of dollars in the construction of inadequate facilities. The abatement of pollution must depend to a large extent on the ability to measure quantitatively its effects.

The section on the improvement of habitat as presented applies almost exclusively to species that inhabit small lakes or streams. The enormous areas of the larger lakes and seas preclude carrying on the

intensive management possible in the smaller water areas. That such
will always be the case is not necessarily true. There is a large and
very productive littoral zone along our coasts in which the fauna
can be influenced profoundly by man. Thus it has been discovered
that the success or failure of spawning of the blue crab in Chesapeake

Fig. 2  The laboratory (left) and residence of the U. S. Fish and Wildlife Service
at Woods Hole, Massachusetts; completed in 1885 this is the oldest marine fishery
station in the United States. Research is being actively conducted on fish and
shellfish of the North Atlantic aided by the research vessel *Albatross III*. (Credit:
U. S. Fish and Wildlife Service)

Bay is greatly influenced by the volume of discharge of the James
River. Engineers already have planned for this river large dams that
eventually will control the seasonal flow.

The productivity of great areas of shallow seas behind the sand
barriers along the Atlantic Coast is influenced by changing salinities
and currents caused by channel dredging. The effect of marsh burning
and marsh draining on the productivity of the shrimp populations has
not been assessed.

Although not yet proved to be economically advantageous, it has
been shown in Scotland that the fauna and flora of large arms of the
sea respond to water fertilization. Even the vegetation of the littoral

zone is influenced by man's cropping of seaweeds and cutting of enormous beds of kelp.

The management of marine fisheries through the control of undesirable species is not without interesting possibilities. Thus for the vast area of the Great Lakes control of the sea lamprey is being attempted.

The tagging of fish has been accorded major attention because it offers one of the best means of obtaining accurate data on speed and direction of migrations, age, growth, boundaries between populations, and the survival of hatchery fish. Because of an unwarranted notion that tagging is a simple process much research money has been wasted on ill-conceived marking experiments. Properly executed experiments provide an insight into life history problems that can be obtained in no other way.

The age and growth rate are two attributes of fish populations of prime importance in estimating the numbers in the population and their response to various types of management measures.

Knowledge of how and why a population varies in abundance, and of man's responsibility for these changes through fishing, pollution, engineering works, and modifications of environment have all been depicted. There remains the question of how man can influence the size and growth of fish populations for his benefit. This is the function of the section, Managing Natural Populations.

Many think that man can continue to flaunt all biological tenets and still retain good fishing merely by continuous rearing and stocking of young fish. This is similar to the faith shown by some in homeopathy. It matters not what causes the ailment—just take continuous doses of little sugar-coated pills. There are some situations that can be aided by artificial propagation, but management of fisheries through hatcheries alone has long been proved futile. Because of this misunderstanding of the proper function of stocking and of the results that can be attained, we have devoted a chapter to the subject. Used as one of the tools of management—used only where it can show results—artificial propagation will always have its place in fisheries.

There are a variety of ways in which fishing can be regulated; however each restriction has certain consequences. One must understand both the effect of a regulation and the population to which it is to be applied to appraise its value correctly in any particular situation.

The final section emphasizes the need for continued and expanded research if the waters are to yield the vast harvest of which they are capable. There is need for expansion of the fisheries to bolster the low protein diet that prevails in vast sections of the world. In the

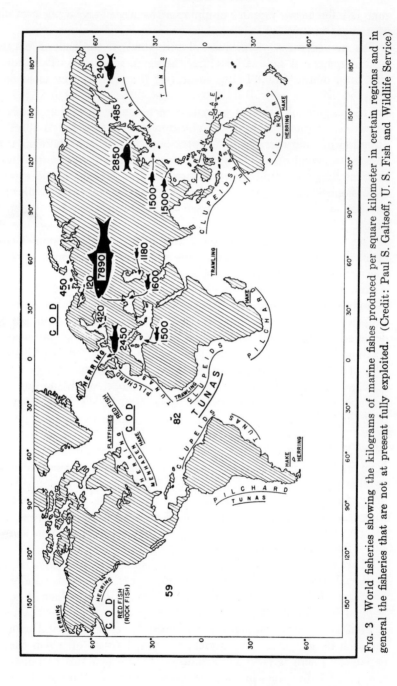

Fig. 3 World fisheries showing the kilograms of marine fishes produced per square kilometer in certain regions and in general the fisheries that are not at present fully exploited. (Credit: Paul S. Galtsoff, U. S. Fish and Wildlife Service)

face of increasing human populations the need is growing ever more pressing.

In many inland areas in undeveloped countries the lack of transport, and of refrigeration and handling facilities, leave but one solution— the fish pond. However, the majority of mankind live close to the sea. A critical appraisal of the possibilities for expansion in the harvest of marine fisheries was made by Galtsoff (1952) in an address before the Second Centennial Academic Conference of Northwestern University. He shows that a very large proportion of the present annual world catch of 37 billion pounds is made in rather small areas, some of which are fished very intensely.

In Figure 3 (kindly supplied by Dr. Paul S. Galtsoff) is shown the present annual catch in kilograms per square kilometer for various areas. The catches range from 59 kilos in the Pacific Ocean to 7890 kilos in the extremely productive Sea of Azov. As the chart shows, there are large areas, especially in the Southern Hemisphere, capable of great expansion.

The greatest share of the world catch (about 37 per cent) is comprised of fishes belonging to the family Clupeidae—herrings, sardines or pilchards, menhaden, etc. These fish feed directly on plankton organisms, and it is not therefore surprising that they are relatively so abundant. The Japanese were the first to attempt large-scale exploitation of the larger pelagic species, tunas, marlins, etc., in the vast midocean. They developed the "flagline" gear which has made this possible. Only experience will tell whether the midoceans can yield a large sustained catch.

**References**

Galtsoff, Paul S.
  1952. Food resources of the ocean. In *World population and future resources.* Edited by Paul K. Hatt. American Book Co.: 108–118.
Ricker, William E.
  1950. Cycle dominance among the Fraser sockeye. *Ecology 31* (1):6–26.

# PART I · ROAD TO MANAGEMENT

# 1 · HOW DO WE PRODUCE KNOWLEDGE?

## 1·1 Difference between data and evidence

The greatest stumbling block in the path of successful management has always been lack of facts. But how many times has a promising lead—hailed as the final solution—been hurriedly translated into action, only to fall far short of the goal? How long will it be before administrators and biologists alike stop reaching conclusions from casual observation—before they subject their hypotheses to critical and objective tests—instead of proclaiming them as established facts?

Few biologists fully realize the difference between data and evidence. The gathering of *facts*, so often referred to (calling an organization a *fact-gathering* agency has become a traditional fetish), is not a simple procedure like picking apples. That is, not unless one is willing to define *fact* in the narrow sense and consider every new temperature record and every length of a specimen duly recorded as a new *fact*. The gathering and filing of data is not, in itself, research. It is but one of the many tasks to be performed in accomplishing a piece of research. The gathering of data bears about the same relationship to research as ploughing does to farming, yet many research projects, "so-called," never get beyond the ploughing stage. We have seen many a laboratory with rows of shining steel filing cabinets proudly bulging with carefully filed sheaves of *data*, collected with fanatical zeal and now doomed to gather dust until someone advances a hypothesis that they may be useful in testing.

One does not build a house by ordering all of the odds and ends of lumber, plumbing, and hardware that can be bought with the money available, by piling them all neatly on the lot, and then, money exhausted, by reclining on the lot admiring the neat piles. Yet that is precisely the manner in which a large share of our *research* money has been squandered.

Why and how do such situations arise? They arise because pressure is put on the administrator to do something to improve fishing.

8

He obtains a sum of money that must be spent within one year or at most two fiscal years. He hires a biologist and admonishes him to go forth and quickly solve the problems.

The problem or problems are not defined. It is not always known for certain that a problem exists; it is taken for granted that a problem must exist, the solution of which will improve fishing, and that data gathering will solve it. Since it is not known what data may be needed vast quantities of unrelated data are gathered. Too often a shotgun is used when a rifle is needed.

A more sane approach demands that research be directed toward specific well-defined objectives; that, regardless of the out-worn idea that anything and everything may be of value, collecting be confined to data that will bear on the problem in hand. It demands that not all of the money and energy be used in collecting, but that an adequate share be allowed for analysis, and that, as a final step, a report be prepared that will present the scientific evidence supporting or disproving whatever hypothesis was being tested.

Basically, research is a mental operation. Few mental operations are performed systematically; few people understand the necessity for the strict mental discipline involved in research. In the past, research has too often been merely a haphazard probing in the hope of stumbling upon truth, in about the same manner as two persons might collide in a dark room.

## 1·2   Fields of research

Before we discuss how research is conducted, the fields of research should be mentioned. These are:

**Basic research.** *Fundamental research.* This is the theoretical experimentation, analysis or exploration of the general principles governing natural or social phenomena. Without fundamental research all other types would eventually perish. Fundamental research has prospered chiefly in the universities, to a much more limited extent in governmental research, and even less in industrial research.

*Background research.* This is the systematic collection, observation, organization and presentation of facts using known principles to reach objectives that are clearly defined before the research is undertaken to provide a foundation for subsequent research or to provide standard reference data. This includes a great deal of the work of the Weather Bureau and the Geological Survey. A large share of the research needed in conservation is also of this character, including most of the lake and stream surveys and habitat surveys. It does not solve any problems, but it is often a necessary concomitant of other types of research, and often serves to point out problems requiring solution.

**Applied research.** This is the extension of basic research to a specific application, which may involve the devising of a specified novel product, process, technique, or device, or the solution of a particular problem. The major share of our fish and wildlife investigations fall into this category, as most of them rely on already established principles to solve particular questions.

**Developmental research.** This is the adaptation of research findings to experimental or demonstration purposes, such as the experimental production and testing of models, devices, equipment, materials, procedures, and processes. Developmental research differs from applied research in that it is done on products, processes, techniques, or devices previously discovered or invented. Thus work on improving the type and design of fishways is developmental research.

## 1·3 Conduct of research

To return now to the conduct of research, one must distinguish between "planning *for* research" and "planning *of* research." Really productive research must be "planned *for*" in that competent staff, adequate facilities, and proper equipment must be obtained. The "planning *of*" research is quite a different matter. *Applied* or *developmental research* can be scheduled and planned, but the planning of *fundamental* research is more difficult. It depends on so many intangibles that results will not always be forthcoming. Great discoveries have usually stemmed from the combination of brilliant minds and the proper environmental climate. This climate has most often been provided by our universities. The syphoning off of much of the best research talent from the universities to great industrial and governmental research bureaus is therefore of grave national concern. It is doubtful whether men like Urey, Fermi, Einstein, or Oppenheimer would have made their discoveries divorced from the university atmosphere.

## 1·4 Steps in solving a problem

The solution of a problem through research consists of several steps. A simplified version is as follows:

**Orientation or awareness** that a problem exists. In basic research the problem is often suggested by the scientist. In applied or developmental research ideas for programs or projects often stem from the clientele served. In fact, program planning for these types of research often provides means for facilitating the flow of suggestions.

**Exploration.** This includes a diagnosis of the possible elements that are causing the trouble, the collection of data and their analysis, to discover what problems may be involved.

**Hypothesis or explanation.** The problems are examined, and a hypothesis is developed to explain them.

An *idea* may be a vagrant thought. All progress, however, starts as an idea. Cherish it; develop it; if it has merit it may form the basis for a hypothesis.

A *hypothesis* is an unproved conjecture or supposition postulated in order to explain provisionally certain facts and to guide in the investigation of others. Sometimes it is called a *working hypothesis* to indicate that it is merely assumed in order to aid in the search for facts.

**Design.** Here a test of the hypothesis is designed and any techniques are developed that will be required in making the test.

**Test.** The hypothesis is tested to determine whether it is or is not a correct explanation of the observed phenomena.

**Communication.** The hypothesis and the results of the test are presented with the data so that others may understand and judge the validity of the solution. Unfortunately, this step is very often omitted. The solution is put into practice without being subjected to scientific criticism. In other cases the results are given without sufficient data to permit anyone to form an accurate estimate of their reliability. Such practices, almost without exception, eventually lead to arbitrary and unwarranted action.

**Trial.** The solution is now used in a limited or pilot area under close observation in order to confirm its correctness. This step is likewise often omitted, and its omission likewise often causes great trouble.

**Use.** The solution is now released for general use.

## 1·5   Interdependence of sciences

**Specialists and teamwork.** A large problem may involve a great many lesser problems that must each be solved in order to solve the larger problem. These so-called minor problems may be minor to the particular problem presented but may of themselves be very difficult to solve. The failure to solve a subsidiary problem may either prevent a solution of the main problem or render its solution obscure and subject to doubt.

For example, the separation of biological races of a species has often been made difficult because of the lack of a single character whose quantitative estimation showed a clear-cut difference between the two or more populations. The failure to solve the subsidiary mathematical problem—how to compare simultaneously more than one character— blocked the solution of the main problem. The recent application of discriminant functions to this problem is now permitting headway on the main problem (Mather 1946).

Here you will note that the solution of an important biological problem was awaiting the solution of a problem in mathematics. As knowledge expands it becomes less and less possible for one man to be conversant with many fields and more and more necessary that research be carried out on a teamwork basis. The great industrial research laboratories have long been fully aware of this truth, but it is not yet fully implanted in governmental and university circles.

A research team must have specialists. They may not all be actually performing active research, but they must be available to suggest means of dealing with matters touching on their field. The leader of the team may or may not be a specialist in a particular field, but he must know how to organize the team effectively. He must so channel the work that the energies of the available force are not dissipated on barren but interesting sidelines, but yet no promising sideline is neglected.

## 1·6   Solving a specific problem

Let us follow the various steps in solving a typical fishery problem. The salmon run of a particular river falls to a mere fraction of its former abundance. The industry becomes worried and appeals for aid. We are now *aware* that a problem exists.

The second step, *exploration*, follows. In order to diagnose the trouble we collect a mass of data showing how many fish were caught, where they were caught, and the amount of fishing effort required to catch them. We also collect data on environmental changes, past records of temperature, rainfall, floods, obstructions to free migration, etc. In order to aid in interpreting these data we also study the age composition of the population. However, we soon discover, as in any research problem, that we cannot make progress until the *field* is clearly defined. What are the *boundaries* of the problem? Fortunately, previous research has shown that this species of salmon returns with a very slight amount of straying to its natal river to spawn. These previous researches were *communicated* (stage 6) in a comprehensive, scientific manner so that we are able to study the evidence on which the hypothesis was formed. We decide that the hypothesis is correct and that we can therefore limit the boundaries of our problem to the salmon population of the one river.

We now have the basic data necessary in order to proceed to step 3 in which we must attempt to explain the cause of the trouble, which was the great decline in abundance. The *hypothesis* is advanced that the decline was caused chiefly by overfishing.

The fourth step is to *design* a test for a hypothesis. The test designed was an index of relative abundance based on the catch of a unit of fishing gear over a definite unit of time.

The *test* was made and showed a significant decline in the catch per unit of fishing effort which was ascribed to overfishing.

The results, together with the supporting evidence, were now communicated as step 6.

This is usually the end of a piece of research, but in this case doubt soon arose as to whether the decline in abundance of the salmon in this river was indeed caused by overfishing or by an obstruction in the river that, at certain water levels, appeared to prevent a large share of the salmon that escaped through the fishery from reaching their spawning grounds. It was now perceived that the cause of the doubt whereby diverse conclusions could be drawn from the same data was the lack of a technique (stage 4) whereby one could abandon the various unsatisfactory measures of relative abundance and determine accurately the true size of the population.

By making several modifications of a new technique developed by D. B. DeLury (1947) the total salmon population for each year was estimated (Rounsefell 1949). On account of the availability of these new population parameters it was now possible to restate the first hypothesis on overfishing in a different manner, namely: The size of each year's run depends on the size of the spawning population that produced it.

This hypothesis was tested by determining the regression of population size on the size of the portion of the parent generation that escaped through the fishery. The resulting correlation of 0.7 showed that about 50 per cent of the variation in the size of the runs was caused by variations in the size of the spawning stock.

A *corollary hypothesis* that a portion of the variation in size of the runs could have been caused by the obstruction to migration showed upon being tested that less than 15 per cent of the residual variation, or about 7 per cent of the total variation in the runs, was caused by the obstruction.

## 1·7  Quantitative approach essential

Perhaps you may have noted that in all of the examples used the proof of a hypothesis depended upon the ability to develop adequate quantitative measures of any observed phenomenon and to design tests that would yield positive quantitative answers. Modern research is no longer haphazard groping. It is orderly production of knowledge by subjection of measurable entities to quantitative statistical analysis. Unless you understand the use of statistical methods you cannot adequately evaluate the complex relationships that may exist between the various factors in your problem.

## 1·8   Importance of design

The fundamental approach to a research problem has been stated. Selection of the problem should be followed by collection and analysis of sufficient data to permit the formation of reasonable opinions as to what factors may be causing the trouble. At this point the research often ends, either actually, or figuratively, for, unless some hypotheses can be formed and tested, one may add continually to the mass of data without reaching any valid conclusions.

When sufficient observations have been analyzed to enable the investigator to form a hypothesis (see Section 1·4) he is ready for the fourth step, design. In research, as in almost any line of human endeavor, anxiety to achieve an end in a hurry may greatly delay accomplishment. At this stage one needs to look carefully into the heart of a problem to decide what questions must be answered before progress can be made. Then one must choose the method of approach best suited to the available facilities and personnel.

Seldom is it sufficient to form an opinion based wholly on casual observation of events. At each step a rigorous test should be applied to show whether a certain premise is either true or false, or that the data on hand are insufficient to form any final judgment. Rigorous tests imply quantitative measurements. Do not introduce lightly factors incapable of measurement or based on pure speculation. Subjective reasoning is usually fatal to sound conclusions. That the unwary can easily fall into this trap may be readily confirmed if one but peruses a number of reports, and notes the incidence of conclusions not substantiated by the evidence presented.

## 1·9   Sampling

Sampling is fundamental. Every quantitative measurement is subject to error. These errors cannot be eliminated, but by proper sampling the range within which any measurement will fall can be stated for various degrees of probability.

In sampling a population it is essential to recall that the statistics of the samples taken are only estimates of the parameters of the true population. If a homogeneous population is being sampled, the accuracy with which the parameters are estimated will depend chiefly on the number of samples, always provided that each sample is so taken that all individuals in the population have equal chances for inclusion.

The sizes and numbers of samples depend on several factors. Thus, if a population consists of fish of several age groups, the size of samples may have to be large if it is desired to represent the least abundant age groups within a narrow range of accuracy. For example, suppose that in a sample of 1000 fish 300 are 6-year-olds and 20 are 10-year-olds; then, if $p$ is the proportion of an age group, and $n$ is the total number in the sample, the standard deviation of an age group is $\sqrt{np(1-p)}$. Then:

For 6-year-olds $\quad \sqrt{1000 \times 0.30 \times 0.70} = \sqrt{210} = 14.5$

For 10-year-olds $\quad \sqrt{1000 \times 0.02 \times 0.98} = \sqrt{19.6} = 4.4$

It will be observed that the sample of 1000 then tells us that the true number of 6-year-olds lies between 262.7 and 337.3 with a probability of 0.01, or will fall outside this range in one direction with a probability of 0.005 (14.5 times 2.57 = 37.3). That is, in one sample out of 100 if drawn from the same population as this sample, the mean can be expected to fall outside of this range. This does not mean exactly one out of every hundred drawn, but one out of every hundred if an infinite number of samples are taken.

For the 10-year-olds the range would run from 8.7 to 31.3 for a probability of 0.01. The mean of the 6-year-olds was thus estimated with an accuracy of 12.4 per cent (37.3/300) for a probability of 0.01, but for the same probability the 10-year-olds were estimated with an accuracy of only 56.5 per cent (11.3/20).

Biological data are highly variable, so that the ideal stable population that underlies many assumptions does not exist for any length of time. Populations change through immigration, emigration, recruitment, mortality, and growth. All factors may be active at once. Because of these changes (which may occur continuously or seasonally and may each be independent of the others) it is often of great importance that biological samples be carefully stratified for time. Great attention must be given to seeming minutiae if one is to satisfy the assumptions on which sampling is based. If one violates these assumptions then the statistics of the samples will give biased estimates of the parameters.

## 1·10    Replication

The value of replication should be fully understood. Innumerable experiments have been performed in which several ponds of fish have each been subjected to different treatment in regard to feeding, disease

FIG. 1·1   This illustrates the use of replication in field experiments. Three series of 3 pens each have been built from one bank to the center of Little Falls Stream on the Moosehorn National Wildlife Refuge, to study the effect of planting density of Atlantic salmon parr on survival and on the abundance of food organisms.

treatment, fertilization, or the like. Too often only one pond is subjected to each type of treatment, so that there is no means of determining any experimental error within treatments. Table 1·1 is an exam-

TABLE 1·1

POUNDS OF FISH PER ACRE PRODUCED BY 3 FERTILIZER TREATMENTS

| | |
|---|---|
| Unfertilized (control) | 80 |
| Fertilizer no. 1 | 100 |
| Fertilizer no. 2 | 160 |
| Fertilizer no. 3 | 140 |

ple without replication. Now obviously there is no means of testing the significance of the differences between treatments because one has no information on the variability within treatments. In Table 1·2

TABLE 1·2

POUNDS OF FISH PER ACRE PRODUCED BY 3 FERTILIZER TREATMENTS

| Treatments | Block $A$ | Block $B$ | Totals |
|---|---|---|---|
| Unfertilized (control) | 85 (2) | 70 (4) | 155 |
| Fertilizer no. 1 | 120 (1) | 80 (2) | 200 |
| Fertilizer no. 2 | 130 (4) | 180 (3) | 310 |
| Fertilizer no. 3 | 170 (3) | 120 (1) | 290 |
| Totals | 505 | 450 | 955 |

the treatments are duplicated. The figures in parentheses indicate the distribution of the ponds within blocks.

In the second trial it is possible to obtain an experimental error (Table 1·3).

TABLE 1·3

| Source of Variation | Degrees of Freedom | Sum of Squares | Mean Square | $F$ |
|---|---|---|---|---|
| Between blocks | 1 | 378 | 378 | |
| Between treatments | 3 | 8,109 | 2703 | 2.67 |
| Within treatments (error) | 3 | 3,035 | 1012 | |
| Total | 7 | 11,522 | 1646 | |

This shows that the difference between treatments was of no significance as $F$ was 2.67 whereas an $F$ of 9.28 is required for a probability of 0.05 with the available degrees of freedom (see Section 4·4 for an explanation of the computations).

As the mean square between blocks was less than that within treatments one can ascribe the block difference to error. In this case the error term is (3035 + 378)/4 or a mean square of 8.53. This yields an $F$ of 3.17 which still has no significance. In the first trial one might decide that the treatments showed significant differences, but there is no basis for such a conclusion.

## 1·11   Use of Latin square and other designs

Many types of fishery experiments lend themselves readily to the same factorial designs used in agricultural research. In fact, when sedentary species, such as clams, are dealt with there is apt to be an environmental gradient similar to that often found in soils in working with plants. These designs permit the removal of a large amount of variation that otherwise would have to be treated as experimental error. Also, by their use it is possible to test several factors at one time. This has several advantages. One is the opportunity to obtain information on interaction between factors. Another is the great economy involved. Most experiments are very expensive and cannot be repeated year after year. Also, experiments performed in different years are subjected to different ecological conditions and cannot be compared directly, but only through some standard, which is itself variable. These designs are given fully by Cochran and Cox (1950) and Fisher (1949).

## 1·12  How many observations to collect

Many research programs bog down under an avalanche of data. Collection of data often is easier than its analysis. If it is decided, for instance, that length measurements of the catch are needed to show changes in the size composition, it may be possible to measure 100, 1000, 10,000, or even 100,000 specimens. Common sense alone will rule out the first figure, but what about the last? Many investigations have measured 50,000 fish per year for many years without it ever being known whether 20,000 would yield estimates of the parameters sought falling within the range of accuracy required. This wasteful procedure can be avoided by determining from random sampling of a large series of samples the minimum number of samples needed to yield a satisfactory estimate (Sette 1926).

At the other end of the scale are observations in which the expense per observation is high. This applies especially to observations taken by research ships and to chemical analyses that require painstaking procedures. Here one often cannot obtain a very large number of observations on which to base a determination of the minimum number required. As a general rule, the greater the variability the larger the number that will be needed.

Because of the diurnal and seasonal variability, scattered observations on such factors as water temperature, for instance, are usually of slight value. If but a few can be collected their value may be enhanced if they are taken so as to discount the daily variation. If a continuous series is being taken at one point then scattered temperatures taken elsewhere can be referred to this base to aid in interpreting their meaning. This is shown in Table 1·4.

The temperatures at station 2 have been adjusted to a standard hour of the day (8 A.M.) by reference to the continuous readings from station 1. Their average 348/5 or 69.6 is 3.0° below the 8 A.M. tem-

## TABLE 1·4

| Day | Station 1, °F at 8 A.M. | Station 2 °F | Hour | Station 1 °F | Station 2, Adjusted to 8 A.M., °F | Differences in 8 A.M. Temperatures, Stations 1 and 2, °F |
|---|---|---|---|---|---|---|
| 1 | 70 | 69 | 10 A.M. | 72 | 67 | 3 |
| 2 | 71 | | | | | |
| 3 | 71 | 68 | 8 A.M. | 71 | 68 | 3 |
| 4 | 72 | | | | | |
| 5 | 73 | 74 | 1 P.M. | 77 | 70 | 3 |
| 6 | 75 | | | | | |
| 7 | 72 | | | | | |
| 8 | 73 | 72 | 11 A.M. | 76 | 69 | 4 |
| 9 | 75 | | | | | |
| 10 | 76 | 78 | 3 P.M. | 80 | 74 | 2 |
| | 363 * | 361 | | 376 | 348 | 15 |

* Five days.

perature 363/5, or 72.6° for the same days for station 1. As the station 2 temperature was consistently lower than that of station 1, it can be confidently inferred that the water at station 2 was colder during the ten days covered.

## 1·13 What to collect

This is a perplexing question that does not always have an easy answer. One approach is to collect observations on practically everything susceptible of measurement. Disciples of this school of thought believe that by collecting everything they will be quite certain that at least some of the measures will prove useful. The results of this approach can be viewed in bulky tables of $pH$, methyl orange alkalinity, and so forth that accompany many papers. The fact that these tables are printed in juxtaposition with the text of an investigational report somehow lends validity to the supposition that they have something to do with the conclusions reached. Occasionally they do, but too often they do not.

There has been an observed tendency to choose observations that are easy to take in preference to those that require more trouble or expense. Thus the $pH$ of most unpolluted natural waters is rarely of any moment to fish. Once the acidity or alkalinity of a lake is known the taking of vast numbers of $pH$ observations is usually a waste of time. Because it is easier to take soluble (inorganic) phosphorus than total phosphorus the former is usually taken, the latter more often neglected. It has been shown by many investigators that soluble phosphorus is practically worthless as an indication of the phosphorus cycle or of the amount of phosphorus available; yet it is still presented as a valuable observation.

Much time and expense can be wasted on indiscriminate sampling of plankton. Plankton populations exhibit such wide and such erratic variation that occasional samples usually cannot be interpreted. It is therefore questionable whether plankton samples should be included in the routine lake surveys occupying a short space of time. Intensive sampling over an extended period, on the other hand, may yield data of great value to management.

One test in deciding what to collect is to ask yourself for each item, "What does it mean?," "What is its variability?," "How can the observations be analyzed so as to relate them to the questions to be answered?" Here again, we return to the fundamental requirement of any research program, namely: It must be designed to answer a specific question. If that question is to be decided, affirmatively or negatively, one needs to take data that will have a bearing on the problem. Other data are superfluous and only serve to confuse and to utilize energy that could be spent to greater advantage.

## 1·14   Field versus laboratory experiments

In the laboratory there has been a great tendency among investigators to attempt rigid control of variability among all factors except the one being tested. In the field it is ordinarily impossible to control any of the environmental factors. Borrowing from the laboratory, many investigators attempt to remedy this by controlling the factor they wish to study. Thus a stream is stocked each year for a number of years with the same number of trout (say 10,000) and the results are recorded in trout caught per angling hour or some similar measure. If one examines this procedure closely one finds that the results will show the variability in returns that can be expected from planting 10,000 trout. But what if one had planted 5000 trout, or 20,000?

It is true that if one measures only the trout caught without troubling to measure any of the other factors involved there is little else to do. Under such circumstances there is no way to relate the returns from different years except in terms of the number released. Perhaps this can be better illustrated by the hypothetical example in Table 1·5.

In this example an attempt has been made to determine the best level at which to stock a stream with trout. If the same number of

TABLE 1·5

| Year | Marked Trout Stocked in May | Daily Stream Flow in August, cfs | Total Catch of Marked Trout Plus Estimate of Their Survival in October |
|------|------|------|------|
| 1940 | 8,000 | 16 | 3,200 |
| 1941 | 4,000 | 25 | 2,200 |
| 1942 | 32,000 | 30 | 5,000 |
| 1943 | 2,000 | 5 | 900 |
| 1944 | 16,000 | 10 | 4,100 |
| 1945 | 4,000 | 12 | 2,000 |
| 1946 | 16,000 | 3 | 1,500 |
| 1947 | 2,000 | 20 | 1,300 |
| 1948 | 8,000 | 10 | 3,000 |
| 1949 | 32,000 | 7 | 2,000 |
| Sum | 124,000 | 138 | 25,200 |
| Average | 12,400 | 13.8 | 2,520 |

trout had been planted each year the experiment would indicate the
stream flow yielding the highest return for the particular number
planted but would give no information on the returns to be expected
from releasing greater or lesser numbers. Some notion of the information obtained from the above system can be gained by a simple re-
tabulation of the results (Table 1·6).

TABLE 1·6

| Number Stocked | Number Returned According to Flow | | | | | Sum | Average |
|------|------|------|------|------|------|------|------|
| | 3–8 | 9–14 | 15–20 | 21–27 | 28– | | |
| 2,000 | 900 * | | 1300 | | | 2,200 | 1100 |
| 4,000 | | 2000 | | 2200 * | | 4,200 | 2100 |
| 8,000 | | 3000 | 3200 * | | | 6,200 | 3100 |
| 16,000 | 1500 | 4100 * | | | | 5,600 | 2800 |
| 32,000 | 2000 | | | | 5000 * | 7,000 | 3500 |
| Sum | 4400 | 9100 | 4500 | 2200 | 5000 | 25,200 | |
| Average | 1467 | 3033 | 2250 | 2200 | 5000 | | 2520 |

* Returns from first 5-year period.

If the first 5 years are compared with the second the total numbers
stocked were identical, but the first 62,000 yielded 15,400 returns
against 9800 for the second. However, the stream flow averaged 17.2
cfs during the first period of 5 years and only 10.4 in the second. The
table shows that the returns were some function of both stream flow
and number planted. How can we use this information?

Obviously, if the stream flow cannot be controlled the important fact is the change in survival of trout as the number stocked is increased. The method of determining the expected survival is to compute the multiple regression of the size of returns on stream flow and number planted. See Snedecor (1946) for the method of computation. Then from the multiple regression equation (Table 1·7) one can determine what survival to expect for any stream flow within the range covered by the data, for any number of trout stocked between 2000 and 32,000.

TABLE 1·7

MULTIPLE REGRESSION OF TROUT PRODUCED $Y$, ON TROUT PLANTED $X_1$, AND AUGUST STREAM FLOW $X_2$

$n = 10$   $SX_1 = 124$   $SX_2 = 138$   $SY = 252$   $\bar{x}_1 = 12.4$   $\bar{x}_2 = 13.8$   $\bar{y} = 25.2$

|  | $X_1$ | $X_2$ | $Y$ |
|---|---|---|---|
| $X_1$ $SX_1^2$, $SX_1X_2$, $SX_1Y$ | 2728.0 | 1798.0 | 3844.0 |
| Correction terms | 1537.6 | 1711.2 | 3124.8 |
| $Sx_1^2$, $Sx_1x_2$, $Sx_1y$ | 1190.4 | 86.8 | 719.2 |
| Cycles − correction 0. |  |  |  |
| $\sqrt{Sx_1^2}$, $\sqrt{(Sx_1^2)(Sx_2^2)}$, etc. | 34.502 | 836.639 | 1194.701 |
| $r_{1.2}$, $r_{Y_1}$ |  | 0.104 | 0.602 |
| $X_2$ $SX_2^2$, $SX_2Y$ |  | 2608.0 | 4002.0 |
| Correction terms |  | 1904.4 | 3477.6 |
| $Sx_2^2$, $Sx_2y$ (total) |  | 703.6 | 424.4 |
| Cycles |  | 115.6 | 190.4 |
| $Sx_2^2$, $Sx_2y$ |  | 588.0 | 334.0 |
| $\sqrt{Sx_2^2}$, $\sqrt{(Sx_2^2)(Sy^2)}$ |  | 24.249 | 839.670 |
| $r_{Y_2}$ |  |  | 0.400 |
| $Y$ $SY^2$ |  |  | 7864.0 |
| Correction term |  |  | 6350.4 |
| $Sy^2$ (total) |  |  | 1513.6 |
| Cycles |  |  | 314.6 |
| $Sy^2$ |  |  | 1199.0 |
| $\sqrt{Sy^2}$ |  |  | 34.627 |

$$\beta_{Y_{1.2}} = \frac{r_{Y_1} - r_{Y_2}r_{1.2}}{1 - r_{1.2}^2} = \frac{0.602 - 0.0416}{1 - 0.010816} = \frac{0.5604}{0.989184} = 0.56653$$

$$\beta_{Y_{2.1}} = \frac{r_{Y_2} - r_{Y_1}r_{1.2}}{1 - r_{1.2}^2} = \frac{0.400 - 0.062608}{1 - 0.010816} = \frac{0.337392}{0.989184} = 0.34108$$

$$\hat{Y} = \bar{y} + \beta_{Y1.2}\frac{\sqrt{Sy^2}}{\sqrt{Sx_1^2}}(X_1 - \bar{x}_1) + \beta_{Y2.1}\frac{\sqrt{Sy^2}}{\sqrt{Sx_2^2}}(X_2 - \bar{x}_2)$$

$$= 25.2 + (0.56653)(34.627/34.502)(X_1 - 12.4)$$
$$+ (0.34108)(34.627/24.249)(X_2 - 13.8)$$
$$= 25.2 + 0.56858X_1 - 7.04959 + 0.48706X_2 - 6.72143$$
$$= 11.429 + 0.56858X_1 + 0.48706X_2$$

$R^2 = r_{Y_1}\beta_{Y1.2} + r_{Y_2}\beta_{Y2.1} = (0.602)(0.56653) + (0.400)(0.34108) = 0.4775$

$R = 0.6910$

From Table 1·7 the regression equation is

$$\hat{Y} = 11.429 + 0.56858X_1 + 1.48706X_2$$

in which $\hat{Y}$ = trout caught and survived in hundreds

$X_1$ = trout stocked in thousands

$X_2$ = stream flow in cubic feet per second for August

To determine the returns from stocking various numbers at any particular stream flow substitute in the equation and list as shown in Table 1·8.

TABLE 1·8

| Number Stocked | Number Caught and Survived at Indicated Flows | | | |
|---|---|---|---|---|
| | 5 cfs | 10 cfs | 15 cfs | 20 cfs |
| 2,000 | 1500 | 1744 | (1987) | .... |
| 4,000 | 1614 | 1857 | 2101 | 2344 |
| 8,000 | 1841 | 2085 | 2328 | 2572 |
| 16,000 | 2296 | 2540 | 2783 | 3027 |
| 24,000 | 2751 | 2995 | 3238 | 3482 |
| 32,000 | 3206 | 3449 | 3693 | 3936 |

The list would indicate that the stream has a definite potential productivity and that stocking high numbers is extremely wasteful. Almost as good returns can be gotten from small plantings as from very large. However, the multiple regression coefficient $R$ (Table 1·7) is 0.691 whereas with 3 variables the total correlation coefficient for a probability of 0.05 should be 0.758 for 7 degrees of freedom (10 minus 2 degrees for the two means, minus 1 degree for the 5-year blocks). This means that the returns, within the ranges covered by the data, cannot be predicted with any confidence from stream flow and number

stocked. This does not mean that it makes no difference how many
are stocked. On the contrary, it means that since the survival cannot
be conclusively shown to have a significant relation to the numbers
stocked (within the range of the data) it is just as efficient to stock
smaller numbers.

## References

Cochran, William G., and Gertrude M. Cox
  1950. *Experimental designs.* John Wiley & Sons: 454 pp., New York.
Cottam, Clarence
  1947. Some improvements needed in wildlife research. *J. Wildl. Management
    11* (4):339–347.
  1949. Further needs in wildlife research. *J. Wildl. Management 13* (4):333–341.
DeLury, D. B.
  1947. On the estimation of biological populations. *Biometrics 3* (4):145–167.
Fisher, Ronald A.
  1949. *The design of experiments.* 5 ed. Oliver and Boyd: 242 pp., Edinburgh.
Leonard, Justin W.
  1949. Research man vs. administrator—the research man's viewpoint. *J. Wildl.
    Management 13* (3):237–244.
Lord, Russell F.
  1946. The Vermont "test-water" study. *Vermont Fish and Game Serv., Fish.
    Res. Bull. 2:* 110 pp.
Marr, John C.
  1951. On the use of the terms abundance, availability, and apparent abundance
    in fishery biology. *Copeia,* 1951 (2):163–169.
Mather, K.
  1946. *Statistical analysis in biology.* Interscience Publ.: 267 pp., New York.
    (Page 152 et seq.)
Mottley, Charles M.
  1942. Experimental designs for developing and testing a stocking policy. *7th
    N. Am. Wildl. Conf.:* 224–238.
  1949. The statistical analysis of creel-census data. *Trans. Am. Fish. Soc. 76:*
    290–300.
Ricker, William E.
  1945. Some applications of statistical methods to fishery problems. *Biometrics
    1* (6):73–79.
Rounsefell, George A.
  1949. Methods of estimating total runs and escapements of salmon. *Biometrics
    5* (2):115–126.
Sette, Oscar Elton
  1926. Sampling the California sardine: A study of the adequacy of various
    systems at Monterey. *Bull. Calif. Div. Fish and Game 11* (3):221 pp.
Snedecor, George W.
  1946. *Statistical methods.* 4th ed. Iowa State College Press, Ames.
Steelman, John R.
  1947. Administration for research. *Science and public policy,* vol. 3, Rept. to
    the President. The President's Scientific Research Board: 324 pp.,
    Washington.

# 2 · RELATION OF LIFE HISTORY
# TO MANAGEMENT

## 2·1   Introduction

Successful management must be based on an understanding of the life histories of the species concerned.  There are numerous textbooks and thousands of scattered reports on various phases of the life history of commercial and game species.  We have, therefore, made no attempt to paraphrase them.  However, because there are certain similarities and differences between the life histories of different species that are all-important in determining the amount and kind of management that is possible or profitable, we attempt to point out a few of these salient features.

Some of the points that we consider have an especial bearing on management are: (1) Is the species resident or migratory?  (2) In what types of habitat does it occur and at what stages in its life?  (3) How does it reproduce?  Are the eggs, young, or adults especially vulnerable during the reproductive season?

## 2·2   Degree of movement

This section is entitled Degree of Movement because there are all gradations from species that spend their lives in a few square yards to others that seasonally cover hundreds of miles in well-defined migrations.  These degrees of movement by species may be roughly classified as:

**Sedentary species.**  These include oysters, clams, mussels, abalones, and scallops that, although perhaps able to crawl about like the abalone or flit about like the scallop, must spend their adult stage in a very circumscribed area.

**Resident species.**  These are species that are able to move about, but apparently prefer to confine themselves to a comparatively small area.  Such species often do perform small movements that may be guided by some natural phenomenon.  Examples are:

*Diurnal movements.*  Fish may move vertically up or down between night and day.  In streams trout may move onto the riffle areas to feed during the hours of twilight or dark, but hide in the pools by day. Many species tend to move closer to the shore at night.

*Tidal movements.* One can observe, especially in shallow bays, fishes that follow the rising tide toward the shores, retreating with the ebb.

*Random dispersal.* In lobsters, flatfishes, and other resident fish there may be a tendency for a gradual nondirectional dispersal.

*Seasonal movements.* Many resident species perform short seasonal movements. Cold-water species may occupy an entire lake in winter but dwell in the cooler hypolimnion in summer. Brook trout will seek out "spring holes" and spring-fed tributaries in summer, or at spawning time, but move freely about during other periods. There is in reality a gradation between the seasonal movements of resident species and the longer journeys of annual migrants so that the distinction may not always be clear-cut.

**Developmental migrants.** These include species that change their habitat at some particular stage in their life history. Thus when salmon parr reach a particular stage of development (governed by a combination of factors: size, age, etc.) they tend to hide their parr marks by an overlying coat of silver in their scales. After this preparation they are ready for their downstream journey to the sea, which in extreme cases may be over a thousand miles. This term may perhaps be applied to the waves of young striped bass that move northward from their spawning centers in more southern waters up along the coast of New England as far as the Bay of Fundy. Since these migrations are more pronounced after years of successful spawning, this may perhaps be merely an extreme case of movement engendered by population pressure. Developmental migrants often move a very short distance; young alewives, for instance, may need to move only a few yards from a seaside pond to reach the sea in which they will make most of their growth.

**Annual migrants.** Many species perform regular annual migrations. These may be for feeding, for spawning, or for both. It is not always possible to ascribe a migration to any particular cause, and indeed a migration may result from the interactions of several factors. Examples of annual migrants are mackerel, tuna, and shrimp.

## 2·3 Zones inhabited

The zones inhabited by different fishes need to be understood in order to decide on the type and possible efficacy of management measures. Since some species inhabit more than one zone, either seasonally or at some developmental stage, it is insufficient merely to name the zones.

Instead we present a classification of types of fish according to the zones inhabited. There are exceptions to almost every grouping, both because the species are plastic and because individual habitats vary widely from region to region. Thus the lake trout (*Cristivomer namaycush*) is always thought of as strictly a lake dweller, but in the far North it is reported to be anadromous.

Fig. 2·1 School of menhaden off Jacksonville Beach, Florida, photographed from the air from a height of about 400 feet showing the density of schooling. The photo was made from a small spotting plane employed by the Nassau Fertilizer Co. of Fernandina, Florida. (Credit: Jan Hahn, Woods Hole, Mass.)

If fish are classified by the zones in which they live it will be noted that within each chief type of habitat there are subhabitats or microhabitats. In a stream some species inhabit the pools, others prefer the riffles, and still others seek the small spring-fed tributaries. When necessary some species may adapt themselves to a wide range of conditions; others may perish.

This classification, then, will not fit all species. Perhaps, if one were to go into sufficient detail one might find almost as many types as species. However, a general classification is very useful so long as one realizes that one type may grade imperceptibly into another. The scheme adopted is to define each category and give one or more species typical of it (Table 2·1). The species inhabiting the ocean

TABLE 2·1

FISH CLASSIFIED EMPIRICALLY BY THE ZONES THEY INHABIT

| Group Designation | General Characteristics of Zones They Inhabit |
| --- | --- |
| *Marine (Sea Living)* | |
| Deep-water forms | |
| Abyssal | Cold, dark great ocean depths |
| Bathypelagic | Cold, dim or dark intermediate ocean depths |
| Archibenthic | On or near bottom below edge of continental shelf |
| Shallow-water forms | |
| Benthic | On or near bottom on continental shelf |
| Oceanic | Far from land and near or on ocean surface |
| Pelagic | Surface-living wanderers |
| Benthopelagic | Seasonally on bottom up to surface |
| Coastal | Never far from shore |
| Estuarine | Estuaries, very tolerant of salinity changes |
| *Dromous (Running)* | |
| Catadromous (down running) | Adults in fresh or brackish water, spawn in oceans |
| Anadromous (up running) | |
| Fluvial anadromous | Ascend streams with or without lakes |
| Lacustrine anadromous | Ascend streams with lakes, young in lakes |
| *Freshwater* | |
| Lacustrine (lake-dwelling) | Live entire life in quiet waters |
| Fluvial (stream-living) | Live entire life in moving waters |
| Adfluvial (to the streams) | In lakes, ascend streams to spawn |

depths are not well known. These zones are at present of little concern to fishery management, but a tentative classification of them is included merely to indicate their existence and for completeness. As might be expected the largest number of types occurs where the land and its fresh waters meet the sea. These are the zones of tides, currents, and the mixing of waters of diverse salinity and temperature.

We begin with perhaps the most stable environment inhabited by living creatures, the gelid waters of the ocean depths, and end with the rushing mountain torrent that fluctuates with every rain squall, freezes in winter and dries up in summer. The classes follow:

**Abyssal.**  Abyssal fish are those found only at great depths in the ocean basins.  Here the water is only slightly above freezing, usually of rather high salinity (close to 35 parts per thousand, 35‰), and light never penetrates the Stygian darkness.  The fishes move about in the eternal gloom, their grotesque forms dimly lighted by a pale ghastly glow from phosphorescent spots.  These species are known only from those few dredged up at great trouble and expense by special equipment.

**Bathypelagic.**  These fish inhabit the intermediate waters of the ocean above the profound deeps of the great basins but below the edge of the continental shelf.  They include the phosphorescent lantern fishes.  A few are taken commercially in Japan.

**Archibenthic.**  These fish live on or near the bottom below the level of the edge of the continental shelf.  They include the chimaera or ratfish.

**Benthic or bank fishes.**  They live typically on the great shallow banks between the land and the edge of the continental shelf.  The depths of these banks usually range from 5 to about 150 fathoms before the edge of the continental shelf abruptly dips toward the ocean floor.  Many of our most prosperous fisheries depend on these bank fish (called groundfish in New England because they live on the bottom).  They include all of the "flatfishes"—halibut, sole, flounders, and plaice—cod, skates, rosefish (*Sebastes*), sablefish (*Anoplopoma fimbria*), cultus cod (*Ophiodon elongatus*), hake (*Urophycis*), cusk (*Brosme*), groupers (*Epinephelus*), and snappers (*Lutjanus*).

**Oceanic.**  These fish live near the surface of the sea and are seldom found near land.  A typical example is the queer-shaped sargassum fish (*Histrio histrio*) whose form imitates the sargassum weed among which it lives and which it grasps with handlike pectorals.  This weed is found in huge floating mats in the Sargasso Sea, a great eddy near the middle of the South Atlantic Ocean.  Another example is the giant sunfish (*Mola mola*) which looks like a great pancake turned edgewise and may weigh several tons.

**Pelagic.**  Pelagic fish usually live close to the surface and are typically wanderers, ranging from the coast to great distances from land.  They are streamlined for speed and include the tunas, the swordfishes, mackerel, and herring.  Many of them swim in dense schools and are the object of some of our great fisheries.  Because many of them are strong powerful swimmers that feed on the surface, they are favorite sport fish.

**Benthopelagic.** This category includes species that are both benthic and pelagic, depending on the season or other conditions. The pollock (*Pollachius virens*) is perhaps the best example. During the late fall and winter large catches of pollock are swept off the bottom by New England otter trawlers in depths up to 90 fathoms; yet during the remainder of the year large quantities are taken by weirs and traps along the shore. Often they forms dense schools at the surface and at such times whole boatloads are captured with purse seines. The dogfish shark (*Squalus*) is another example of a fish that is found at all depths from the bottom to the surface.

**Coastal.** These are marine fishes that are seldom found far from shore. The cunners, both the common cunner (*Tautogolabrus adspersus*) and the tautog (*Tautoga onitis*) are fine examples. Almost the entire population lives within a mile or two of shore, and usually within a few fathoms below the low tide level. They rarely enter brackish water. The weakfish, squeteague, or sea trout (*Cynoscion*) is another example of a coastal fish seldom taken far from the shore.

**Estuarine.** This group of fishes is quite tolerant of changes in salinity and temperature, living typically in estuaries where the water may vary from fairly salt to nearly fresh. The best example is afforded perhaps by the tomcod (*Microgadus tomcod*) a small member of the cod family. Tomcods seldom are found on the outer coast, but live in the estuaries, running into fresh water in the winter. They spawn during late winter at any salinity. The white perch (*Morone americana*) is also an estuarine species, living close to shore in the estuaries and spawning in fresh or slightly brackish water. In a few localities populations of white perch have become "landlocked." The striped bass (*Roccus saxatilis*), although usually listed as anadromous, that is, running up freshwater rivers to spawn, should probably be classified as estuarine. Although they do enter the mouths of some streams they may spawn in brackish water, and the majority spawn in the lower reaches, within the influence of the tides.

**Catadromous.** These are fish which spawn at sea and occupy two or more environments, from the sea to fresh water. The eel (*Anguilla*), always given as the classical example, ascends streams in the elver stage, usually to a pond or lake. The adult eels, after several years of growth, migrate downstream (hence the word "catadromous," or down running) before reaching full maturity, and then ripen and spawn in the deep ocean waters off Bermuda. However, the facts are not all so clear-cut as is generally supposed. Large eels are often abundant in river mouths and tidal estuaries. In many streams in eastern Maine the fishermen set their weirs to fish in either direction and catch numbers of *large* eels moving *upstream* out of salt and brackish waters. The evidence suggests that eels are tolerant of salinity and that at least a portion of the population may never enter fresh water. The mullet (*Mugil cephalus*) is occasionally a catadromous fish, but it is doubtful if fresh water is a necessity.

**Fluvial anadromous.** These are fish that typically inhabit at least two environments—the sea or an estuary in their adult stage and a stream in their young stage. Some of these species utilize the stream merely as a spawning ground. In the spring, for instance, the smelt (*Osmerus mordax*) ascends many small brooks to spawn. Since the beds of many of these streams are dry in summer, the young smelt cannot remain long. The majority of the smelt ascend streams for a very short distance, often only a few hundred yards, and many spawn in slightly brackish water.

The shad has always been regarded as an anadromous species, and in former years they ascended the larger rivers for a considerable distance. However, small runs of shad have persisted in river estuaries blocked by impassable dams at tidewater. The shad apparently can adapt itself to a considerable extent to an estuarine existence provided the salinity is sufficiently low for successful incubation of the eggs. Leim (1924) found that the larvae developed best in slightly saline water (7.5 parts per thousand).

The pink salmon (*Oncorhynchus gorbuscha*) is an excellent example of a fluvial anadromous species. The adult salmon enter the streams in the late summer and autumn, bury their eggs in nests in the coarse gravel and stones of the riffles, and then die. The young emerge from the redds or nests in the spring as soon as they have absorbed their yolk sac. Hiding by day and traveling by night they descend immediately to the sea.

**Lacustrine anadromous.** These are species the adults of which ascend streams from estuarine or marine environments to spawn, seeking a lake or pond. A good example is the alewife (*Pomolobus pseudoharengus*). Alewives will spawn in freshwater ponds only a few feet from the sea or they may battle rivers for many miles to reach a pond or lake. Small runs of alewives sometimes manage to exist in sluggish streams with stretches of deadwater. However, as the young are plankton feeders they cannot prosper in normal streams that lack lakes.

A second example is the sockeye, red, or blueback salmon (*Oncorhynchus nerka*). Like the alewife the adults enter streams that issue from lakes. In many localities the bulk of the sockeye spawn in streams tributary to the lake, but in western Alaska a very large proportion will spawn in the lake itself. The young sockeye like the young alewives are plankton feeders and live pelagically in the lake until they are ready to migrate downstream to the rich ocean feeding grounds, where they make their most rapid growth.

Fig. 2·2   A pair of sockeye salmon spawning in a redd.   (Credit: J. T. Barnaby, U. S. Fish and Wildlife Service)

**Lacustrine.** These are fish that normally pass their entire existence within a pond or lake. Examples are the cisco (*Coregonus artedii*) although found in streams in the far north, the burbot or ling (*Lota lota lacustris*) in much of the Great Lakes region and New England, often the horned pout or brown bullhead (*Ameiurus nebulosus*), and the lake trout (*Cristivomer namaycush*). To these fish a lake is merely a sea with a very low salinity. Actually one could subclassify these lake dwellers into categories quite similar to those used for marine species. Some live pelagically and others, like the horned pout, are benthic. However, as such a classification would be of value chiefly in the larger lakes it will not be attempted.

**Fluvial.** These are species that live in streams. The paddlefish (*Polyodon spathula*) is an example of a fish that inhabits the larger rivers of the Mississippi Valley. Many members of the minnow family, i.e. the redside dace (*Clinostomus elongatus*), are found typically in clear gravelly creeks. Most of the darters, subfamily Etheostomatinae, are almost entirely stream dwellers.

**Adfluvial.** This last category includes species or populations that do not go to sea, but live in lakes, and enter streams to spawn. Many of them are landlocked races of species typically anadromous, i.e., the freshwater form of the smelt (*Osmerus mordax*) and the landlocked forms of the rainbow trout (*Salmo gairdneri*).

## 2·4   Classification by manner of reproduction

The grouping of fish by their manner of reproduction is often useful in estimating the effect of various factors on their abundance. A simple outline follows:

I. Viviparous (eggs hatched internally, free-swimming young extruded).

This group includes many of the sharks, many of the surf perches (Embiotocidae), the rosefish (*Sebastes marinus*), and a few other fishes. The term viviparous used here includes a wide range of conditions from that in which the egg hatches just before extrusion to that in which the yolk is absorbed and the young obtain nourishment from the parent before extrusion. Sometimes the intermediate term ovoviviparous is used to indicate the cases in which the young receive nourishment only from the egg, but the exact limits of these two categories are not easily determined.

II. Oviparous (eggs hatched externally).

A. Eggs planktonic (float passively). Examples: mackerel, halibut, haddock, sardine.

B. Eggs semibuoyant. Examples: shad, striped bass.

C. Eggs demersal (sink to bottom).

1. Eggs loose—lake trout.

2. Eggs buried—trout, salmon, grunion (*Leuresthes tenuis*).

3. Eggs adhesive.

(a) Eggs not attended—sea herring, winter flounder, smelt (*Osmerus*).

(b) Eggs attended—smallmouth black bass, bluegill.

**References**

Leim, A. H.
  1924. The life history of the shad, *Alosa sapidissima* (Wilson), with special reference to the factors limiting its abundance. *Contr. Can. Biology N. S. 2* (11)(1925):163–284.

Merriman, Daniel
   1941. Studies on the striped bass (*Roccus saxatalis*) of the Atlantic Coast.
         *U. S. Fish and Wildl. Serv., Fish. Bull. 50* (35):1–77.
Myers, George S.
   1949. Usage of anadromous, catadromous, and allied terms for migratory fishes.
         *Copeia,* 1949 (2):89–96.

# PART II · NATURAL POPULATIONS

A population or stock of fish is a biological entity. Knowledge of the ranges, migrations, and seasonal overlapping in ranges of different populations is essential for successful management. Unless one knows whether one is dealing with one or with several populations the field of the problem is ill-defined.

Populations may be limited in their distribution either by natural barriers or by certain circumstances that favor their existence in particular localities. A knowledge of the effect on fishes of certain physical, chemical, and biological factors of the environment also aids in discovering the causal factors of natural fluctuations in their abundance.

Whether a population is declining in abundance or maintaining itself at a stable level (subject to the expected variations due to natural factors) can sometimes be detected from changes in age composition, shifts in the grounds fished, or changes in yield.

The estimation of the abundance of a population can occasionally be accomplished directly, as by counting salmon through a weir. Usually indirect methods must be employed. The accuracy of the estimate, and whether total population size or an index of abundance is made, depends on what information is at hand.

# 3 · FACTORS LIMITING ABUNDANCE

## 3·1  Introduction

In order to perpetuate themselves all species must produce a surplus of young. Conversely, all species are held in check by one or more forces. When one of these forces fails a species may become tremendously abundant for a time, but always the same or another factor steps in to re-establish a balance. Some species vary widely in abundance from time to time. Such variations may not indicate that a species is out of balance. Thus the enormous differences in the size of the odd- and even-numbered year runs of pink salmon (*Oncorhynchus gorbuscha*) in Puget Sound are a normal occurrence. Likewise, the differences in survival of successive age groups of some species are very large. But dominant age classes are usual to many species; it has been suggested that there is some relation between the maximum age attained by individuals of a species and the long span of years that may occasionally elapse between successful spawnings.

The elimination of the older age classes, possibly by overfishing, may have a profound effect on the normal life cycle. Thus the reduction in numbers of the older individuals among the Pacific sardine (*Sardinops caerulea*) in recent years has virtually eliminated the fishery north of San Francisco (as far as British Columbia) which depended on the northward migration of the older fish.

The purpose of this chapter is to indicate some of the factors that keep fish populations in check and that cause fluctuations in their abundance. Some of these factors are purely physical; others are directly or indirectly biological.

The part played by purely physical factors is of great interest. For nearly a century biologists have noted, for instance, the dearth of species in the northern seas contrasted with the myriad species surrounding tropical shores. Nevertheless, the abundance of individual species is almost always in favor of those in the more northern latitudes where biological competition is less severe but physical conditions are harsher.

## 3·2  Fecundity

In order for each species to maintain on the average the same relative abundance it is clear that the same relative numbers must survive from generation to generation. This means that the average survival to maturity from the individual spawning of 2 million eggs can be no higher than the average survival from the spawning of a species with only 2000 eggs.

Species with a low fecundity survive because each individual egg has a greater chance of survival. As a general rule species with a low fecundity exhibit smaller fluctuations in abundance both because of the greater protection from natural phenomena and because the limited number of eggs does not permit so sudden an increase when conditions are exceptionally favorable.

## 3·3  Critical stages in the life history

The success or failure of a species in any particular environment may not depend on the suitability of the environment as a whole, but rather on whether the species is able to survive during some particular phase of its life history. This fact often has been overlooked, especially in the introduction of new species. For example, it is well known that many species of the Salmonidae must have the proper type of spawning conditions if they are to reproduce; yet many lakes without proper or sufficient spawning areas have been repeatedly stocked in the vain expectation of establishing a species.

Among marine fishes great fluctuations in abundance may occur because of the annual variation in the success of spawning. This has been variously attributed to temperature, salinity, currents, absence of suitable food for the very young fish at the proper time, and an overabundance of predators.

## 3·4  Vanishing species

In considering limiting factors it will be noted that with most species there is a portion of their range in which their maximum abundance is reached, while there are marginal zones, in which the species is scarce or rare. As environmental conditions change the range may expand or contract or shift in one direction or another. There are some species that, owing perhaps to overspecialization which prevents their quick adaptation to changing conditions, are nowhere abundant. Some of these species may be losing the battle for existence and perhaps should be regarded as vanishing species. The first-mentioned species may be considered marginal on the periphery of this range.

## 3·5   Salinity

Salinity is a very important limiting factor for many species both directly and indirectly. All species tolerate a range in salinity since even the so-called fresh waters contain dissolved salts in greater or lesser degree. The range of tolerance varies widely from species to species. Thus Rawson and Moore (1944) show the distribution of several species of fish in relation to salinity in 60 lakes in Saskatchewan. The long-nosed dace (*Rhinichthys cataractae*) and the black-nosed shiner (*Notropis heterolepis*) were not found in salinities above 0.6 part per thousand. Salinities approaching 10 parts per thousand or above were tolerated by the fathead minnow (*Pimephales promelas*), the common sucker (*Catostomus commersoni*), the yellow perch (*Perca flavescens*), the pickerel or pike-perch (*Stizostedion vitreum*), the Iowa darter (*Poecilichthys exilis*), the five-spined stickleback (*Eucalia inconstans*), and the nine-spined stickleback (*Pungitius pungitius*). Introduction of several species into these saline lakes proved that lakes with salinities up to 15 parts per thousand were suitable for whitefish (*Coregonus clupeaformis*) and pike-perch. Only one fish, the nine-spined stickleback, survived in a salinity of 20 parts per thousand. The general conclusion is that lakes with a salinity exceeding 15 parts per thousand are unsuitable for most freshwater fishes.

Marine fishes also vary widely in their tolerance of salinity changes. In the Laguna Madre off the Texas coast there are occasional heavy mortalities of fish caused by high salinities because of insufficient exchange of water between the lagoon and the Gulf of Mexico. Evaporation raises the salinity to as high as 75 to 100 parts per thousand and fish die by the ton. This is an extreme case as normal ocean water usually runs from 34 to 35 parts per thousand.

Estuarine species are tolerant of salinity changes and may be found in salinities ranging from normal sea water to brackish or even fresh. Examples are the tomcod (*Microgadus tomcod*), the striped bass (*Roccus saxatilis*), and the white perch (*Morone americana*). The white perch supports a commercial catch of half a million pounds in Chesapeake Bay but is landlocked in many freshwater lakes in New England.

Anadromous species are considered tolerant of great salinity changes, but there is evidence that the young of many such species cannot tolerate a high salinity until they approach the normal time of migration to the sea.

Sandoz and Rogers (1944) showed that the hatching rate of blue crab eggs usually fell below 50 per cent when the salinity dropped below 18 parts per thousand and increased with a rise in salinity up to at least about 27 parts per thousand. Pearson (1948) showed a significant high negative correlation between the survival of each brood of blue crabs from 1930 to 1944 and the discharge of the James River. This river discharges at the mouth of Chesapeake Bay near the area of the greatest spawning concentration of blue crabs.

The oyster drill (*Urosalpinx cinerea*) is not tolerant of low salinities. Federighi (1931) found that it dies at salinities as low as 12.5 parts per thousand and that drills from environments with high salinities die at about 15 parts per thousand. This has great economic significance as it is the river estuaries with low salinities that produce most of the seed oysters for transplanting.

## 3·6  Oxygen

The minimum oxygen requirements of fish are gradually becoming understood. It is pointed out by Ellis, Westfall, and Ellis (1946) that the effect of oxygen depends on other factors and that it is not always safe to accept any definite oxygen limit without considering other hazards that are present.

Fish have been found living in a healthy condition at extremely low oxygen concentrations. Such fish show a high red-blood cell count. Stocking fish from waters with a high oxygen concentration into waters poor in oxygen is often lethal, though such waters may contain an abundance of fish that are physiologically adjusted to the oxygen level.

Oxygen can become a limiting factor when it is reduced by substances with a high oxygen demand. Thus the decaying organic matter on lake bottoms tends to exhaust the oxygen below the thermocline during the summer months. In some lakes the oxygen level becomes too low to support most species of fish. During the winter months the shutting off of light by ice and especially by snow-covered ice causes plants, including planktonic algae, to consume more oxygen than they produce, thus contributing heavily to oxygen depletion. Greenbank (1945) explains that the amount of oxygen consumed by the fish themselves would usually not be much of a factor in oxygen depletion. The formation, by the decay of organic matter on the bottom, of methane, hydrogen sulfide, carbon dioxide, ammonia, nitrogen, and possibly other gases, may consume much oxygen and contribute heavily to winterkill in shallow or very fertile lakes. The role of the decay of suspended material may also be important.

There are many small shallow lakes in the northern states in which winterkill occurs frequently. Usually a few fish survive, although some species, often the game species, may be killed completely. When a lake suffers from winterkill during only the more severe winters it is economic to keep it stocked.

There is evidence that the 5-ppm oxygen tolerance level set by Ellis, Westfall, and Ellis (1946) is too high. Thus Greenbank (1945) found that values of less than 1.5 ppm with some samples ranging from 0.01 to 1.0 ppm for several consecutive days killed bluegills, but did not kill bullheads.

Jahoda (1947) reported that brook trout fingerlings survived a period of nearly 2 months in a New Hampshire brook with oxygen ranging from 3.3 to a low of 1.1 ppm. Temperatures ranged from 52° to 60° F with the lowest at 52° when the oxygen was at 1.1 ppm. Similarly, Lindroth (1949) studied the oxygen tolerance of Atlantic salmon parr in Swedish streams and stated that salmon parr are capable of living in water at 8° C (46° F) with an oxygen pressure of 30 mm Hg (about 2.2 ppm) for at least 5 days. He says that this corresponds fairly well to the critical tension.

Most warm-water species are apparently capable of existing at even lower oxygen concentrations than cold-water species as is reflected in Table 3·1 which gives the oxygen tolerances reported by several authors.

In rare instances fish mortalities have occurred as a result of supersaturation of water with oxygen. Thus Woodbury (1942) examined a large number of fish that died in Lake Waubesa, Wisconsin, apparently from blocking of the capillaries in the gill filaments by gas emboli. The dissolved oxygen content of water samples taken at the time varied from 16.8 to 32.1 ppm, the saturation being 171 to 327 per cent.

## 3·7   Hydrogen sulfide

It was pointed out by Chamberlain (1947) that hydrogen sulfide is a very severe limiting factor in Florida waters. The Florida Everglades muck soil is composed of 0.33% by wet weight of sulfur. Hydrogen sulfide is formed by anaerobic bacteria, but the chief means of its formation is by fire. The soil has such a high organic content that when it becomes dry it frequently burns and combustion tends to be incomplete, forming chiefly sulfides rather than sulfates. When rain carries the alkaline sulfides into contact with the slightly acid unburned wet muck, hydrogen sulfide is formed and is carried off in solution. This accounts for heavy unpredictable fish mortalities. He states that 6 ppm of hydrogen sulfide will kill carp in a few hours,

TABLE 3·1

MINIMUM OXYGEN REQUIREMENTS OF CERTAIN SPECIES OF FISHES

| Species | Oxygen Require-ment, Ppm | Authority |
|---|---|---|
| Brook trout (*Salvelinus fontinalis*) | 1.1 | Jahoda (1947) |
| Atlantic salmon (*Salmo salar*) | 2.2 | Lindroth (1949) |
| Largemouth bass (*Micropterus salmoides*) | 2.3 | Moore (1942) |
| | 0.6 | Cooper & Washburn (1949) |
| | 0.38 | King & Smith (1947) |
| Northern pike (*Esox lucius*) | 2.3 | Moore (1942) |
| | 0.3–0.4 | Cooper & Washburn (1949) |
| Yellow perch (*Perca flavescens*) | 1.5 | Moore (1942) |
| | 0.3–0.4 | Cooper & Washburn (1949) |
| Black crappie (*Pomoxis nigromaculatus*) | 1.4 | Moore (1942) |
| Pumpkinseed (*Lepomis gibbosus*) | 0.9 | Moore (1942) |
| | 0.3–0.4 | Cooper & Washburn (1949) |
| Bluegill (*Lepomis macrochirus*) | 0.8 | Moore (1942) |
| | 0.6 | Cooper & Washburn (1949) |
| | above 0.56 | King & Smith (1947) |
| Black bullhead (*Ameiurus melas*) | 0.3 | Moore (1942) |
| | 0.2–0.3 | Cooper & Washburn (1949) |
| Golden shiner (*Notemigonus crysoleucas*) | 0.0 * | Moore (1942) |
| | below 0.2 | Cooper & Washburn (1949) |
| Grass pickerel (*Esox vermiculatus*) | 0.3–0.4 | Cooper & Washburn (1949) |
| Lake chubsucker (*Erimyzon sucetta*) | 0.3–0.4 | Cooper & Washburn (1949) |
| Warmouth bass (*Chaenobryttus coronarius*) | 0.30–0.56 | King & Smith (1947) |

* Not measurable.

that he found concentrations in feeder canals up to 40 ppm, and that at the time tested the rim canal encircling Lake Okeechobee contained 7 ppm. This confines most of the fish to the wind-aerated waters away from the shores.

## 3·8  Temperature

Temperature plays an important role for all living organisms. Fish vary considerably in their tolerance both of the range of temperature and of the abruptness of temperature changes. Fish that ordinarily live in an environment with a stable temperature are apt to be quite sensitive to change. Thus most of the freshwater fishes of the tropics, as all aquarists know, succumb readily to a drop of a few degrees in temperature. Many marine fishes approach the shores in spring as the water warms up but desert the shoals in late summer when the water temperature approaches its peak.

Many of the so-called "warm-water fishes" such as the black bass become extremely sluggish as the water cools, and when the ice starts forming on ponds they may sometimes be observed lying entirely motionless and practically powerless to move.  On shallow coasts a sudden cold spell will occasionally kill large quantities of marine fish that are trapped by the sudden cooling of the shallow waters.

All fishes are affected by temperature, the differences between the reaction of different species being in the width of the band of temperatures tolerated, in the position of the upper and lower limits, and in the optimum temperature.  For short periods fish will tolerate temperatures that might otherwise be lethal.  Thus Atlantic salmon parr will survive temperatures over 80° F and are known to withstand temperatures up to 90° F during the day if the total period is but a few days and there is a lowering of the temperature at night.  Even closely related species exhibit differences in their tolerance of high temperatures.  Thus on Atlantic salmon rivers the brook trout (*Salvelinus fontinalis*) cannot endure such high temperatures as the salmon parr.  In midsummer while the parr are thriving in the main stream the brook trout desert these warm waters and gather in cool spring holes or enter cooler spring-fed tributaries.  High temperatures are thus a definite limiting factor for many species.

The growth rate of fish depends to a large extent on temperature.  Digestion proceeds very slowly at low temperatures.  This is often shown by the differences in growth rate between populations of the same species inhabiting waters of different temperature.  Thus Rounsefell and Stringer (1945) show that the alewives in the Taunton River which enters the Atlantic Ocean south of Cape Cod mature very predominantly at 3 years of age, while alewives running up the Damariscotta and Orland Rivers in Maine, which enter the colder waters of the Gulf of Maine, mature chiefly at 4 years of age.

This decrease in rate of growth with lowered temperature is also well marked in the Pacific salmons.  Thus most of the sockeye salmon of the Fraser River mature at 4 years while those in the Karluk River on Kodiak Island mature chiefly at 5 years, in the rivers of the Alaska Peninsula and Bristol Bay large numbers mature at six years, and in some years the 6-year-old fish may predominate in some rivers.

Obviously a species inhabiting a temperature zone that is unfavorable to it is at a disadvantage in competing with species that are better adapted to the conditions.  This fact is often neglected in stocking ponds and lakes.  Thus, if a lake during midsummer has only a very restricted area of hypolimnion suitable for cold-water species it is very unlikely that they can be made abundant by heavy stocking as the amount of food available to the species is too limited during this period. Conversely, the stocking of deep cold lakes that have a limited littoral zone with warm-water species may be equally bad, resulting in sparse populations of slow-growing fish that yield little fishing but that prey on the young of the cold-water species. The amount of warm and cold water available in a lake, especially at critical periods, is thus a definite limiting factor.

One of the ways in which temperature affects populations is by its effect on reproduction. Thus most species do not spawn unless the water temperature is within certain limits. As the temperature rises later in the year in northern latitudes spawning is correspondingly delayed. Thus the Pacific herring (Rounsefell 1930) may spawn as early as December at San Diego, but they spawn later and later northward along the coast, as late as June at St. Michaels in Alaska. For many species the temperature raises a barrier to their reproduction in northern waters. Thus the oyster (*Crassostrea virginica*) fails to spawn with success in northern New England or on the Pacific Coast, even though young oysters (spat) brought from the south and planted in the same areas may thrive. The low maximum summer ocean temperatures in northern New England have precluded the successful raising of the oyster in these waters except in shallow bays which warm in summer. Experiments with hardier species of oysters may ultimately lead to success.

In addition to the direct effect of limiting or precluding spawning itself temperature also limits reproduction by its effect on the survival of the young. This may come about either by the lack of sufficient food of the proper kind at a critical period or by a greatly reduced growth rate which leaves the young susceptible to certain predators over a longer period. Thus, Foerster (1938) has shown that the mortality of young sockeye salmon in a lake is extremely high during their earlier stages, falling off steadily as the fish advance in size. If the younger fish grow slowly their high mortality rate is prolonged, causing a great reduction in numbers.

## 3·9   Space

Many species are limited in their abundance by the amount of space available during some phase of their life history. Very often this is suitable spawning area. For instance, many of the ocean smelt spawn only on beaches of certain texture washed by the surf. The grunion (*Leuresthes tenuis*) (Thompson and Thompson 1919) spawns on beaches of fine sand just after the tide commences to recede. The fish allow themselves to be washed onto the beach, and the eggs are buried in the wet sand. On the next series of high tides, a fortnight later, the eggs are washed out and hatch immediately. The silver smelt (*Hypomesus pretiosus*) (Thompson and associates 1936, Loosanoff 1937) also spawns in the surf but lower down the beach. The eggs are not

Fig. 3·1 A salmon attempting to leap Celilo Falls on the Columbia River. Note the Indian hanging-basket trap in the foreground. This illustrates the role of obstructions in limiting access to spawning grounds. (Credit: U. S. Fish and Wildlife Service)

buried in pods like those of the grunion but adhere firmly to the larger grains of coarse sand. They are not spawned on the higher night tides as are those of the grunion, but on the day tides, so that they will be washed every day by the water. The grunion needs beaches of fine sand, the silver smelt beaches of coarse sand. In both cases spawning is regulated by the tides, and both species are severely limited by the available spawning area.

Most of the Salmonidae spawn by burying their eggs in redds in

clean coarse gravel or rubble where there is sufficient seepage of water
through the bottom to aerate the eggs and to prevent silting. In some
streams the areas of suitable bottom, flow, and depth of water are so
severely limited as to constitute the chief factor limiting the abundance
of the fish.

The idea that marine species are able to spawn anywhere is erroneous. Because of the existence of strong ocean currents fish with
buoyant eggs must often spawn in rather circumscribed areas if the
young are not to be swept out to sea and lost. For example, the Pacific
halibut (*Hippoglossus stenolepis*) that inhabit the Gulf of Alaska
spawn chiefly on the grounds off Yakutat, and many of the eggs and
the developing young are carried hundreds of miles westward along the
Alaska Peninsula by the northern branch of the Japan Current. The
young are thereby spread along the shore when they reach the proper
stage for settling to the bottom. When they mature, halibut inhabiting
this stretch of coast must migrate far to the eastward to spawn.

Space may be a critical factor also at later stages of the life history.
Thus the alewife (*Pomolobus pseudoharengus*) makes most of its
growth in the sea, has a very high fecundity, and is able to spawn
under a variety of conditions as the adhesive eggs hatch in a matter
of 2 or 3 days. However, the young which are plankton feeders spend
their first summer in fresh water. The abundance of each run of
alewives depends therefore in large measure on the area of lake available during this first summer. The size of the nursery area for the
young fish is a limiting factor for many species.

## 3·10   Total productivity

The total productivity of any body of water is limited. In the case
of farm ponds and other small bodies of water it sometimes may be
practical to increase the natural productivity by fertilization or other
measures. Such intensive management is not however practical on a
large scale. This fact sets a very positive theoretical limit to the
maximum abundance obtainable by any species. In practice, a body
of water is usually inhabited by several species of fish that compete
for the available food. The type of food chain that exists also determines how nearly the total theoretical productivity is attained. Thus
a body of water can support a larger poundage of plankton feeders
than of fish that must exist by converting fish flesh into fish flesh.

In speaking of limiting factors, no distinction has been made so far
between standing crop and yield. If too many of a species are competing for the same amount of food, then less will be converted into
growth and more will be used in basal metabolism. The standing crop
may be large but the yield is small. The maximum yield in pounds

of fish flesh is attained when the largest quantity of food is being converted into flesh. This requires a rather delicate balance between available food and numbers of fish that is seldom attained.

Total productivity applies to the sea as well as to the fresh waters. Possibly the best example is afforded by the European plaice (*Pleuronectes platessa*). On the shallow banks off the coasts of the Netherlands and Denmark young plaice are very numerous, and even though these shallow banks are highly productive, the competition is so keen that growth is very slow. Thousands of these small plaice were transplanted onto the larger and less populated banks of the North Sea, where their increase in rate of growth was remarkable.

## 3·11   Competition

Competition can be considered separately from direct predation, and it can take more than one form. Ricker and Gottschalk (1941) explain how the game fish in Bass Lake, Indiana, were very badly depleted because rough fish, chiefly carp, had uprooted and destroyed the aquatic vegetation and made the water very turbid. Removal of 71 tons of coarse fish from this 1600-acre lake by seining had an immediate beneficial effect, demonstrating that the alteration of habitat is one form of competition that may limit abundance.

Another form of competition takes place on the spawning grounds, that may sometimes be very severe. Among the five species of Pacific salmon there are often times and places where two or more species are attempting to use the same spawning beds. In 1924 the sockeye salmon run to the Karluk River, Alaska, was badly damaged by an unprecedented run of millions of pink salmon (*Oncorhynchus gorbuscha*). These pink salmon not only spawned in their accustomed areas in the 20 miles of river below Karluk Lake, but, on account of the tremendous population pressure, they pressed on into the lake and ascended its tributaries, which are the usual spawning grounds for a large share of the sockeye. They dug up great quantities of the sockeye eggs already deposited there.

A third form of competition, if it can be called this, comes from overpopulation. Once the senior author ascended a stream in Gambier Bay in southeast Alaska, during the fall when the pink salmon were spawning. Thousands of herring gulls circled above the forest, and the air literally reeked. The stream was full of rotting salmon that had not spawned, and the water was so foul that many dead trout were among them. Overpopulation had reached its climax, and the cycle would have to start over again from the possible survivors.

## 3·12    Predation

Predation is one of the most powerful forces in maintaining a balance.  In many bodies of water the removal of a large share of the larger predator fish by intensive fishing has not resulted in better fishing.  On the contrary, in waters with favorable conditions for re-

FIG. 3·2   Showing millions of herring (*Clupea pallasi*) which died suddenly in the salt-water lagoon at Craig, Alaska, in the spring of 1925.  Such mass mortalities occur sporadically.  In 1913 a similar mortality was recorded here in which the fish crowded into the bay and millions died, covering the beach to a depth in places of several feet.

production the removal of predators often permits a survival of young fish too great for the available food supply.  The result is overcrowding of the waters by an abundance of slow-growing fish that are unable to attain normal size.

This does not necessarily apply in special cases.  For example with anadromous fishes in which the young migrate from fresh water to the sea where they make most of their growth, the control of predators may cause a greater survival and hence a lower growth rate, but up to a certain point the increased numbers of young may outweigh the disadvantage of their smaller size.

Predation may be an especially serious limiting factor for species that are very vulnerable during some particular phase of their life cycle.

FIG. 3·3  Showing the beach littered with great quantities of marine forms killed by the red tide during the 1947 outbreak in Florida. (Credit: *St. Petersburg Evening Independent* Staff Photograph)

### 3·13   Intraspecific competition and predation

The size of a population is often limited by intraspecific competition. This may take the form of competition for available food (see Section 3·10 on total productivity). Ricker (1950) postulates the theory that the dominance of one out of four of the cycles in sockeye salmon is caused by intraspecific competition, which may take the form of actual predation. The sockeye of the Fraser predominantly mature at 4 years of age, and all die after spawning, so that each cycle is really a different population of the same species. In this case the populations of the three cycles following a dominant cycle do not achieve the size permitted by the available food, so that the actual limiting factor is the abundance of the preceding dominant cycle.

## 3·14   Diseases and parasites

How effective diseases and parasites are in limiting fish populations
is not well established.  It is known that fish are occasionally subjected to heavy mortalities that bear the stamp of epidemic disease,
although the evidence is not always forthcoming.  The sudden tremendous mortality that almost exterminated the huge smelt population

FIG. 3·4  Showing the heavy mortality of fish caused by the red tide.  Airplane
view from 150 feet of dead fish (grunts, tarpon, groupers, jewfish) floating on the
surface of the Gulf of Mexico 8 miles southwest of St. Petersburg, Florida.
(Credit: *St. Petersburg Evening Independent* Staff Photograph)

of the Great Lakes about 1944 is an example.  Marine fish are also
subject to such outbreaks, perhaps the best-known case being the
recurrent epidemics, about every 15 or 16 years, of a fungus disease
that is found in the sea herring (*Clupea harengus*).  The dreaded
furunculosis or "boil" disease has limited populations of brown trout
and Atlantic salmon in many European rivers.

## 3·15   The red tide

For decades scientists have noted discoloration of water associated
with luxurious growth of one or another of several species of plankton
(Galtsoff 1949).  At times these outbursts have caused damage to

pearl oysters, fishes, crabs, shrimp, and even turtles. The illustrations shown are from the 1947 outbreak along the Florida west coast. It started in the fall of 1946 and lasted until March 1947. It recurred in July 1947, and it is said that the second outbreak was the more destructive. Galtsoff (1949) conservatively estimates that the second outbreak destroyed between 100 and 200 million pounds of fish. Tightly packed masses of dead fish (see figure) in bands 100 to 200 feet wide, and extending over a great distance along the coast, were observed several miles offshore. The exact manner in which the red tide kills is not fully known, but it appears to be by means of powerful toxins.

## References

Chamberlain, T. K.
    1947. Investigations of the effect of the water hyacinth on the fish of Florida waters. *U. S. Fish and Wildl. Serv., Spec. Sci. Rept. 39,* App. B: 66–71.
Cooper, Gerald P., and George N. Washburn
    1949. Relation of dissolved oxygen to winter mortality of fish in Michigan lakes. *Trans. Am. Fish. Soc. 76:* 23–33.
Ellis, M. M., B. A. Westfall, and Marion D. Ellis
    1946. Determination of water quality. *U. S. Fish and Wildl. Serv., Res. Rept. 9:* 122 pp.
Federighi, Henry
    1931. Studies on the oyster drill (*Urosalpinx cinerea,* Say). *Bull. U. S. Bur. Fish. 47* (4):85–115.
Foerster, R. Earle
    1938. Mortality trend among young sockeye salmon (*Oncorhynchus nerka*) during various stages of lake residence. *J. Fish. Res. Bd. Canada 4* (3):184–191.
    1944. The relation of lake population density to size of young sockeye salmon (*Oncorhynchus nerka*). *J. Fish. Res. Bd. Canada 6* (3):267–280.
Galtsoff, Paul S.
    1948. Red Tide. *U. S. Fish and Wildl. Serv., Spec. Sci. Rept. 46:* 44 pp.
    1949. The mystery of the red tide. *Scientific Monthly 48* (2):108–117.
Greenbank, John
    1945. Limnological conditions in ice-covered lakes especially as related to winter-kill of fish. *Ecol. Mono. 15:* 343–392.
Jahoda, W. J.
    1947. Survival of brook trout in water of low oxygen content. *J. Wildl. Management 11* (1):96–97.
King, Joseph E., and Arthur L. Smith, Jr.
    1947. Investigations of the effect of the water hyacinth on the fish and fish habitats of Louisiana waters. *U. S. Fish and Wildl. Serv., Spec. Sci. Rept. 39,* App. A: 30–65.
Lindroth, Arne
    1949. Vitality of salmon parr at low oxygen pressure. *Institute of Freshwater Res., Fish. Bd. Sweden, 29:* 49–50. Drottningholm.

Loosanoff, Victor L.
  1937. The spawning of the Pacific surf smelt, *Hypomesus pretiosus* (Girard).
    *Inter. Revue der gesamten Hydrobiologie und Hydrographie 36:* 170–183.
Moore, Walter G.
  1942. Field studies on the oxygen requirements of certain freshwater fishes.
    *Ecology 23:* 319–329.
Pearson, John C.
  1948. Fluctuations in the abundance of the blue crab in Chesapeake Bay.
    *U. S. Fish and Wildl. Serv., Res. Rept. 14:* 26 pp.
Rawson, D. S., and J. E. Moore
  1944. The saline lakes of Saskatchewan. *Can. J. Res., D, 22:* 141–201.
Ricker, William E.
  1950. Cycle dominance among the Fraser sockeye. *Ecology 31* (1):6–26.
Ricker, William E., and John Gottschalk
  1941. An experiment in removing coarse fish from a lake. *Trans. Am. Fish.
    Soc. 70:* 382–390.
Rounsefell, George A.
  1930. Contribution to the biology of the Pacific herring, *Clupea pallasii,* and
    the condition of the fishery in Alaska. *Bull. U. S. Bur. Fish. 45:* 227–320.
Rounsefell, George A., and Louis D. Stringer
  1945. The New England alewife fisheries, with special reference to Maine.
    *Trans. Am. Fish. Soc. 73:* 394–424.
Sandoz, Mildred, and Rosalie Rogers
  1944. The effect of environmental factors on hatching, moulting, and survival
    of zoea larvae of the blue crab, *Callinectes sapidus,* Rathbun. *J. Ecol-
    ogy 25* (2):216–228.
Thompson, W. F., and Associates
  1936. The spawning of the silver smelt, *Hypomesus pretiosus. Ecology, 17*
    (1):158–168.
Thompson, W. F., and J. B. Thompson
  1919. The spawning of the grunion (*Leuresthes tenuis*). *Calif. Div. Fish and
    Game, Fish. Bull. 3:* 29 pp.
Woodbury, Lowell A.
  1942. A sudden mortality of fishes accompanying a supersaturation of oxygen
    in Lake Waubesa, Wisconsin. *Trans. Am. Fish. Soc. 71:* 112–117.

# 4 · CRITERIA FOR SEPARATING POPULATIONS

## 4·1 Introduction

In managing a particular fishery it is essential to know whether the catch comes from one population or perhaps from several. When an entire fishery depends wholly on one stock of fish it will be affected by the quantities caught in any one locality. If on the contrary the stocks of fish are local in their distribution, each must be treated as a separate unit, and it becomes possible to reduce the numbers of fish in one locality greatly without affecting them elsewhere. Migratory fish present a further complication. Different races of Pacific herring are taken together where their ranges overlap on their summer feeding grounds. Salmon bound for their own natal rivers are caught at the same point as they pass through the same marine channels. Recent experiments have shown that the shad from many Atlantic coast rivers congregate in the same area off the Maine coast in summer.

The tracing of the migrations of fish by the direct method of marking and releasing individuals and later noting where they are recaptured is a positive method of determining the areal distribution of a population. Where and when it can be employed it is superior to the indirect method of comparing morphometric characters. However, it can be used only to determine if fish are migrating into fishing areas, not to determine if the same stock of fish extends beyond the boundaries of the existing fishery, as, obviously, no marked fish can be expected to be recaptured without a modicum of fishing effort. Knowledge of the existence of stocks as yet untouched by the fishery is often of great importance in judging the future of a fishery; racial analyses are needed to determine this.

For one reason or another, some species of fish have not been particularly suited to marking experiments, and here again recourse is had to racial characters. The same is sometimes true when the expense of tagging is prohibitive.

## 4·2   Selection.of racial characters

The selection of the characters to be used for comparisons to determine whether or not different samples of fish belong to the same race may present considerable difficulty.  Different investigators have often studied different characters for the same species.  Some investigators have employed a multiplicity of characters whereas others have used but a few or have put their entire effort on the study of one character. The selection of characters will of course depend somewhat on circumstances but a few general rules can be stated:

1. Choose between using many characters, thus being limited by funds or time to small samples, perhaps inadequate, and using one or at most four or five characters with correspondingly larger samples. The seeming benefit of using many characters in the hope of finding one or more yielding a statistically significant difference, is usually more than offset by the inadequacy of the samples.  This should not preclude preliminary study of many characters in order to select those that exhibit a useful range of variation.

2. Avoid characters that admit of much error in their determination. Thus it is often a laborious task to determine separately the unbranched and branched fin rays.  The presence or absence of the first tiny fin ray may also be difficult to decide.  Where there is a large range in the number of fin rays the difficulty of determining the first ray (without a careful dissection) may not be of great moment, but if the range is small then such a difficulty will throw doubt on the results.

3. Do not use two or more characters that are dependent upon one another; thus the length of the base of the dorsal fin is largely a function of the number of fin rays.

Characters used in racial determinations are of two main types, counts and measurements, although other features of the populations, such as age composition, or spawning habits, may be important evidence of races.

In selecting characters remember that one that may be excellent for differentiating races of one species may be quite worthless for another.  Thus the number of vertebrae is a valuable racial character for the herring but is worthless among many fish with a low number of vertebrae, because, as the number of vertebrae decreases, the range of variation also decreases, and in many fish the number is practically constant.  Select therefore a character in which there is a certain amount of variation.  Otherwise you can hardly expect to find an intraspecific difference.  Also it may be difficult to employ a character with extreme variation as only large samples will locate the mean accurately.

The counts ordinarily used include both meristic characters such as vertebral counts, fin ray counts, and scale counts, and enumerations of gillrakers, branchiostegals, caeca, ova, etc. In recording the number of vertebrae many investigators have distinguished between the abdominal and caudal vertebrae, making the distinction between vertebrae with or without a completely closed haemal arch. This distinction is difficult to make and is not recommended. However, it appears from studies on the Pacific sardine by Charles Clothier (1950) that a well-developed haemal spine is a better indication of a caudal vertebrae than the closed haemal arch. The hypural element, which is flattened to support the caudal rays, is included in the vertebral counts of some investigators as one vertebra and excluded by others. In a few fishes that have definite intervertebral sutures in the hypural element, each portion may be counted as a separate vertebra.

## 4·3  Genetic and environmental variation

It has been shown repeatedly that meristic characters of fishes are determined only partially by inheritance. Thus Rounsefell and Dahlgren (1932) showed that the means of the vertebral count for nine successive year classes of Pacific herring (*Clupea pallasi*) were negatively correlated, $r = -0.85$, with the temperatures during the 4-month period (March–June) when spawning and incubation occur.

This circumstance makes it necessary to compare only counts from samples of fish of the same year class, unless one first measures the range of the possible environmental variation and only accepts differences significantly in excess of such variation. Even when significant differences are found between sample counts of fish from the same year class they may still be caused by environmental differences between the localities compared. However, if statistically significant differences between sample counts of fish of the same year group persist, it indicates that the fish are not all from the same stock, regardless of whether the differences are genetic or environmental in origin.

A word of caution should be inserted concerning the collection of samples intended to be used for determining whether or not different stocks of fish exist in a region. Experience has demonstrated that different races of fish may be mingled on a migration route, or in a feeding area, and yet repair to their natal area at spawning time. Therefore, whenever possible, attempt to collect samples from spawning fish if pure samples of each stock are desired.

## 4·4 Analysis of enumeration characters

The $z$ test devised by Fisher (1930, p. 201) is rather tedious to calculate, but Snedecor (1940) gives a convenient adaptation for testing the significance of the differences between the variances (mean squares). The ratio of the variances from Table 4·1,

$$F = \frac{\text{larger variance}}{\text{smaller variance}} = \frac{0.5262}{0.4756} = 1.11$$

is compared with a table of $F$ values for the 0.05 and 0.01 probability points. The table is entered with the $n_1$ degrees of freedom corresponding to the greater mean square, in this case 8. The table shows that for the 0.05 point the distribution of $F$ with $n_1$ equal to 8 and $n_2$ equal

TABLE 4·1

ANALYSIS OF VERTEBRAL COUNTS OF HERRING OF THE 1926 YEAR CLASS FROM NOYES ISLAND TO ILLUSTRATE METHOD OF TESTING FOR HOMOGENEITY OF THE POPULATION

| A | B | C | D | E | F | G |
|---|---|---|---|---|---|---|
| June 21, 1930 | 51.786 | 14 | −0.402 | 0.161604 | 2.262456 | 6.357 |
|  | 52.250 | 24 | .062 | .003844 | .092256 | 12.500 |
| June 23, 1930 | 52.348 | 23 | .160 | .025600 | .588800 | 15.217 |
| June 24, 1930 | 52.226 | 31 | .038 | .001444 | .044764 | 13.419 |
|  | 52.000 | 9 | −.188 | .035344 | .318096 | 2.000 |
| June 27, 1930 | 51.857 | 7 | −.331 | .109561 | .766927 | 2.857 |
| June 28, 1930 | 52.240 | 25 | .052 | .002704 | .067600 | 10.560 |
| July 18, 1930 | 52.231 | 39 | .043 | .001521 | .059319 | 16.923 |
| July 28, 1930 | 52.214 | 14 | .026 | .000676 | .009464 | 4.357 |
| Total |  | 186 |  |  | 4.209682 | 84.190 |

General mean, 52.188; column $A$, date of sampling; column $B$, mean of sample; column $C$, number in sample; column $D$, column $B$ minus general mean; column $E$, column $D$ squared; column $F$, column $C$ times column $E$; column $G$, sum of squared deviations of individual counts from their sample means.

| Variance | Degrees of Freedom | Sum of Squares | Mean Square |
|---|---|---|---|
| Between arrays or samples | 8 | 4.209682 | 0.5262 |
| Within arrays or samples | 177 | 84.190 | .4756 |

Note that the degrees of freedom between samples are one less than the number of samples and that the degrees of freedom within samples are the total number of counts minus one for each sample.

to 177 (table gives values for $n_2$ of 150 and 200) is between 2.00 and 1.98. Since the observed $F$ is only 1.11 the conclusion is reached that the samples could all have been drawn from the same population.

#### 4·5 Normal distribution of variances required

In using the analysis of variance it should be noted that the method is based on the assumption that the distribution of the variances of the samples must approach normality. Whenever there is any doubt on this point the distribution of the variances should be examined. An example of the frequency of the variances of 162 individual samples of the vertebral count of herring from various localities in southeastern Alaska (from Rounsefell and Dahlgren 1935) is given in Table 4·2.

TABLE 4·2

| Variance | Number | Variance | Number |
|---|---|---|---|
| 0.16–0.23 | 1 | 0.88–0.95 | 2 |
| 0.24–0.31 | 16 | 0.96–1.03 | |
| 0.32–0.39 | 25 | 1.04–1.11 | |
| 0.40–0.47 | 38 | 1.12–1.19 | |
| 0.48–0.55 | 30 | 1.20–1.27 | 1 |
| 0.56–0.63 | 19 | 1.28–1.35 | |
| 0.64–0.71 | 15 | 1.36–1.43 | 2 |
| 0.72–0.79 | 9 | 1.44–1.51 | 1 |
| 0.80–0.87 | 3 | 1.52–1.59 | |

The variances of the last four samples (variances from 1.20 to 1.51) are obviously far outside the normal range and must be discarded before making an analysis.

#### 4·6 Effect of errors in age determination

In comparing enumeration data on fish of the same year class it must be remembered that with practically all species there is a certain amount of error in the determination of age. In comparing counts from two localities it is wise to forego comparison between samples of less than about 50. As an added precaution probabilities greater than 0.01 should not be interpreted as necessarily significant.

#### 4·7 Comparison of means. Pooled estimate of the variance

If an analysis of variance has disclosed that the samples from a region are not all drawn from the same population you may wish specific information as to the significance or nonsignificance of differences between counts from individual localities. The usual method of determining the significance of the difference between two means, $\bar{x}$ and $\bar{y}$, is to divide their difference by the standard error of the difference computed by the formula

$$\sigma_{\bar{x}-\bar{y}} = \sqrt{\sigma_{\bar{x}}^2 + \sigma_{\bar{y}}^2}$$

in which $\sigma_{\bar{x}}$ and $\sigma_{\bar{y}}$ are the standard errors of the respective means.

However, when two samples differ in size the standard error of the difference computed in this manner is not an efficient statistic. To extract all of the relevant information and at the same time to avoid over- or underestimating the significance of the difference, which can be done easily if the standard deviations of the two samples are dissimilar, the standard error of the difference should be estimated by making a pooled estimate of the variance. The formula is

$$\sigma_{\text{difference}} = \sqrt{\frac{S(x - \bar{x})^2 + S(y - \bar{y})^2}{n_1 + n} \left(\frac{1}{n_1 + 1} + \frac{1}{n_2 + 1}\right)}$$

if $x_1, x_2 \cdots x_{n_1} + 1$ and $y_1, y_2 \cdots y_{n_2} + 1$ be two samples, and $\bar{x}$ equals $1/(n_1 + 1)S(x)$, $\bar{y}$ equals $1/(n_2 + 1)S(y)$.

An example of such a comparison between the means of the vertebral counts of herring of the 1926 year class from Juneau and Petersburg is given in Table 4·3.

TABLE 4·3

Number of Vertebrae

| Locality | 49 | 50 | 51 | 52 | 53 | 54 | 55 | Number | Mean | $S(x - \bar{x})^2$ |
|---|---|---|---|---|---|---|---|---|---|---|
| Juneau | | | 1 | 37 | 183 | 150 | 18 | | 389 | 52.378 | 207.450 |
| Petersburg | 1 | 3 | 64 | 274 | 144 | 7 | 1 | 494 | 52.178 | 250.324 |

$$\sigma_{\text{difference}} = \sqrt{\frac{207.450 + 250.324}{388 + 493} \left(\frac{1}{389} + \frac{1}{494}\right)} = 0.049$$

Difference between means equals 52.378 − 52.178 or 0.200

$\dfrac{0.200}{0.049} = 4.08$ which is a deviate of a normal curve and the probability of its occurrence can be ascertained from any probability integral table or from the $t$ tables of Fisher (1930) or Snedecor (1940).

Since for 881 degrees of freedom a $t$ of 2.58 yields a probability of occurrence of 0.01 it is obvious that a $t$ of 4.08 is highly significant, its expected occurrence being only one in 10,000 to 100,000 similar comparisons.

### 4·8 Morphometric characters. Analysis of covariance

These are measurements of various body proportions, such as the length of the head, of the snout, the interorbital width, and the distances from the tip of the snout to the insertions of the various fins. These measurements are usually expressed as percentages of the body length, or of some other measurement. However, the proportion between the measurements usually changes as fish increase in size. Most of the methods used for comparing morphometric measurements do not yield efficient comparisons.

The efficient method is that of the analysis of covariance, developed by Fisher (1930) and adequately explained by Snedecor (1940). Application of this method to morphometric data was made by Mottley (1941) to determine whether or not there was a significant difference in head length between the populations of Kamloops trout, a variety of *Salmo gairdneri,* in two lakes.

The first step is to transform both head lengths and the body lengths into logarithms. The example in Table 4·4 is adapted from Mottley, using the notation of Snedecor.

TABLE 4·4

SHOWING THE TEST OF SIGNIFICANCE OF THE DIFFERENCE BETWEEN MEAN HEAD LENGTHS ($\bar{y}$) OF MALE TROUT, ADJUSTED FOR DIFFERENCES IN MEAN BODY LENGTH ($\bar{x}$) (Adapted from Mottley 1941.)

| Lakes | Number in Sample | Degrees of Freedom | Sum $x^2$ | Sum $xy$ | Sum $y^2$ | Degrees of Freedom | Sum of Squares | Variance |
|---|---|---|---|---|---|---|---|---|
| | | | | | | | Standard Error of Estimate * | |
| Kootenay | 50 | 49 | 2.04777 | 2.17892 | 2.35846 | 48 | 0.03999 | |
| Wilson | 10 | 9 | .13389 | .14850 | .16570 | 8 | .001 | |
| Within lakes | 60 | 58 | 2.18166 | 2.32742 | 2.52416 | 57 | .04124 | 0.000724 |
| | | | | | | | | |
| Total | | | | | | 58 | .04926 | |
| Within lakes | | | | | | 57 | .04124 | .000724 |
| | | | | | | | | |
| Between adjusted means | | | | | | 1 | .00802 | .00802 |

$$F = 0.00802/0.000724 = 11.08, \quad n_1 = 1, \quad n_2 = 57$$

\* Sum of squares = $Sy^2 - (Sxy)^2/Sx^2$, $2.35846 - (2.17892)^2/2.04777 = 0.03999$

Variance = sum of squares/degrees of freedom: $0.04124/57 = 0.000724$

In Table 4·4 the sums of $x^2$, $y^2$, and $xy$ are computed by standard regression methods; the sums are not shown for the total, but they were computed from the mean for the combined samples. The sum of squares for the standard error of estimate (this is the dispersion of the $y$ values about each regression line) is calculated by the formula

$$Sy^2 - (Sxy)^2/Sx^2$$

$y$ is the logarithm of the head length, $x$ the logarithm of the body length. Section 4·4 explains $F$.

What this analysis measures is whether or not the head lengths in each sample fit their own regression line (logarithm of head length on logarithm of body length) significantly better than they fit the regression line of the combined samples, after allowance has been made for the differences in body length.

## 4·9   Comparison of age composition.   Use of chi-square

The age composition of samples may furnish a clue to racial stocks. As an example the following age distributions of herring are from samples taken 60 miles apart, one from Shuyak Strait on Afognak Island and the other from lower Kachemak Bay at the mouth of Cook Inlet, Alaska.

The formula for $X^2$, the measure of discrepancy, is $X^2 = S(x^2/m)$ when $m$ is the number expected and $m + x$ is the number observed. Where the expected number is the same for both distributions we may add $x^2$ and $x'^2$ before dividing by $m$.

TABLE 4·5

<small>AGE FREQUENCIES OF HERRING FROM TWO LOCALITIES AND THEIR COMPARISON BY CHI-SQUARE</small>

| Age | Observed | | | Expected | | Differences | | Measure of Divergence | |
| --- | --- | --- | --- | --- | --- | --- | --- | --- | --- |
| | Shuyak Strait, July 1926 $(m + x)$ | Lower Kachemak Bay, August 1926 $(m' + x')$ | Sum | Shuyak Strait $(m)$ | Lower Kachemak Bay $(m')$ | $x$ | $x$ | $x^2/m$ | $x'^2/m'$ |
| 1 | | | | | | | | | |
| 2 | | 5 | | | | | | | |
| 3 | | 3 | | | | | | | |
| 4 | 1 | 5 | 14 | 3.3 | 10.7 | −2.3 | 2.3 | 1.603 | 0.494 |
| 5 | 6 | 14 | 20 | 4.7 | 15.3 | 1.3 | −1.3 | .360 | .110 |
| 6 | 10 | 30 | 40 | 9.5 | 30.5 | .5 | −.5 | .026 | .008 |
| 7 | 2 | 9 | 11 | 2.6 | 8.4 | −.6 | .6 | .138 | .043 |
| 8 | 16 | 55 | 71 | 16.8 | 54.2 | −.8 | .8 | .038 | .012 |
| 9 | 16 | 58 | 74 | 17.5 | 56.5 | −1.5 | 1.5 | .129 | .040 |
| 10 | 3 | 12 | 15 | 3.6 | 11.4 | −.6 | .6 | .100 | .032 |
| 11 | 6 | 14 | 20 | 4.7 | 15.3 | 1.3 | −1.3 | .360 | .110 |
| 12 | 13 | 33 | 46 | 10.9 | 35.1 | 2.1 | −2.1 | .405 | .126 |
| 13 | 1 | 5 | 10 | 2.4 | 7.6 | .6 | −.6 | .150 | .047 |
| 14 | 2 | | | | | | | | |
| 15 | | 1 | | | | | | | |
| 16 | | | | | | | | | |
| 17 | | 1 | | | | | | | |
| Total | 76 | 245 | 321 | 76.0 | 245.0 | | | 3.309 | 1.022 |

$$X^2 = 3.309 + 1.022 = 4.331, \quad df = 9, \quad P = 0.90\%$$

The age frequencies from 2 to 4 and from 13 to 17 years have been grouped, as $X^2$ is not reliable for too small frequencies. Usually frequencies less than 5 are grouped together. The probability of $X^2$ is obtained from $X^2$ tables (see Fisher 1930 et seq., Snedecor 1940 et seq.). The probability obtained of 0.90 indicates that in nine times out of ten samples from the same population would be expected to diverge as much as these two. Therefore, the probability is very high that the two samples came from the same population.

### 4·10    Other indicators

The existence of separate populations may be indicated in other ways. For instance, the rate of growth may often show marked differences. These may be of two kinds:

1. Differences in the general rate of growth throughout the life span of the fish.

2. Differences in the rate of growth during a particular portion of the life span, especially the early stages. The second is usually caused by some difference in the environment whereby the fish spawned in one locality grow significantly larger in the early stages. Such differences in growth may be indelibly stamped on the scale so that fish from a particular spawning locality can be traced. Methods for analyzing growth data are given in Chapter 19.

Differences between populations are sometimes shown by differences in the years of periodic abundance and scarcity. Thus the pink salmon (*Oncorhynchus gorbuscha*), which matures at two years of age and dies after spawning, is very abundant in the streams of Puget Sound and the Fraser River in the odd-numbered years, but is totally absent from most of these streams in the even-numbered years. In the region to the north the cycles tend to be more equal, although in some streams the odd-year run is scarce or missing.

### 4·11    Recovery of marked individuals

The most direct means of studying populations is through the release and recapture of marked individuals. In the example in Table 4·6, 1000 marked fish were released near the center of a 500-mile stretch of coastline several months in advance of the regular fishing season. The actual recoveries made during the fishing season were then compared to the number of recoveries expected in each area if the catch was all from one population and if the marked fish were randomly distributed throughout such a population. It is clear that the recoveries do not conform to this hypothesis. In cases where there is doubt the observed and expected should be compared by the chi-square method of Section 4·9.

TABLE 4·6

HYPOTHETICAL EXAMPLE TO ILLUSTRATE METHOD OF COMPARING RECOVERIES
OF MARKED FISH TO THE CATCH

| Area, Miles of Coast | Number Marked | Numbers in Catch * | Number of Recoveries Observed | Number of Recoveries Expected |
|---|---|---|---|---|
| 0–100 | | 150 | 0 | 84 |
| 100–200 | | 200 | 50 | 113 |
| 200–300 | 1000 | 120 | 200 | 68 |
| 300–400 | | 50 | 40 | 28 |
| 400–500 | | 30 | 20 | 17 |
| Total | 1000 | 550 | 310 | 310 |

* In hundred thousands.

**References**

Clothier, Charles R.
   1950. A key to some southern California fishes based on vertebral characters. Calif. Div. Fish and Game, *Bur. Mar. Fish., Fish Bull. 79:* 83 pp.
Fisher, R. A.
   1930. Statistical methods for research workers. 3 ed. Oliver and Boyd: 283 pp., Edinburgh.
Heincke, F.
   1898. Naturgeschichte des Herings. I. Die Lokal formen und die Wanderungen des Heringes in den europaischen Meeren. *Abh. Deutsch. Seefischerei Ver., 2* (1):CXXXVI, 128 pp.
Mottley, Charles M.
   1941. The covariance method of comparing the head-lengths of trout from different environments. *Copeia,* 1941 (3):154–159.
Rounsefell, George A., and Edwin H. Dahlgren
   1932. Fluctuations in the supply of herring, *Clupea pallasii* in Prince William Sound, Alaska. *Bull. U. S. Bur. Fish. 47* (9):263–291.
Rounsefell, George A., and Edwin H. Dahlgren
   1935. Races of herring, *Clupea pallasii,* in southeastern Alaska. *Bull. U. S. Bur. Fish. 48* (17):119–141.
Snedecor, George W.
   1940. *Statistical methods.* 3 ed. Iowa State College Press: 422 pp., Ames.

# 5 · EFFECTS OF EXPLOITATION

## 5·1  Introduction

The ability to recognize the stage of abundance of a population is very important.  The population growth curve is typically a sigmoid curve similar to the growth curve of an individual, the relative growth rate of a population like that of an individual constantly declining with increasing size (see Chapter 19).  There is one distinction that should be noted.  Any population growth curve describes a population for only one set of conditions; for example, when a population has almost reached its maximum size so that the curve is approaching close to the asymptote a sudden increase in available food or space may cause the population to resume rapid growth.  In terms of an individual one might say that a senescent population had been rejuvenated.  The population curve for the new set of conditions has a higher asymptote so that the existing population in terms of the new curve is closer to the point of inflection where population growth is most rapid.

Students of fisheries do not all agree on the relative importance of the various criteria that have been used to indicate the relative stage of population abundance, but each one will be treated on its merits.

## 5·2  Decrease in age and size

A decrease in the age and size of the individuals in a fish population has long been regarded as an indication of a diminution in numbers. To be a valid indication it must not be accompanied by a decrease in rate of growth.  In fish populations in which several age classes are normally present such an indication is usually valid if it is a long-term trend.  Obviously, this criterion has little practical value for species in which the annual success of spawning is highly variable, since it depends largely on the relationship in numbers between age classes, which is upset by uneven annual recruitment to the population. In recent years because of the adoption and use of various other means for measuring population size it is not so often necessary to employ this measure.

One fault of this method is that it only yields an indication of what is happening during the time that a change in population level is taking place. Once a population has become diminished to the point where the increase in reproductive potential plus increased growth rate permits the population to maintain itself at a lower level of abundance, the age and size again remain stable. Samples taken at this time will give no indication that the population was formerly more abundant.

## 5·3   Change in species composition

One criterion of abundance for the total populations of all species in a body of water is changes in the relative numbers of the different species. This occurs because practically all forms of fishing gear are more or less selective as to the species taken. Under such circumstances a species that is especially vulnerable will decrease more rapidly than the others.

If the most vulnerable species is not the principal object of the fishery, but it is taken by the same gear and at the same time and in the same localities as the principal species sought, then it may reach an exceedingly low level. This follows because it is still taken by the gear fishing for the dominant species long after it is so scarce that its pursuit would not be profitable. On the North Atlantic fishing banks the large otter trawlers seek chiefly for haddock or rosefish but take halibut incidentally. The result is that the halibut, which is very vulnerable to the otter trawl, has declined to a low level. The only exception is on certain exceedingly rough trawling grounds on La Have and Quereau Banks where the bottom terrain serves as a protection.

This change in species composition is sometimes made evident when a fishery finds it necessary to shift fishing effort from one species to another. Thus the New England otter trawl fleet once concentrated its effort on haddock (*Melanogrammus aeglefinus*), but as the population declined they became scarce over vast areas of Georges Bank, South Channel, and the Gulf of Maine. The vessels then began fishing at times principally for cod (*Gadus morrhua*), pollock (*Pollachius virens*), rosefish (*Sebastes marinus*), gray sole (*Glyptocephalus cynoglossus*), and yellowtail flounder (*Limanda ferruginea*).

## 5·4   Stunting of populations by removal of predators

One effect of exploitation that surprised many conservationists has been the overpopulation of many bodies of water by stunted fish. This is especially true in warm-water sport fisheries. As the larger fish are taken there often remains no effective control on the survival of young with the result that many lakes and ponds are unable to furnish sufficient food to permit normal growth. The size limits that are imposed in many areas only aggravate the situation.

## 5·5   Decrease in areal distribution and abundance of young

The decline of a population is sometimes shown by the contraction of the area formerly inhabited by the young. In schooling pelagic species with buoyant or semibuoyant eggs the decline in size of the adult spawning population may be indicated by the shrinkage of the area in which spawning occurs, as shown by the catches of eggs and larvae by tow nets.

In some fisheries, such as that for the Pacific halibut (*Hippoglossus stenolepis*), in which it is difficult to estimate the numbers and distribution of spawning adults over a vast area, the abundance of young as estimated from widely scattered tow net catches has been used to indicate changes in the actual numbers of spawners (Thompson and Van Cleve 1936).

## 5·6   Decline in catch per unit of effort

One of the most immediate and noticeable effects of declining abundance is usually a drop in the catch per unit of fishing effort. This may not be infallible for, as explained in Chapter 7, it may be caused in part by competition between increased numbers of fishing units. Because of many factors that influence the availability of fish to the fishing gear any sudden drop in the catch per unit of effort should be regarded with suspicion. It may be only a temporary phenomenon. A gradual decline over a long period of time is more apt to indicate an actual decrease in numbers.

## 5·7   Economic levels of abundance

The abundance of fish is governed to a very large extent by economic laws. The distance that vessels travel from port to the grounds fished is determined by the price received, the time consumed in travel, and the abundance of fish. It is therefore axiomatic that fish populations are almost always least abundant close to port and that the abundance tends to rise as the distance increases. If the price remains fairly stable over a long period the abundance of fish in each area will tend to vary directly with its distance from port. Whenever the price rises, it will become economically feasible to fish for populations that were formerly below a profitable level of abundance, and the populations close to port will be driven to a lower level. The change from gasoline to Diesel engines had almost the same effect as a price rise as it permitted more economical vessel operation, but it also greatly extended the total distance from port that could be fished profitably. Whenever the price of fish falls these economic levels of abundance assume major importance. Often the only vessels that can operate profitably are those that can fish the more abundant populations on the distant

FIG. 5·1  A large modern otter trawler. This is the type that takes the largest share of the haddock and other groundfish landed in New England. (Credit: Howard Schuck, U. S. Fish and Wildlife Service)

grounds and vessels with a short cruising radius may be eliminated.

This economic level of abundance for commercial species is paralleled by similar conditions in sport fisheries. In heavily populated areas all easily accessible waters are usually overfished. The result is seen in the heavy and continued stocking of legal-sized trout in streams close to large cities. These streams are fished beyond the "profitable" level, and fishing of a sort can be maintained only by artificial means. The advent of the airplane, like the adoption of the Diesel engine by the fishing fleet, has tremendously expanded the areas exploited by the sport fisherman and lowered the level of abundance in areas that were once too distant to be subjected to heavy fishing.

## 5·8 Shift in fishing grounds

One effect of exploitation often has been a shift in fishing grounds. As the populations on one bank become reduced in numbers the fleet moves to another. This shift in fishing grounds may keep the catch per unit of effort from falling, thus masking a successive depletion until the fleet has exploited all banks within a profitable cruising radius or until the fleet reaches banks exploited by vessels from another port.

**References**

Graham, Michael
  1943. *The Fish Gate.* Faber and Faber, Ltd.: 196 pp., London.
Russell, E. S.
  1942. *The overfishing problem.* University Press: 130 pp., Cambridge.
Thompson, W. F., and Richard Van Cleve
  1936  Life history of the Pacific halibut. (2) Distribution and early life history. *Rept. Int. Fish. Comm. 9:* 3-184.

# 6 · FACTORS AFFECTING ESTIMATION
## OF POPULATION SIZE

## 6·1 Introduction

The harvesting of a crop of fish presents most of the same problems encountered in raising livestock. Enough must be sold each year to prevent overcompetition for food. The youngest are left because they are growing most rapidly and are therefore converting a larger proportion of the available food into body substance. A sufficient number of adults are left to insure an adequate number of young in future years. Seldom, however, does the fishery biologist have at his command all of the information at the disposal of the livestock breeder. He must employ indirect methods to estimate the amount of available food, the total number of fish in the population, and the number at each age.

A great deal has been written concerning the estimation of population parameters, such as size, mortality, and growth. Many of the methods for estimating these parameters or "constants" involve the use of formulas which depend for their validity on certain assumptions concerning either the fishery, the population, or both. Although it is granted that when *all* of the assumptions hold true the populations may be more accurately estimated by the employment of these methods, it is evident that they do not, in themselves, yield any proof of the correctness of the underlying assumptions.

Before discussing the methods by which population size may be estimated it would be well to consider a few practical aspects of the application of the information to fishery management. In managing a fishery it is rarely possible either to adjust the intensity of fishing within narrow confines or to predict within a small range what effect any particular intensity of fishing will have on the catch. The effect of the number of adults on the number of young produced, the survival rate of these young, and the season and age at which the young will become available to the fishery are also variable, depending largely on hydrographic or climatic conditions that cannot be foreseen at the time the management measures are put into effect. Because of these facts the size of populations can usually be estimated as closely as is compatible with the use to be made of the information without resort to minute refinements.

## 6·2    Total catch as an indicator of population size

Perhaps the only information available on which to base an estimate of the size of a population may be the total annual catch.  Despite the reasons that can be advanced against employing it to indicate population size it may often yield sufficient information for management purposes.  This is especially true if it be coupled with general knowledge of the fishery and of the biology of the species.  Here one may wish to distinguish between knowledge that indicates the necessity for action and knowledge that indicates what action needs to be taken.  Total catch data may point out that a fishery is in a dangerous condition, but they must be supplemented in order for the underlying causes to be understood, so that the difficulty may be diagnosed and a plan of action formulated.

Examples are given in Table 6·1 of total catch figures for two fish populations: the sockeye salmon of the Fraser River and the Pacific halibut south of Cape Spencer, Alaska.  A cursory examination is enough to reveal that in both cases the fisheries had reached a peak and then declined.  Additional information is necessary for interpretation.  This information can be of two kinds—biological information and information concerning the conduct of the fishery.

The items of paramount interest are those that affect the stability of the population.  Some of these items are as follows:

|  | Sockeye | Halibut |
|---|---|---|
| 1. What is the age at maturity? | 4 years, a few 5. | 8–16 years, average 12. |
| 2. How many age groups are caught? | One plus. | Many. |
| 3. Is natural mortality high? | Yes, total. | No. |
| 4. Are immature fish caught? | No. | Yes. |
| 5. How uniform is survival of young? | Quite. | Very. |
| 6. Where do they spawn? | Stream gravel bars. | Ocean banks. |
| 7. How often is each adult subject to capture? | During spawning migration. | Continuously. |
| 8. Are they captured throughout their range? | No. | Yes. |
| 9. What is their habitat classification? | Lacustrine anadromous. | Benthic. |
| 10. At what seasons are they captured? | Summer and autumn. | All seasons. |
| 11. With what types of gear are they caught? | Traps, seines, gill nets, reef nets. | Hook and line. |

TABLE 6·1

EXAMPLES OF TOTAL ANNUAL CATCHES OF FISH

| Year | Fraser River Sockeye Salmon * | Halibut South of Cape Spencer † | Year | Fraser River Sockeye Salmon * | Halibut South of Cape Spencer † |
|------|------|------|------|------|------|
| 1893 | 624  | ...  | 1914 | 569 | 453 |
| 1894 | 428  | ...  | 1915 | 183 | 450 |
| 1895 | 515  | 43   | 1916 | 129 | 302 |
| 1896 | 430  | ...  | 1917 | 688 | 316 |
| 1897 | 1442 | ...  | 1918 | 81  | 271 |
| 1898 | 504  | ...  | 1919 | 125 | 274 |
| 1899 | 1137 | 89   | 1920 | 121 | 332 |
| 1900 | 439  | ...  | 1921 | 169 | 375 |
| 1901 | 2576 | ...  | 1922 | 109 | 313 |
| 1902 | 718  | 223  | 1923 | 86  | 288 |
| 1903 | 425  | ...  | 1924 | 121 | 270 |
| 1904 | 240  | 281  | 1925 | 183 | 239 |
| 1905 | 2068 | 221  | 1926 | 138 | 258 |
| 1906 | 410  | ...  | 1927 | 178 | 246 |
| 1907 | 172  | 500  | 1928 | 94  | 272 |
| 1908 | 275  | ...  | 1929 | 206 | 263 |
| 1909 | 2093 | ...  | 1930 | 459 | 226 |
| 1910 | 446  | 518  | 1931 | 143 | 225 |
| 1911 | 218  | 569  | 1932 | 159 | 229 |
| 1912 | 336  | 604  | 1933 | 245 | 236 |
| 1913 | 3134 | 562  |      |     |     |

\* Number of fish in tens of thousands.
† Pounds of fish in hundreds of thousands.

The total catch figures of Table 6·1 begin to take on meaning when viewed in the light of the above questions and answers. Thus the answers to questions 1, 2, and 3 explain the unmistakable 4-year periodicity in the sockeye catches. The answers to the first five questions largely explain the gradual trend in the halibut landings. Of course it is generally realized that the size of the catch does not necessarily closely reflect the true size of the population. The catch depends not only on the actual abundance of fish but also on the number and efficiency of the units of fishing gear, on the length of time they operate, and on the availability of the fish to be captured.

## 6·3   Errors inherent in ratio method

Because all of the adult population of each cycle of sockeyes dies after spawning there is no carryover from year to year, and each 4-year cycle is in reality a more or less distinct stock of fish as far as management is concerned. In lieu of any of the better-known methods for indicating abundance attempts have been made to determine sockeye abundance by obtaining the ratio between the catch in one year $Y_4$ and the catch 4 years previously $Y_0$. This overlooks one very important point. In using the $Y_4/Y_0$ index one must realize that if the regression is linear and of the form $y = a + bx$ then the rate $y/x$ or $Y_4/Y_0$ is not constant. Only if $a = 0$ does the line pass through the origin on both scales, making the rate $y/x$ always equal to the constant $b$. We do not recommend this method for interpreting total catches despite its deceptive simplicity.

## 6·4   Fishing effort and availability

As the total catch is a product of fishing effort times availability we should next consider these two factors. By "fishing effort" we mean any combination of time and gear that can be readily standardized, such as one set of a skate of halibut gear, one day's fishing of a trapnet, one night's drifting of a gillnet, one hour of flycasting, and so forth. By "availability" we mean whether or not the fish are always taken with equal readiness by any particular form of gear. Most species of fish vary from one portion of the fishing season to another in their vulnerability to the fisherman. Such changes in seasonal availability must be measured and allowed for in computing abundance.

## 6·5   Effect of competition on catch per unit of effort

For many years the catch per unit of fishing effort has been regarded as a reliable measure of relative abundance. Though often this may be true, when the fishery annually catches a large proportion of the population it may be quite the reverse. This follows from the competition between units of fishing effort. Some fishery workers have assumed that "competition" applies only in situations where fish such as salmon enter a restricted area so that there is an obvious physical interference between the units of fishing gear. This view of "competition" is statistically unsound on two counts. First, there is no essential difference between catching salmon or halibut. Both populations are limited, and a large proportion of each is taken annually, so that the notion that units of gear would divide salmon but not halibut must be discarded. Second, the implied idea that the catch bears little relation to the amount of fishing effort but is merely divided among the units is also unsound, as the degree of competition between units of fishing effort, as will be shown later, is not a constant, but decreases logarithmically as the number of units increases.

## 6·6   Adjustment of catch per unit of effort to obtain relative abundance at beginning of each season

Another reason for the catch per unit failing to portray the actual population size can often be found in the fact that the catch per unit is the average catch over the entire fishing season, whereas we desire to know the relative abundance at the beginning of the fishing season.   Schuck (1949) has developed a method for obtaining the relative abundance at the beginning of the fishing season for haddock, which can be used for other fisheries in which age can be readily determined.

Essentially the method consists of first determining the relative numbers of fish of each age group in the catch, weighted by the abundance index.   The numbers for the last half of one year are then combined with those from the first half of the next year and the average is taken.   The last half of the year must contain the fish that will be added to the population as recruits of the succeeding age group in the first half of the next year.   Thus for haddock the 3-year-olds from the last half of one year are added to the 4-year-olds of the first half of the next year to estimate the relative abundance of 4-year-olds at the beginning of the year.

## 6·7   Halibut as an example of a stable population

The halibut fisheries perhaps present the least complicated situation for determining the relative abundance of a population.   The fish are benthic; only the very large (mature) specimens are at all migratory; they are slow growing so that many age classes are represented in the catch, and annual recruitment to the population tends to be uniform, or at least the incoming age class is such a small part of the numerous age classes present that recruitment apparently does not often disturb the trend.of abundance.

The fishery itself is also very simple in character.   Until the very recent appearance of otter trawlers, fishing on the halibut banks was solely by hook and line.   The take of one set of a unit of hook-and-line gear (called a "skate" by the fishermen owing to the shape of the canvas in which each unit is tied) forms a convenient and easily standardized unit of fishing effort.   Study of this example will serve as a background for developing methods to fit more complicated conditions.

The total annual catch, the number of units of gear fished, and the catch per unit of fishing effort for the halibut from the banks south of Cape Spencer, Alaska, from 1910 to 1933 have been taken from a report of the International Fisheries Commission (Thompson and Bell 1934). A summary is given in Table 6·2.

TABLE 6·2

| Period | Catch, Hundred Thousands | Skates Fished, Thousands | Catch per Skate, Pounds | Increase in Number of Skates, % | Decrease in Catch per Skate, % | Decrease in Total Catch, % |
|---|---|---|---|---|---|---|
| 1—1910–13 | 2253 | 1,210 | 186 | | | |
| 2—1914–17 | 1521 | 1,397 | 109 | 15.5 | 41.4 | 32 |
| 3—1918–21 | 1252 | 1,523 | 82 | 9.0 | 24.8 | 18 |
| 4—1922–25 | 1110 | 1,950 | 57 | 28.0 | 30.5 | 11 |
| 5—1926–29 | 1039 | 2,215 | 47 | 13.5 | 17.5 | 7 |
| 6—1930–33 | 916 | 2,102 | 44 | −5.0 | 6.4 | 12 |
| Total | 8091 | 10,397 | 78 | 74.0 | 76.5 | 59 |

These data show several things about the population of halibut. The catch per skate had fallen by the sixth period to 24 per cent of its level in the first 4-year period, but the total catch fell to only 41 per cent of its first level. The interplay of total catch and catch per unit of effort is somewhat obscured by a concomitant increase in the number of skates of gear fished. It increased 74 per cent in the same period of time. As the total catch decreased markedly in the face of increased fishing effort there is no doubt about a decrease in the total population, but there is likewise little question that the decrease in population was greater than the decline to 41 per cent of the former level as shown by the catch.

Because many of the formulas that have been advanced and that are being used in estimating relative or absolute population size are predicated upon a lack of competition between units of fishing effort it is of interest to note what that assumption would entail in this case.

If we exchange numbers of skates of gear in the first and sixth periods, and assume that as the gear is noncompetitive the catch per skate would have remained the same, the catch in the first period would have been 3910 and in the sixth period 532, or a decrease by the sixth period to 13.5 per cent instead of 41 per cent of the first period level. Obviously then, competition existed between units of fishing effort that tended to lower the efficiency of the units as their number increased.  This is clearly shown by Figure 6·1 in which the logarithms of the three variables are plotted.  Owing to this competition the catch per skate fell at a faster rate than the total catch.

It will be noted that the greatest drop in catch occurred in the early periods before the fishery reached its greatest intensity.  This often

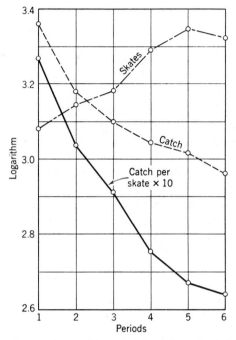

Fɪɢ. 6·1   Showing skates of gear fished, total catch, and catch per skate for the halibut fishery.

occurs in the first heavy exploitation by man of a species as the natural population usually has a large number of older individuals that cannot be quickly replaced.  However, the maximum that a population can produce on a sustained basis is reached when the largest proportion of the available food is being converted into fish flesh instead of being utilized for maintenance of basal metabolism.  Growth is slow when the population is too old, so that a drop in numbers when a fishery is first intensively exploited is usually inevitable.  If the population is overexploited the increase in rate of growth and in survival rate of the young may not be sufficient to maintain the population at its most productive level.

Not all populations are as stable as the halibut. Most fish populations exhibit a greater variability in the annual recruitment of young,
especially coastal, estuarine, and pelagic species.

## 6·8   Herring as an example of a fluctuating population

The herring is an excellent example of a species subject to great
natural fluctuations in abundance. Fluctuations of this type appear
to be caused by great differences from year to year in the survival
of young. In the Pacific herring the survival rate is related to surface
water temperature during and after the spawning season (Rounsefell
1930), whereas survival in the Pacific sardine has been shown by
Walford (1946) to be closely correlated with ocean salinity. In bank-
dwelling species survival may often depend on whether the ocean
currents drift the pelagic larvae away from or toward the banks at
the stage when they are ready to settle to the bottom.

Owing to this uneven survival the age composition of the population
may be extremely unstable; in some years the average age will be
greatly decreased if an exceedingly abundant year class of recruits is
added to the population. Conversely, a period of several years may
elapse in which survival is poor, and the population will consist chiefly
of older (and larger) individuals.

This uneven survival of young causes great economic losses to the
fishing industry which must sometimes shift its type of product from
year to year to utilize whatever size of fish are available and must
accumulate sufficient reserves in good years to tide over periods of
scarcity.

The estimation of abundance is for several reasons rendered more
difficult by these variations in survival. The younger and older fish
may not frequent the same areas. The large sardines, for instance,
feed in the northern part of their range and at times have supported
fisheries as far north as British Columbia while the smaller sizes tend
to remain off the California coast, there being a gradation in size from
British Columbia south to San Diego. When the average size of the
individual is small the northern fishery may be very poor.

In gregarious species the age composition also affects the behavior
of the fish in another manner. Fish tend to mingle more or less according to size, with adjacent age groups schooling together. When
one or more successive age classes are extremely scarce there is a sharp
break in the size continuity, resulting in distinct schools of fish of
quite different size. It becomes a serious problem to obtain accurate
estimates of the relative abundance of the two groups as usually they

are not available to the fishing gear equally at all seasons or localities. Fish that form dense schools may present a further problem. Some of these species congregate heavily in restricted localities so that good catches may be made even when the population is small. Thus the relationship between actual numbers and the measure used to estimate abundance will not be linear. In such cases a population may be greatly reduced before the fact suddenly becomes evident.

## 6·9   Requirements of measures of fishing effort

The first step in estimating abundance is to try to obtain a measure of fishing effort that will satisfy the following requirements:

1. It should be a time and/or gear unit used by the fisherman or dealer in transacting business.

2. If only a portion of the fishery can be covered the gear units used should be selected objectively.

3. The time portion of a unit of effort should cover definite periods of fishing, and if necessary be stratified for time.

4. Any time breaks should coincide with any factors affecting the availability insofar as these are sufficiently regular to be determined.

5. In a mixed fishery consideration must be given to depths and localities fished, especially in considering fishing effort for species making up only a minor share of the catch. These requirements are discussed in more detail below.

## 6·10   Selection of type of effort unit

If the dealer buys each day's catch from the fisherman, then a day may be a convenient unit of time. For offshore vessels where absences of a few days to a few weeks are common a very good unit of effort becomes more difficult to obtain except when the number of sets of line trawl gear, of lobster pots, scouting time of a purse seine vessel, or the number of drags of an otter trawl are available from vessel log books. In most fisheries good fishing log books are kept only on the larger vessels. For vessels without log books the calculation of fishing time has to allow for running time of the vessel from port to the fishing grounds and back.

## 6·11   Selection of portion of effort data to analyze

It is sometimes necessary to make a selection of the portion of the records to be analyzed when the facilities for analysis are limited, or when the data are either incomplete or too extensive for complete collection.  Several bases for selection are indicated.  If for instance one were studying a harpoon fishery in which the skill of the individual harpooner was the most important factor, then it would be more important to attempt to obtain the catch records of the same fisherman for successive years than to follow individual vessels.  In a great many fisheries there is a large range in the catching ability of different gear units.  In the otter trawl fisheries, for example, the smaller vessels drag a smaller trawl and usually tow it at a lower speed so that their fishing time represents less fishing effort than that of the larger vessels.

One method—and this has some advantages—is to take a random sample each year.  But one great disadvantage lies in the fact that there is a tendency for fishing gear to improve; any decline in abundance would tend to be masked by such gear improvement.  Another method is to select one or more groups of similar vessels and follow their records of catch from year to year.  The method used depends to an extent on the type of index to be calculated, as will be discussed later.

### 6·12    Defining of time units, stratification of time for a creel census

When the unit of fishing effort involves a variable quantity of time it becomes very important that the time be carefully defined.  Certain types of fishing gear operate properly only at specified hours of the day.  Gill nets in clear water usually take fish only at night.  In some river estuaries fish are gillnetted only by day as the luminescence from phosphorescent organisms betrays the net by night whereas the turbidity is sufficient to allow it to fish by day.  The North Atlantic otter trawlers catch the ocean perch (rosefish) only during daylight hours as the fish apparently rise off the bottom at night.  Thus the actual effective fishing day varies in length between winter and summer, and is shortened appreciably by cloudy weather.

When information on the catch per unit of fishing effort must be sought by personal canvass, as when collecting records of sportsmen's catches, complete coverage cannot always be obtained.  To get the most representative sample it is advisable to divide the season into periods and sample a certain number of days in each period.  Because more sportsmen usually fish during the weekends it is usually necessary to also stratify the sample by days of the week, as follows:

| Day of the Week | Period 1 Week No. | | | | | Period 2 Week No. | | | | | Period 3 Week No. | | | | | Total |
|---|---|---|---|---|---|---|---|---|---|---|---|---|---|---|---|---|
| | 1 | 2 | 3 | 4 | 5 | 6 | 7 | 8 | 9 | 10 | 11 | 12 | 13 | 14 | 15 | |
| Sunday | | X | | | X | | X | X | | | | | | X | X | 6 |
| Monday | | | X | X * | | | X | | | | | | X | | | 4 |
| Tuesday | | | | X | | X | | | | | X | X * | | | | 4 |
| Wednesday | | | X | | | | | | X | | | | | X | | 3 |
| Thursday | | X | | | | | | | X | X * | | X | | | | 4 |
| Friday | X | | | | | | | X | | | | | X | | | 3 |
| Saturday | X | | | | X | X | | | | X | X | | | | X | 6 |
| Total | 2 | 2 | 2 | 2 | 2 | 2 | 2 | 2 | 2 | 2 | 2 | 2 | 2 | 2 | 2 | 30 |

* Holidays.

The above gives a sample of how to randomize a creel census. During a period of 105 days a census is taken on only 30 days, but by stratification one obtains a random sample by periods and by days of the week. The three holidays are taken because they cannot otherwise be allowed for, as there will undoubtedly be more fishing on them than on other weekdays. Because more people will fish on weekends they have been sampled more thoroughly. If the first day of the season is highly important, as it is in many areas, it should perhaps be added to the list and treated in the same manner as a holiday.

## 6·13 Removal of effect of lunar cycles and other periodic influences

Oftentimes the unit of fishing effort is the fishing attempts by a piece of fishing gear over a period of several days or even as much as a month. In dividing up time for such purposes it is highly important to synchronize the time divisions to fit in with any influences affecting the catches. Many times we have observed the use of 10-day periods merely because 10 days is about one third of a month. In rough work the 11-day period at the end of a 31-day month may even be included as a 10-day period. Sometimes in these same fisheries there is a weekly period when no fishing is permitted. In such cases the use of a weekly period is almost mandatory. In thus removing any periodic influence it makes no difference on what day the chosen period ends so long as the period is of the same length as that of the influence to be eliminated.

Another influence of no mean importance is that exerted by the lunar cycle. This is of especial importance in many purse seine fisheries for pelagic species, some of which are extremely difficult to take during moonlit nights as the fishermen depend on the luminosity of the school for its detection. Where such is the case the data should be summarized by 29-day periods so that each period will contain all phases of the cycle. In other fisheries the periods of high and low tides must be considered.

## 6·14    Fishing effort in a mixed fishery

Whenever gear is fishing for more than one species extreme caution is necessary to guard against crediting fishing effort directed primarily toward the catching of one species to another species. In Puget Sound the purse seiners fish for sockeye salmon during each season but also fish for the abundant pink salmon on the odd-numbered years. In studying their catches of sockeye salmon it was found that the average catches were consistently lower on the odd-numbered years. The reason was soon discovered. In the fall after sockeye became too scarce to support a profitable fishery the vessels quit fishing on the even-numbered years, but on the alternate years they continued to fish for the pinks, taking small numbers of sockeye in the process.

The same may be said of the North Atlantic otter trawl fishery. As the main species sought after is the haddock, the vessels follow them into whatever depth of water they frequent at any particular season. However, an estimation of the abundance of a minor species may be based on the same records of vessel catches if one credits only the effort expended in the depth zone occupied by that species. For example, when lemon sole, which occupy the shallow areas of the bank, are taken during fishing over the whole bank, only that portion of the time spent in fishing on the shallow areas can be used in estimating their abundance.

## 6·15    Fishing effort involving variable amounts of time

It will be observed that units of effort cannot always be completely standardized. One haul of a seine is an easily comprehended unit that under identical conditions of abundance and availability should yield catches over a small range of sizes. However, when data on effort consist of varying amounts of fishing time no such simple relationship exists. Such a *variable* unit of effort is in reality composed of one or more basic units.  Thus, in the otter trawl fishery, where the drag should be the ideal unit a vessel may average 10 drags a day; but, if the unit of effort is not number of drags but fishing days and is collected by trips, each trip may consist of anywhere from perhaps 10 to 70 or 80 drags.  Fishing trips of a few days' duration will yield usually an average catch per day higher than trips in which the fishing time was much longer because the boats return to port whenever

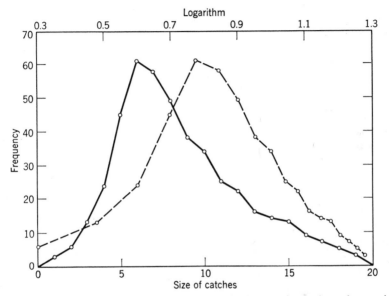

Fig. 6·2  Showing the original and the logarithmic transformation of a typical skewed catch curve.

they have made a reasonable catch.  Nevertheless, on the long trips catches of individual drags may have been just as high as on the short trips.  The records of catches made by varying amounts of fishing effort cannot always be analyzed in exactly the same manner as those collected by identical units of fishing effort.

## 6·16   Skewed catch curves and their transformation

When the records of catches are collected as single units of effort (like one set of a gill net), or by a time period always of equal length—although such a period may contain several sets it is necessarily considered the basic unit in such cases—then the size of the resulting catches usually forms a positively skewed frequency distribution.  The example in Table 6·3 gives the hypothetical size frequency of daily catches of trout by a number of fishermen.

TABLE 6·3

| Size of Catch | Logarithm of Size of Catch | Number of Catches |
|---|---|---|
| 1 |  | 3 |
| 2 | 0.301 | 6 |
| 3 | 0.477 | 13 |
| 4 | 0.602 | 24 |
| 5 | 0.699 | 45 |
| 6 | 0.778 | 61 |
| 7 | 0.845 | 58 |
| 8 | 0.903 | 49 |
| 9 | 0.954 | 38 |
| 10 | 1.000 | 34 |
| 11 | 1.041 | 25 |
| 12 | 1.079 | 22 |
| 13 | 1.114 | 16 |
| 14 | 1.146 | 14 |
| 15 | 1.176 | 13 |
| 16 | 1.204 | 9 |
| 17 | 1.230 | 7 |
| 18 | 1.255 | 5 |
| 19 | 1.279 | 3 |

The distribution is markedly skewed with the mode at six trout. With a logarithmic transformation these characteristic catch frequency curves usually form a curve closely approximating a normal curve as shown by Figure 6·2.

**References**

Rounsefell, George A.
  1930. The existence and causes of dominant year classes in the Alaska herring. *Contributions to marine biology,* Stanford University: 260–270.
Rounsefell, George A., and George B. Kelez
  1938. The salmon and salmon fisheries of Swiftsure Bank, Puget Sound, and the Fraser River. *Bull. U. S. Bur. Fish. 49* (27):693–823.
Schuck, Howard A.
  1949. Relationship of catch to changes in population size of New England haddock. *Biometrics 5* (3):213–231.
Thompson, W. F., and F. Heward Bell
  1934. Biological statistics of the Pacific halibut fishery. (2) Effect of changes in intensity upon total yield and yield per unit of gear. *Rept. Int. Fish. Comm. 8:* 49 pp.
Walford, Lionel A.
  1946. Correlation between flunctuations in abundance of the Pacific sardine (*Sardinops caerulea*) and salinity of the sea water. *J. Mar. Res. 6* (1):48–53.

# 7 · METHODS OF ESTIMATING POPULATION SIZE

## 7·1  Introduction

The size of a population can be obtained either directly or indirectly, but only in special cases can a direct method be employed. In the preceding chapters we have explained many of the difficulties encountered in gathering the necessary basic data, such as availability, standard units of fishing effort, catches by populations, that are prerequisites in making population estimates. Because each author has used his own symbols for the various values used, we have found it necessary to define and use a standard set of symbols throughout this chapter to facilitate comparison of the different methods and of the statistics obtained (see Section 7·15).

## 7·2  Enumeration methods

The simplest methods of estimating population size depend on direct enumeration of a whole or a selected portion of a population. This method when applied to the whole population is of strictly limited application and can be used only when the total population may be confined sufficiently at some stage or stages of its life history to permit taking an actual tally or other quantitative measure of the individuals composing it. It has been applied successfully to salmon and trout populations for 30 years and is applicable to any truly anadromous or adfluvial species wherever the size of the stream and the importance of the information warrant the expense of the necessary trapping facilities.

No estimate of a population can surpass this method for accuracy, and the expense involved in trapping and counting the population may often be as low as the expense of collecting and analyzing data to obtain a population estimate by an indirect method. In order to obtain the total population it is of course necessary to add the catch to the number tallied in the stream. Establishing this catch may sometimes be a serious limitation, as the populations migrating toward two or more adjacent streams may be mingled. The recovery of marked fish in the catch has aided in many cases in disclosing the migration routes toward different rivers, thus yielding a basis for allocating the catch amongst the rivers.

The estimate of the population from this method equals catch plus escapement (survival), that is, $C + S = P$. But by definition (Section 7·15) $P_n = C_n + N_n + S_n$. Therefore this estimate of population size is underestimated by the amount of natural mortality from the time fishing starts until the survival $S$ is counted, if the population is estimated for the beginning of the fishing season. For most anadromous species this is a short period, and the fish are all or predominantly adults in full vigor so that natural mortality can be presumed to be very low.

Not only is this method useful in determining the numbers of adult fish migrating in a stream, but also it has been employed in several instances to obtain the number of young fish that are descending to the lake or sea. Knowledge of the number of young that have survived through their earlier stages to the seaward (or lakeward) migrating stage is of considerable value in predicting the future numbers of older fish.

Farm fish ponds require an occasional population estimate for proper management. Wherever possible they should be built with a large drain emptying into a concrete basin or kettle so that the ponds may be completely drained and a tally of the fish population made. This sort of tally yields the true parameter $P$ for the moment of counting.

The *area-density method* is a means of estimating populations paralleling the total tally method. It likewise depends on enumeration, but differs in that it also depends upon representative sampling. The application is somewhat limited because of the strictness of the underlying assumptions. It is assumed that the population is nonmigratory, at least during the period of sampling. If a population is migratory the method can be employed by simultaneous sampling throughout the population range; however this is seldom possible. This method also assumes that the investigator has sufficient knowledge of the environment to be able to summarize the areas of similar habitat.

The method is especially useful for determining populations in streams sufficiently small to permit sections to be completely blocked with seines and the total population in each section captured by seining, electric shock, or other means. It is important that the sections of stream to be sampled be selected at random. If two or more distinct types of habitat are represented it is best to sample each type in proportion to its area. A hypothetical example follows:

| Habitat | Total Area, 100 Square Yards | Number of Sections | Average Number of Fish per Square Yard |
|---|---|---|---|
| Shallow riffles | 18 | 6 | 4.2 |
| Deep riffles and pools | 30 | 10 | 2.1 |
| Deadwater | 50 | 17 | 0.4 |
| Total | 98 | 33 | |

Clearly the average population per square yard is

$$\frac{(1800)(4.2) + (3000)(2.1) + (5000)(0.4)}{1800 + 3000 + 5000} = \frac{15,860}{9800} = 1.61837$$

and the estimate of the total population is 15,860.

Unless good information is available on which to base exact classification of habitat it is wise to avoid any such attempt. In such cases it is best to sample at regular distances along the stream to avoid any conscious selection of habitat, and to give each type an equal chance to be represented.

One advantage of sampling by different categories is that it may yield valuable information on the distribution of fish by size, age, and abundance in each type of habitat. Of course one may sample a stream by a strictly objective method such as locating sampling points at regular intervals and still use the data to show habitat distribution as well as population size.

The area-density method may be applied also to any bottom-dwelling forms or to nonschooling fish, especially benthic species, in specified areas. The assumption must be made that each sample is from a definite-sized area of the bank. Otherwise the result will be an over- or underestimation of the true population, although the estimate may still be of value as a measure of relative abundance. This method has been applied to clam populations, a clamshell bucket being used that picks up all of the top layer to a depth of several inches over an area of 5 square feet.

It is extremely difficult to determine the exact size of the area from which each sample is taken by any of the conventional types of fishing gear. Perhaps recent developments in underwater photography will overcome this handicap and the method may then find wide use. Either of two methods of procedure seems to be indicated depending upon the manner in which the fish are distributed. If the bank is rather uniformly populated it can be divided into many equal-sized units and each one assigned an identifying symbol.  Any number of these units may then be selected at random to be sampled.

If it is known or strongly suspected that the density of fish on the bank is not uniform but varies according to depth or some other factor, a different procedure may be indicated.  The one we suggest we shall

Fig. 7·1  Taking quantitative samples of quahogs in Rhode Island waters with a clam-shell bucket.  (Credit: Alden P. Stickney, U. S. Fish and Wildlife Service)

call the *density-contour* method.  In this method the bank is divided as before into equal-sized units and a sample or samples are taken near the center of each unit.  Let us assume that each unit is one nautical mile square or 4 million square yards and that the fish population is sampled on 4000 square yards at or near the center of each unit.  The samples yield the numbers of fish shown in Table 7·1.

One now draws density contours on graph paper laid out in squares or on tracing paper laid directly over the nautical chart that has the station positions marked on it.  A sketch is laid out in contours that show densities, for example, of 5, 10, 20, 30, 40, 50, 60, 70, 80, and 90 fish per 4000 square yards. With a planimeter one can quickly deter-

FIG. 7·2  Scup (*Stenotomus*) at 80 fathoms in the Gulf of Mexico, off the Apalachicola River. Taken from the research vessel *Atlantis* with the Ewing underwater camera. (Credit: Woods Hole Oceanographic Institution, by David M. Owen)

mine the number of square miles enclosed by each contour and set up a table thus:

| Density Contour | Square Miles | Difference | Midpoint of Interval | Population per Square Mile Times Number of Miles (Times 1000) |
|---|---|---|---|---|
| 90 | 1.0 | 1.0 | 95 | 95,000 |
| 80 | 2.6 | 1.6 | 85 | 136,000 |
| 70 | 4.5 | 1.9 | 75 | 142,000 |
| 60 | 10.0 | 5.5 | 65 | 357,500 |
| etc. | | | | |

By completing such a table and summing one can arrive at a reasonable estimate of the population.

Another direct-count method, used in Alaska in estimating the escapement of salmon, is to take aerial photographs in strips while flying at a low altitude and then count the salmon in the photographs.

TABLE 7·1

HYPOTHETICAL SAMPLES OF FISH FROM MILE-SQUARE AREAS

|    | A | B | C | D | E | F | G | H | I | J | K | L | M | N | O |
|----|---|---|---|---|---|---|---|---|---|---|---|---|---|---|---|
| 1  |   | 0 | 0 | 0 | 0 | 0 | 1 | 0 | 0 | 0 | 0 | 0 | 0 | 0 |   |
| 2  | 0 | 0 | 2 | 2 | 3 | 5 | 15 | 8 | 5 | 4 | 2 | 0 | 1 | 0 |   |
| 3  | 0 | 1 | 4 | 8 | 12 | 20 | 40 | 20 | 10 | 4 | 10 | 6 | 2 | 0 |   |
| 4  | 0 | 2 | 10 | 40 | 50 | 80 | 60 | 30 | 5 | 10 | 20 | 15 | 5 | 0 | 0 |
| 5  | 1 | 5 | 17 | 60 | 70 | 100 | 90 | 50 | 15 | 20 | 30 | 25 | 10 | 1 | 0 |
| 6  | 0 | 6 | 15 | 35 | 50 | 70 | 80 | 60 | 25 | 40 | 50 | 20 | 8 | 2 | 1 |
| 7  | 0 | 2 | 8 | 10 | 20 | 30 | 50 | 20 | 5 | 10 | 15 | 10 | 3 | 1 | 0 |
| 8  | 0 | 0 | 3 | 5 | 10 | 15 | 7 | 3 · | 1 | 0 | 0 | 0 | 0 | 0 | 0 |
| 9  |   | 0 | 0 | 2 | 5 | 10 | 4 | 1 | 0 |   |   |   |   |   |   |
| 10 |   |   | 0 | 0 | 3 | 10 | 2 | 0 | 0 |   |   |   |   |   |   |
| 11 |   |   |   | 0 | 1 | 5 | 0 | 0 |   |   |   |   |   |   |   |
| 12 |   |   |   | 0 | 0 | 3 | 0 |   |   |   |   |   |   |   |   |

## 7·3   Estimation of total mortality rates from age frequencies

Another method in vogue for determining population size is the age-frequency method, in which one obtains the total mortality rate $r$ from an age-frequency curve and then estimates the population by dividing the total catch by the mortality rate. This method probably owes its popularity to the fact that apparently all the data required are the total catch and a sample of fish scales.

The statistic obtained is $r$, so that one cannot estimate the population $P$. The parameter obtained is $Y_\infty$:

$$Y_\infty = \lim_{t \to \infty} Y = \sum_{t=0}^{\infty} C = \frac{C_0}{r} = \frac{ZP_0}{\Delta}$$

Obviously as $Z$ the instantaneous fishing rate, approaches the total instantaneous mortality rate, $Y_\infty$ approaches $P_0$:

$$\lim_{Z \to \Delta} Y = P_0$$

The method depends on the following assumptions:

1. That the annual recruitment to the population was constant at the time each age group used in the calculations entered the fishery.

2. That the ages can be deciphered with a high degree of accuracy.

3. That natural mortality has been constant over the period involved.

4. That fishing mortality has been uniform over the period involved.

5. That the mortality rate of those age groups that have become fully vulnerable to the fishery is equal between age groups.

6. That the age samples are representative of the vulnerable age groups.

The method furthermore presupposes that enough age groups are present to permit a reliable estimate of the slope of the frequency curve. This practically eliminates many anadromous species such as Atlantic salmon in which the mortality between first and second spawning is of a very high order and largely unrelated to fishing effort. The same probably applies to the shad in which the proportion of fish surviving to spawn more than once falls very markedly toward the southern end of their range. In both species runs to some rivers consist almost entirely of maiden fish.

Assumption 1 eliminates the method for most pelagic species, such as mackerel, herring, or tuna; for striped bass; for such groundfish as cod and haddock with pelagic eggs; and indeed for most marine species that have been investigated, except perhaps the flatfishes.

Assumption 2 is of great importance; yet it is seldom even mentioned in fishery reports. Anyone who has had much experience with deciphering the age of fish from their scales, otoliths, or other hard parts knows that there is always a residue, sometimes a considerable residue of scales that cannot be accurately assigned to an age group. This is especially true among the older fish. Discarding these specimens introduces errors; assigning them by guess to the wrong age group also introduces errors. In fact it may well account for some of the great overlapping of the length frequencies in age groups of older fish.

Assumption 3 is of course difficult to establish. Natural mortality is usually considered to occur at a rather constant rate, but for many species this does not apply. Fluctuations in natural mortality may be caused by epidemics, such as the herring disease; unknown factors, possibly epidemic, such as sudden failure of the smelt fishery of the Great Lakes; winterkill in northern lakes, or cyclic changes which cause populations to wax and wane in abundance.

Assumption 4 (that fishing mortality must be uniform over the period involved) immediately removes the method from consideration in many fisheries; fishing intensity is almost invariably linked closely with economic conditions, and, especially in marginal fisheries, there may be wide annual variations.

Assumption 5 is usually fairly well satisfied although in many species the very old individuals tend to adopt a somewhat different mode of life, changing food, habitat, or migration habits. Thus, although the Pacific halibut normally lives in depths of many fathoms on the banks, the senior author has observed a few halibut of tremendous size preying upon salmon in the shallow mouths of salmon streams.

Assumption 6 (that the age samples are representative of the population) is one that can generally be satisfied by adequate sampling, keeping in mind that the scarce older age groups will not be adequately represented by the same samples that are adequate for the more abundant younger age groups. This method depends upon the determination of the correct slope for the population. As each age group usually is given equal weight in the calculations it is especially important to have these older fish adequately sampled so as to have a sufficient number of reliable age groups. An approximation to the error involved can be obtained by considering the number in each age group in the sample to be the true ratio in the population. Then, if $p$ is the proportion of an age group, and $n$ is the total number in the sample, the standard deviation of the age group is $\sqrt{np(1-p)}$. For example, in a sample of 1000 ages if 200 are 5-year-olds and 20 are 8-year-olds the standard deviations would be calculated thus:

For 5-year-olds    $\sqrt{1000 \times 0.20 \times 0.80} = \sqrt{160} = 12.6$

For 8-year-olds    $\sqrt{1000 \times 0.02 \times 0.98} = \sqrt{19.6} = 4.4$

## 7·4    Computation of total mortality rates from age frequencies

There follows (Table 7·2) an example of the computation of total mortality and survival rates from age frequency. The notation used is:

$f(y)$ = age frequency at any age $(y)$
$y_x$ = age at which all of population become "catchable"
$r$ = annual mortality rate
$s$ = rate of survival
$\Delta$ = instantaneous mortality rate
$1/\log_{10} \epsilon = 2.303$

To compute $\Delta(y)$ the signs of the log differences in column $D$ are changed and then multiplied by 2.303. The equation is

$$\Delta = [\log_{10}(1/s)(1/\log_{10}\epsilon)] = \log \epsilon (1/1 - r)$$

This amounts to multiplying each value in column $D$ by 2.303 and changing the sign. The resulting $\Delta(y)$ for each interval between

TABLE 7·2

EXAMPLE OF COMPUTATION OF MORTALITY AND SURVIVAL RATES

| A | B | C | D | E | F | G | H |
|---|---|---|---|---|---|---|---|
| Age | Age Frequency | Logarithm of Age Frequency | Logarithm of $f(y)$ minus log $f(y-1)$ | $D$ times 2.303 or $1/\log_{10} \epsilon$ | $1-D$ or log $s$ | Antilog of $F$ | $D$ weighted by $f(y)$ |
| $y$ | $f$ | $\log f$ | $\log (1/s)$ | $\Delta(y)$ | $\log s$ | $s(y)$ | $\log (1/s)(w)$ |
| 1 | | | | | | | |
| 2 | 31 | 1.491 | | | | | |
| 3 | 252 | 2.401 | | | | | |
| 4 | 360 | 2.556 | | | | | |
| 5 | 180 | 2.255 | −0.301 | 0.693 | 0.699 | 0.500 | −4.033 |
| 6 | 85 | 1.929 | −.326 | .751 | .674 | .472 | −2.999 |
| 7 | 49 | 1.690 | −.239 | .550 | .761 | .577 | −1.673 |
| 8 | 30 | 1.477 | −.213 | .491 | .787 | .612 | −1.172 |
| 9 | 7 | .845 | −.632 | 1.455 | .368 | .233 | −1.643 |
| 10 | 6 | .778 | −.067 | .154 | .933 | .857 | −.161 |

|  |  |  |
|---|---|---|
| | −1.778 | 4.222 | −11.681 |
| −1.778/6 = | −.2963 | .682 .703 | .505 |

$$\Delta = 0.682$$
$$s = 0.505$$
$$r = 0.495$$

$$-11.681/40.1 = -0.291$$
$$\Delta(w) = \quad 0.670$$
$$1 - 0.291 = \quad 0.709$$
$$s(w) = \quad 0.512$$
$$r(w) = \quad 0.488$$

years is shown in column $E$. The values in column $D$ (with the sign changed) are the logs of $1/s$. To compute $s(y)$ subtract each value from 1 and obtain the antilog. For all·the years $s$ is in reality the geometric mean rate. The equation is

$$\log s = \frac{\left(\sum_{y=x}^{n-1} \log f(y)\right) - \left(\sum_{y=x+1}^{n} \log f(y)\right)}{n}$$

The annual mortality rate, $r = (1 - s)$ or $(1 - \epsilon^{-\Delta})$.

In the example given it is obvious that the values of $f$ at $y = 9$ and $y = 10$ are not so reliable as the values of $f$ from $y = 4$ to $y = 8$. In column $H$ are shown the log differences of column $D$ weighted by the square root of the smaller $f$ in each pair of comparisons. From this we have calculated $\Delta(w)$ and $s(w)$. These values do not depart far from the values computed by the conventional method, and, although it may be an advantage to weight when the samples are small, it is better to take a large enough sample so that no age groups need to be used that are not well represented. This follows because the differences in the rate of decrease are as apt to be caused by actual differences in slope between years as by sampling error.

## 7·5  Fishing mortality ratio from seasonal recovery of marked fish

Estimates of population size often are made from the data of marking experiments. Let us consider an extremely simple case. Of a hypothetical population of 100,000 fish, 5000 are marked and released before the opening of the fishing season. During the fishing season 40,000 fish are captured of which 1600 are found to have been marked. What was the total population?

$$P_1 = 100{,}000, \text{ an unknown parameter}$$
$$T_1 = 5000, \text{ tagged fish released}$$
$$C_1 = 40{,}000, \text{ seasonal catch}$$
$$H_1 = 1600, \text{ tagged fish recaptured}$$

The fishing ratio $f$ from these data is apparently 1600/5000 or 0.32. The estimate of the population $P$ would then be 40,000/0.32 or 125,000.

What caused the estimate of the population to exceed the true initial population? The possible reasons are:

1. That the marked fish suffered a higher natural mortality than the unmarked. Thus if the 40,000 fish caught had included 2000 instead of 1600 marked fish the estimate would have been correct. That is, 2000/5000 equals an $f$ of 0.40 and 40,000/0.40 = 100,000.

2. That a proportion of the marked fish lost their mark during the fishing season. If the marked fish are distributed at random before the fishing season begins, this may be tested by determining if there is a significant decrease in the proportion of marked fish as the season progresses.

3. That the marked fish were not as easily caught as the remainder of the population. This assumption cannot easily be proved. A low proportion of recovery early in the season followed by a higher proportion of recovery later may indicate that the marking temporarily affected the habits of the fish.

4. That the catch was taken from the whole population while the marked fish were not distributed randomly throughout the range of the population. This can be determined by comparing the catches and recoveries of marked fish from various areas.

5. That a proportion of the marked fish recaptured were either not detected or not reported, or both. This is to be expected in all marking experiments. As the investigator seldom can examine all of the catch personally it is necessary when possible to correct for this error. By careful examination of random samples throughout the fishing season a factor may be developed to correct for nondetection or nonreporting of marked fish.

6. That the number of fish in the catchable population was increased during the season by recruitment. This error can be eliminated in many instances by subtracting the recruits from the catch. They may be detected by either age- or size-frequency distributions of the catch compared to the age or size frequencies of the marked group.

The chief drawback of this method lies in the assumptions that the tagged fish do not suffer any heightened mortality and that all recaptured fish are observed and recorded. If by other means one has a reliable estimate of the total mortality ratio $r$ it can be compared with the fishing mortality $f$ derived from tagging, and $r - f$ should give an estimate of $n$, the natural mortality ratio. However, if the estimated $f$ is lower than the true $f$, $n$ will be too high.

## 7·6  Estimation of total population by short-period simultaneous marking and recovery

A second method of using marking to estimate population size is to continue marking and fishing intensively for a short period of time. Each time interval yields an independent estimate of population size. This method was proposed by Schnabel (1938) and has been used with variations by many workers since.

Essentially it consists of fishing and marking simultaneously and estimating the population from the proportion that the recaptured marked fish are of the catch, considering the number of unaccounted-for marked fish at large when each catch is made.

In the example of Table 7·3 column $A$ represents a short time interval $t$. Column $B$ is the number of unaccounted-for marked fish at liberty at the end of each time interval $M(t)$. Column $C$ represents

TABLE 7·3

EXAMPLE OF ESTIMATING SIZE OF A POPULATION BY INTENSIVE MARKING

| Time Inter-val ($t$) | Marked Fish at Large by End of Interval $M(t)$ | Fish Cap-tured $C(t)$ | Number of Marked Fish Re-captured $R(t)$ | $M(t-1)C(t)$ | $\dfrac{M(t-1)C(t)}{R(t)}$ | Cumula-tive $E$ | Cumula-tive $D$ | $G/H$ |
|---|---|---|---|---|---|---|---|---|
| A | B | C | D | E | F | G | H | I |
| 1 | 100 | | | | | | | |
| 2 | 250 | 200 | 1 | 20,000 | 20,000 | 20,000 | 1 | 20,000 |
| 3 | 410 | 220 | 4 | 55,300 | 13,750 | 75,300 | 5 | 15,060 |
| 4 | 500 | 180 | 6 | 73,800 | 12,300 | 149,100 | 11 | 13,555 |
| 5 | 630 | 250 | 15 | 125,000 | 8,333 | 274,100 | 26 | 10,542 |
| 6 | 760 | 200 | 8 | 126,000 | 15,750 | 400,100 | 34 | 11,768 |
| 7 | | 300 | 20 | 228,000 | 11,400 | 628,100 | 54 | 11,632 |
| | | | 54 | 628,100 | 11,632 | | | |

Number of recaptures is 54 ± 7.348.
1.96 standard errors or probability of 0.05 is 14.4.
Population at $P$ of 0.05 is 11,632 (7403 to 15,861).

the total number of fish captured during each time interval $C(t)$. Column $D$ shows the number of marked fish recaptured during each time interval $R(t)$. Column $E$ is the total number of fish captured during any interval $C(t)$ multiplied by the number of marked fish at liberty at the end of the previous time interval $M(t-1)$. Column $F$ is column $E$ divided by column $D$, $R(t)$. Columns $G$ and $H$ are the cumulative summations of columns $E$ and $D$. Column $I$ is column $G$ divided by column $H$.

It will be noted that the independent estimates of the population yielded by each time interval in column $F$ are much more variable than the cumulative estimates of column $I$. Because only a small proportion of the total population is marked, the numbers of recaptures by intervals are distributed in a Poisson distribution. The total number of recaptures, 54, is then also so distributed and its variance is equal to 54 and its standard deviation is equal to its square root, 7.348.

For such a large number, the distribution approximates the normal form so that 7.348 may be attached to 54 as its standard error. For the 5 per cent limit of probability, multiplying the standard error by 1.96 equals 14.4. Thus only once in 20 times would one expect the population estimate to differ by as much as 4229.

Obviously a population estimate based on so few recoveries is not too reliable, but it may suffice in many cases in which the magnitude of the population is unknown. This method is most suitable for a small body of water in which the marked fish can quickly become distributed throughout the population.

## 7·7  Mortality rates from long-period marking experiments '

It is possible to estimate fishing mortality $f$ from long-period marking experiments. It must be based on the assumptions that:

1. The tagged fish behave like the remainder of the population in respect to mortality, movements, availability, etc.
2. Loss of tags is proportional in different years.
3. Fishing intensity is constant.

From the recaptures in successive years $s$ may be calculated as follows, the suffix $T$ being used to designate tagged fish:

$$s = \sum_{x=2}^{n} C_{T_x} / \sum_{x=1}^{n-1} C_{T_x}$$

Once the survival rate $s$ is determined then $f$ can be found:

$$f = \sum_{x=2}^{n} C_{T_x} / s P_T (1 + s + s^2 + \cdots + s^{n-2})$$

As an example 1000 fish are marked and released. The recoveries for 3 successive years are 500, 200, and 80. Then

$$s = 280/700 = 0.40$$
$$f = 280/0.40 \times 1000(1 + 0.40 + 0.16 + \cdots +)$$
$$= 280/(400 + 160)$$
$$= 280/560 = 0.50$$

If both $f$ and $r$ $(r = 1 - s)$ are known, it is obvious that the annual natural mortality ratio is $r - f$ or $0.60 - 0.50 = 0.10$.

Note that $P_T = C_{T_1}/f = 500/0.50 = 1000$.

In using this method it has been assumed that there was no extra initial mortality from tagging, but this is rarely the case. Therefore it may not be possible to estimate $f$, but only $r$. Without $f$ it is not possible to determine the initial population from the catches.

If for instance the above tagging recoveries had been made from a tagged population of 2000 of which 1000 fish died immediately, then $s$ (and $r$) would have the same values, but $f$ would be

$$f = 280/0.40 \times 2000(1 + 0.40)$$
$$= 280/1120$$
$$= 0.25$$

and $n$ would be $0.60 - 0.25 = 0.35$.

Because of the strictness of the necessary assumptions it is plain that $f$ calculated from recoveries of tagged fish may be too low and lead to erroneous conclusions concerning both the size of the population and the natural mortality.

### 7·8    Illustration of population parameters

Table 7·4 is introduced to clarify the relationships that exist between the various population parameters (see Section 7·15 for symbols

TABLE 7·4

ILLUSTRATING CERTAIN POPULATION PARAMETERS

| Symbols | No. of Fish | Ratios | | Rates | | Instantaneous Rates | |
|---|---|---|---|---|---|---|---|
| | | Symbol | Value | Symbol | Value | Symbol | Value |
| $P_0$ | 2500 | | | | | | |
| $C_0$ | 1250 | | | | | | |
| $N_0$ | 250 | | | | | | |
| $D_0 = C_0 + N_0$ | 1500 | | | | | | |
| $P_1$ | 1000 | | | | | | |
| $C_1$ | 500 | $f_1$ | 0.50 | $F_1$ | 0.5357 | $Z_1$ | 0.767 |
| $N_1$ | 100 | $n_1$ | .10 | $M_1$ | .1416 | $\Lambda_1$ | .153 |
| $D_1 = C_1 + N_1$ | 600 | $r_1$ | .60 | $r_1$ | .6000 | $\Delta_1$ | .920 |
| $S_1 = P_1 - D_1 = P_2$ | 400 | $s_1$ | .40 | $s_1$ | .4000 | | |

$$Z/f = \Lambda/n = \Delta/r = 1.53$$

used). This is a hypothetical example of a population, $P_0 = 2500$, in which no recruitment is postulated. Note that the ratios of deaths to total population from fishing $f$ and from natural causes $n$ are additive and equal $r$. The rates of death $F$ and $M$ are the rates at which each cause would remove the population if the other cause of death were nonoperative. Obviously, as $M$ approaches $O$, $F$ approaches $f$ in value, and vice-versa. The instantaneous, or exponential rates $Z$ and $\Lambda$ are additive, making them extremely useful in population calculations.

The total yield $Y$ of $P_0$ (or 2500) at rate $r$ is by definition $C_0/r =$ 1250/0.60 = 2083 fish. In actual practice the biologist often does not have sufficient information at hand to determine all of these parameters. He must then be satisfied with estimates of varying degrees of re-

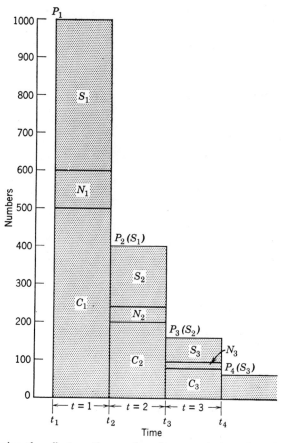

FIG. 7·3  Showing the effect on the numbers in a population of catch and natural mortality when no recruitment is occurring.

liability. In order to interpret his results, however, he should know what the parameters are, and realize in what regard his estimate may be biased.

Figure 7·3 shows the effect of removals from the population by fishing and natural mortality in the absence of recruitment. Figure 7·4 illustrates the relations among the ratios $f$, $n$, and $r$. Note that $C_1$ and $N_1$ are the quantities of fish removed *between* times $t_1$ and $t_2$.

As explained in Section 6·6, the value $C_1$ is the catch taken during the entire season, not the quantity taken at time $t_1$. It will also be noted that the true rate of decline $r$ is exactly the same rate as shown by $r_{1_f}$ or $r_{1_n}$ if fishing and natural mortality are both constant. Thus

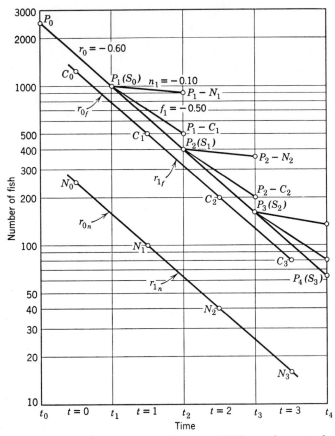

Fig. 7·4 Showing the relations among the annual fishing ratio, natural mortality ratio, and the total rate of mortality.

the rate of decline found from comparing catches is not the fishing rate, but the total rate, and includes both $f$ and $n$.

Figure 7·5 shows the difference between the number of fish that actually die from fishing and natural causes, $f$ and $n$, and the rate at which each cause, $F$ and $M$, would remove the fish if the other cause of death were not present.

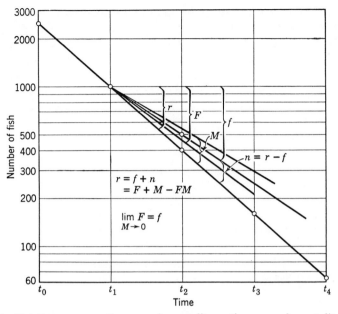

FIG. 7·5 Relations among the annual mortality ratios, annual mortality rates, and the total mortality rate.

## 7·9 Indices of relative abundance

In lieu of estimates of actual population size, an index of relative abundance is often calculated.

The simplest form of index is merely the total catch divided by the number of fishing units with no allowance for changes in availability:

$$I_R = C/U$$

This simple form has been widely used in fisheries work, and for benthic species that tend toward fairly even dispersal (nonschooling) it may differ little from an index in which availability $V$ is discounted.

The relation between the true parameter $P$ and the index depends on several factors. If the natural mortality rate $M$ is low, or is low in relation to the fishing mortality $F$, then the index may follow closely the changes in actual population provided that availability is either rather constant or can be discounted. The number of units of fishing effort $U$ also affects the relation since competition between units lowers the efficiency of the individual unit as their number increases.

The fact that skewed catch curves usually approximate normal curves when transformed into logarithms (Section 6·16) is taken advantage of in calculating one of the most effective indices of relative abundance in which changes in availability $V$ are minimized. The underlying assumption is that in determining abundance the changes in size of the smaller catches are just as important as changes of the same relative magnitude in the larger catches. By comparing the logarithm of the catch of each vessel or fisherman in one year with the logarithm of the catch of the same vessel on the same date in another year (or usually on an adjacent date if the same date does not yield a comparison), three objectives are accomplished:

1. The resulting index is a geometric mean showing the rate of change from the first year to the second.

2. The difference in efficiency between vessels or other unit of gear is fully discounted.

3. Small catches have as much influence as large catches in determining the geometric mean so that it is less necessary to employ a norm of seasonal availability (this will be discussed in the next method). This minimizes the effect of changes in availability so that the resulting index in effect is

$$I_E = C/E$$

as defined in Section 7·15.

The formula for this method is as follows:

$a_{0_1}, a_{0_2} \cdots a_{0_n}$ = catches of a vessel in the first year

$a_{1_1}, a_{1_2} \cdots a_{1_n}$ = catches of same vessel on corresponding dates in the second year

$b_{0_1}, c_{0_2} \cdots z_{0_n}$ = catches of other vessels in first year

$n$ = total number of pairs of catches compared

$I_E$ = geometric mean of the ratios of catches in first year to corresponding catches in second year

$$V = \left[ \sum_{x=1}^{n} \log a_{0_x} + \sum_{x=1}^{n} \log b_{0_x} + \cdots + \sum_{x=1}^{n} \log z_{0_x} \right] - \left[ \sum_{x=1}^{n} \log a_{1_x} \right.$$

$$\left. + \sum_{x=1}^{n} \log b_{1_x} + \cdots + \sum_{x=1}^{n} \log z_{1_x} \right]$$

$$\log I_E = \frac{V}{n}$$

Although this index is a more efficient statistic than most of those to be discussed later it has certain disadvantages as we well know from once computing this type of index for a fleet of tuna vessels over a 10-year period. To begin with, *all* catches have to be converted to logarithms—an exceedingly tedious and exacting task—then all pairs of comparisons between logarithms must be either recopied or marked by symbols on each vessel's record. The coding or marking is necessary if one desires a high degree of accuracy from this method.

By coding comparisons one can pick the logarithms off the records on an adding machine. Also by coding one can compare each year not only with the years adjacent to it but with every other year in the series. By so doing one can dispense with seasonal availability curves and still derive an accurate index. Because of the tremendous amount of labor involved and the difficulty of accurately checking the logarithms this method is unsuitable for large masses of data.

A more usual way to calculate an index is to take the daily arithmetic means of the catches of a group of similar units of fishing effort. These daily means are then converted into logarithms and compared with a seasonal curve of average availability. The calculation is as follows:

$a_1, a_2 \cdots a_n$ = averages of the catches on one date in various years
$b_1, b_2 \cdots b_n$ = averages of catches on successive days in same year
$V$ = standard average catch for one date (availability curve)
$n$ = number of years
$N$ = number of days in one year
$I_E$ = geometric mean of the ratios of each day's average catch in one year to the standard curve

$$V = \frac{a_1 + a_2 + \cdots + a_n}{n}$$

$$\log I_E = [(\log b_1 - \log V_1)$$
$$+ (\log b_2 - \log V_2) + \cdots + (\log b_N - \log V_N)]/N$$

An index computed in this manner is frankly a compromise between the method described just previously and any method using arithmetic means throughout. However, this second index is much easier to compute than the first. In the large number of cases in which the unit of fishing effort covers a sufficiently long period of time to involve several sets or attempts by a unit of gear, the catches involved are actually each a total of an undetermined number of attempts and so do not really satisfy the requirements of the first method.

## 7·10    Seasonal norm of availability

In the method just described the daily catches were compared to a seasonal curve of availability. In computing an index of relative abundance such a curve of seasonal availability or occurrence must be used unless:

1. The fishing effort of each year is evenly distributed throughout the fishing season, or
2. There are no significant differences in availability (occurrence) during the fishing season.

In the great majority of fisheries there are significant seasonal changes in availability. As a general rule the major changes are not sporadic but follow a well-defined pattern from season to season. This pattern is usually closely linked with biological and environmental phenomena. For this reason the pattern shifts but slightly from year to year. Thus, although the northward migration of the sardine shoals occurred a little earlier or a little later in accordance with hydrographic conditions the fundamental pattern was there. An excellent illustration of the stability of this pattern of seasonal occurrence and of the tremendous changes involved is furnished by the runs of salmon in the Puget Sound area (Table 7·5). It will be noted that the modes of the five species occur about a month apart, and that the great bulk of each run is available over a period of but a few weeks.

In computing a curve to portray the normal seasonal availability it is important to obtain the correct shape for the curve. In order to do this it is usually necessary to weight the catches so that each year will have equal influence in determining the curve. To illustrate how this is accomplished the example in Table 7·6 gives the average weekly catches of a unit of fishing effort for 8 years. The totals are summed for all of the periods which are represented in all of the years. In this case the total was 5809 fish for the periods 4 to 15 inclusive. The average was 726 per year. This average was then divided by the total for periods 4 to 15 in each year to obtain a weight factor. The average catches in each year were all multiplied by their respective weight factor. These weighted catches were then summed by periods and divided by the number of years of fishing in each period to obtain an availability curve.

When but a few years' records are available a smooth curve is not likely to be obtained. Minor fluctuations in the data may be removed

## TABLE 7·5

SEASONAL OCCURRENCE OF SALMON CAUGHT BY PUGET SOUND TRAPS *

| Week Ending | Percentage Occurrence | | | | |
|---|---|---|---|---|---|
| | King † | Red ‡ | Pink § | Coho ‖ | Chum ¶ |
| Apr. 21 | 0.4 | | | | |
| 28 | 1.4 | | | | |
| May 5 | 2.3 | 0.4 | | | |
| 12 | 3.2 | 0.4 | | | |
| 19 | 3.6 | 0.3 | | 0.1 | |
| 26 | 3.8 | 0.1 | | 0.1 | |
| June 2 | 4.2 | 0.1 | | 0.1 | |
| 9 | 4.8 | | | 0.1 | |
| 16 | 5.1 | | | 0.1 | |
| 23 | 5.9 | 0.1 | | 0.2 | |
| 30 | 6.3 | 0.5 | | 0.2 | |
| July 7 | **7.3** | 2.2 | | 0.4 | |
| 14 | 6.7 | 4.5 | | 0.4 | |
| 21 | 6.3 | 8.4 | 0.2 | 0.5 | 0.1 |
| 28 | 6.2 | 16.1 | 1.5 | 0.5 | 0.2 |
| Aug. 4 | 6.1 | **26.3** | 3.7 | 0.7 | 0.4 |
| 11 | 6.1 | 20.9 | 6.9 | 1.0 | 0.8 |
| 18 | 5.6 | 11.2 | 10.1 | 1.4 | 1.2 |
| 25 | 4.5 | 5.5 | 21.1 | 2.7 | 1.9 |
| Sept. 1 | 3.4 | 1.5 | **23.8** | 3.9 | 1.8 |
| 8 | 2.9 | 0.5 | 19.6 | 7.0 | 2.0 |
| 15 | 2.1 | 0.1 | 8.7 | 10.8 | 2.3 |
| 22 | 1.1 | 0.1 | 3.5 | **12.7** | 3.2 |
| 29 | 0.5 | 0.1 | 0.8 | 12.1 | 7.4 |
| Oct. 6 | 0.2 | | 0.1 | 12.6 | 9.2 |
| 13 | 0.1 | | | 12.0 | 11.8 |
| 20 | | | | 8.4 | 12.7 |
| 27 | | 0.1 | | 5.3 | **13.6** |
| Nov. 3 | 0.1 | 0.1 | | 3.1 | 10.3 |
| 10 | | 0.3 | | 1.6 | 7.1 |
| 17 | | | | 1.5 | 5.7 |
| 24 | | | | 0.7 | 3.3 |
| Dec. 1 | | | | 0.1 | 1.9 |
| 8 | | | | | 1.1 |
| 15 | | | | | 0.4 |
| 22 | | | | | 0.7 |
| 29 | | | | | 0.6 |
| Jan. 5 | | | | | 0.1 |

* Modified from Rounsefell and Kelez (1938), the modes are in **boldface**.
† *Oncorhynchus tshawytscha*, 1900–1934, 17 traps.
‡ *O. nerka*, 1896–1934, 12 traps.
§ *O. gorbuscha*, 1919–1933, odd-numbered years, 16 traps.
‖ *O. kisutch*, 1900–1934, 26 traps.
¶ *O. keta*, 1900–1934, 13 traps.

## TABLE 7·6

CALCULATION OF A SEASONAL AVAILABILITY CURVE TO USE AS A NORM IN
COMPUTING AN INDEX OF RELATIVE ABUNDANCE

| Period | Observed Average Catches by Years | | | | | | | |
|---|---|---|---|---|---|---|---|---|
| | 1 | 2 | 3 | 4 | 5 | 6 | 7 | 8 |
| 1 | ... | 19 | ... | ... | ... | ... | ... | ... |
| 2 | 44 | 94 | ... | ... | ... | ... | ... | ... |
| 3 | 141 | 174 | ... | ... | 32 | 38 | ... | ... |
| 4 | 147 | 122 | 117 | 61 | 27 | 31 | 123 | 120 |
| 5 | 135 | 121 | 130 | 35 | 31 | 34 | 90 | 174 |
| 6 | 151 | 39 | 110 | 34 | 10 | 86 | 97 | 223 |
| 7 | 103 | 77 | 47 | 20 | 14 | 70 | 121 | 256 |
| 8 | 102 | 2 | 6 | 9 | 51 | 63 | 109 | 184 |
| 9 | 141 | 5 | 8 | 9 | 5 | 78 | 48 | 155 |
| 10 | 34 | 0 | 35 | 0 | 1 | 17 | 43 | 95 |
| 11 | 0 | 0 | 42 | 71 | 0 | 26 | 51 | 17 |
| 12 | 13 | 0 | 8 | 4 | 9 | 77 | 22 | 166 |
| 13 | 89 | 33 | 55 | 2 | 48 | 60 | 0 | 343 |
| 14 | 7 | 0 | 8 | 9 | 49 | 68 | 21 | 184 |
| 15 | 12 | 3 | 0 | 31 | 16 | 50 | 3 | 56 |
| 16 | 0 | 0 | 0 | 0 | 28 | 23 | 0 | ... |
| 17 | 2 | 0 | 0 | 0 | 30 | 0 | 50 | ... |
| 18 | 1 | 0 | ... | ... | ... | ... | 25 | ... |
| 19 | 34 | 8 | ... | ... | ... | ... | 23 | ... |
| 4–15 | 934 | 402 | 566 | 285 | 261 | 660 | 728 | 1973 |

$5809/8 = 726$

Weight factor   0.78   1.80   1.28   2.55   2.78   1.10   1.00   0.37

| Period | Weighted Average Catches by Years | | | | | | | | Total | Total ÷ Years | Smoothed by 3's |
|---|---|---|---|---|---|---|---|---|---|---|---|
| | 1 | 2 | 3 | 4 | 5 | 6 | 7 | 8 | | | |
| 1 | ... | 34 | ... | ... | ... | ... | ... | ... | 34 | 34 | |
| 2 | 34 | 169 | ... | ... | ... | ... | ... | ... | 203 | 102 | 91 |
| 3 | 110 | 313 | ... | ... | 89 | 42 | ... | ... | 554 | 138 | 118 | 110 |
| 4 | 115 | 220 | 150 | 155 | 75 | 34 | 123 | 44 | 916 | 114 | 120 | 114 |
| 5 | 105 | 218 | 166 | 89 | 86 | 37 | 90 | 64 | 855 | 107 | 104 | 106 |
| 6 | 118 | 70 | 141 | 87 | 28 | 95 | 97 | 82 | 718 | 90 | 93 | 92 |
| 7 | 80 | 138 | 60 | 51 | 39 | 77 | 121 | 95 | 661 | 83 | 79 | 79 |
| 8 | 79 | 4 | 8 | 23 | 142 | 69 | 109 | 68 | 502 | 63 | 64 | 62 |
| 9 | 110 | 9 | 10 | 23 | 14 | 86 | 48 | 57 | 357 | 45 | 43 | 48 |
| 10 | 27 | 0 | 45 | 0 | 3 | 19 | 43 | 35 | 172 | 22 | 36 | 36 |
| 11 | 0 | 0 | 54 | 181 | 0 | 29 | 51 | 6 | 321 | 40 | 30 | 37 |
| 12 | 10 | 0 | 10 | 10 | 25 | 85 | 22 | 61 | 223 | 28 | 45 | 40 |
| 13 | 69 | 59 | 70 | 5 | 133 | 66 | 0 | 127 | 529 | 66 | 45 | 45 |
| 14 | 5 | 0 | 10 | 23 | 136 | 75 | 21 | 68 | 338 | 42 | 45 | 39 |
| 15 | 9 | 5 | 0 | 79 | 44 | 55 | 3 | 21 | 216 | 27 | 28 | 31 |
| 16 | 0 | 0 | 0 | 0 | 78 | 25 | 0 | ... | 103 | 15 | 20 | 21 |
| 17 | 2 | 0 | 0 | 0 | 83 | 0 | 50 | ... | 135 | 19 | 14 | 17 |
| 18 | 1 | 0 | ... | ... | ... | ... | 25 | ... | 26 | 9 | 16 | |
| 19 | 27 | 14 | ... | ... | ... | ... | 23 | ... | 64 | 21 | | |
| 4–15 | | | | | | | | | 5808 | | |

by smoothing once or twice by 3's. Ordinarily smoothing is not important, and there is much to be said for making only those adjustments in the data that can be shown to accomplish a specific purpose.

### 7·11   Limitations of indices of relative abundance

An index of relative abundance has certain limitations. Seldom is there available any usable information on gear competition; yet the index is essentially a measure of the quantity of fish taken by a definite amount of fishing effort. The effectiveness of this fishing effort, however, varies with the total number of units that are competing. There is also the question of whether the relationship between catch per unit and population size is always linear.

### 7·12   Advantages of the geometric mean

The geometric mean should be employed whenever possible in computing indices for three reasons:

1. When indices are geometric means the year selected as a base can be shifted without difficulty, but with arithmetic means it cannot be so shifted.

2. When arithmetic means are used an index tends to become higher and higher as each year is added because of the method of computation. Using arithmetic means for an index is equivalent to averaging ratios. Ratios must be averaged by geometric means.

3. Geometric means give the rate of change from year to year. Thus an increase of 100 per cent in one catch and a decrease of 50 per cent in another would yield an arithmetic mean of 125 per cent, but a geometric mean of 100 per cent. In other words one catch was doubled and the other was halved so that the rate of change was zero.

### 7·13   Regression method of DeLury

The regression method for estimating population size which was developed by DeLury (1947) depends upon the fact that the decrease in the catch per unit of effort as the population becomes depleted bears a direct relationship to the extent of the depletion. This method cannot be used if the fishery does not take a significant proportion of the population, as it depends on the ability to estimate the slope of the regression of catch per unit on either accumulated catch or effort. When a very small proportion of the population is taken the slope is either nil or so slight that a slight change in slope makes a tremendous difference in the point at which the projection of the regression line cuts the $x$-axis. It must be assumed also that:

1. The "catchability" of the fish remains constant during the sampling period.

2. The population is all available to the fishery and that natural mortality and recruitment may be ignored.

3. There is no competition between units of fishing gear. This provision can be ignored if the number of units remains constant throughout the period considered.

The statistics needed for the computation of population size by this method are either total catch or total fishing effort by time in-

TABLE 7·7

EXAMPLE OF A POPULATION WITH NO RECRUITMENT OR NATURAL MORTALITY DURING THE PERIOD OF SAMPLING

| Period | Catch | Cumulative Catch $C(t)$ | Effort $U$ | Catch per Unit of Effort $C/U(t)$ | Cumulative Effort $U(t)$ | Logarithm of Catch per Unit of Effort $\log C/U(t)$ | Column $F^2$ | Column $E^2$ | Column $FE$ |
|---|---|---|---|---|---|---|---|---|---|
| | A | B | C | D | E | F | G | H | I |
| | | | | | X | Y | $Y^2$ | $X^2$ | $XY$ |
| 1 | 100 | 0 | 10 | 10.0 | 0 | 1.000 | 1.000 | 0 | 0 |
| 2 | 90 | 100 | 10 | 9.0 | 10 | .954 | .910 | 100 | 9.54 |
| 3 | 81 | 190 | 10 | 8.1 | 20 | .908 | .824 | 400 | 18.16 |
| 4 | 73 | 271 | 10 | 7.3 | 30 | .863 | .745 | 900 | 25.89 |
| 5 | 66 | 344 | 10 | 6.6 | 40 | .820 | .672 | 1,600 | 32.80 |
| 6 | 59 | 410 | 10 | 5.9 | 50 | .771 | .594 | 2,500 | 38.55 |
| 7 | 53 | 469 | 10 | 5.3 | 60 | .724 | .524 | 3,600 | 43.44 |
| 8 | 48 | 522 | 10 | 4.8 | 70 | .681 | .464 | 4,900 | 47.67 |
| 9 | 43 | 570 | 10 | 4.3 | 80 | .633 | .401 | 6,400 | 50.64 |
| 10 | 39 | 613 | 10 | 3.9 | 90 | .591 | .349 | 8,100 | 53.19 |
| | | | | | 450 | 7.945 | 6.483 | 28,500 | 319.880 |

$$n = 10, \quad \bar{x} = 45, \quad \bar{y} = 0.7945$$

$$SX^2 = 28\,500, \qquad SY^2 = 6.483, \qquad SXY = 319.880$$
$$(SX)^2/n = 20\,250, \qquad (SY)^2/n = 6.312, \qquad (SX)(SY)/n = 357.525$$

$$Sx^2 = 8\,250, \qquad Sy^2 = 0.171, \qquad Sxy = -37.645$$

$$\hat{Y} = \bar{y} - \frac{Sxy}{Sx^2}(X - \bar{x}) \quad \text{or} \quad 0.9998 - 0.004563X$$

Antilog of 0.9998 = 9.996 or $kP(0)$

$$\frac{0.00456}{0.4343} = 0.01 \text{ or } k$$

$$P(0) = \frac{9.996}{0.01} = 999.6 \text{ or estimate of initial population} = Y_\infty$$

tervals, and at least a representative sample of catch per unit of effort for the same time intervals.

Although this method is of theoretical value and marks a new approach to the problem of estimating populations, it is difficult to apply in actual practice. It really measures only the "catchable" portion of the population, and since the proportion that is vulnerable varies from time to time in most fish populations it is difficult to obtain a linear relationship between catch per unit of fishing effort and accumulated catch to each time interval. Mottley (1949) for instance found that in order to obtain a linear relationship he had to use the square of the effort.

The assumption that the population is closed, i.e., it does not change during the sampling period by recruitment, is only fully satisfied in certain cases, especially those in which the entire annual recruitment of young joins the adult population before the fishing season. However, this particular difficulty may be overcome if the ages of representative samples of the population can be obtained during the season. The new recruits can then be separated by subtracting their age group from the population.

The assumption that the population shall all be equally vulnerable assumes of course that the fishery extends to all of the population and that conversely no large share of the population migrates into or out of the fishing area. This condition is best satisfied on a small body of water such as a farm pond, a small lake, or an enclosed bay.

If the natural mortality rate is uniform it will not affect the linear relationship between catch and catch per unit, but the estimate of total population will be low. This follows because the method in reality estimates not $P_0$ but total yield $Y_\infty$. If there is no natural mortality then $P_0 = Y_\infty$.

Section 7·15 defined $Y_\infty$ as

$$\underset{t \to \infty}{\mathrm{Lim}}\ Y = \sum_{t=0}^{\infty} C = \frac{C_0}{r} = \frac{ZP_0}{\Delta}$$

Now obviously if there is no natural mortality, then $Z = \Delta$ and $P_0 = Y_\infty$. Since this is seldom a practical assumption we shall call the parameter derived by this method $Y_\infty$.

The method is illustrated by a hypothetical example in which

$C/U$ = catch per unit of fishing effort
$P$ = number in catchable population at any time $t$
$U(t)$ = number of units of fishing effort to interval $t$

$C(t)$ = total catch to interval $t$

$t$ = any interval $t$

$b$ = $k \log_{10} \epsilon$ in which $k$ is a constant

$k$ = the proportion of the population captured by one unit of fishing effort when $t$ = 0.

Stated briefly the method consists of plotting $C/U$ against $C(t)$ or $U(t)$, determining the intercept on the $y$-axis, and then dividing the intercept, $kP(0)$, by $k$, which yields an estimate of the total population. Two formulas can be used according to whether one wishes to plot $C/U$ against $C(t)$ or against $U(t)$. The formulas are:

$$\log [C/U(t)] = \log [kP(0)] - bU(t)$$

and

$$C/U(t) = kP(0) - kC(t).$$

It will be observed that both formulas are equivalent to a linear regression in which

$$y = a - bx$$

In the example that follows (Table 7·7) each unit of fishing effort catches the same proportion of the remaining population during each interval; and there is either no natural mortality or recruitment, or both exactly balance. This satisfies the necessary assumptions on which the method is based. An initial population of 1000 is postulated.

By using the first formula the regression of $\log C/U(t)$ on $U(t)$ is computed by standard regression methods as shown in Table 7·7. The resulting equation is

$$\log C/U(t) = 0.9998 - 0.004563 U(t)$$

As $b$ = 0.004563 and $b$ = $k \log_{10} \epsilon$ then $k$ = $b$ divided by the modulus $\log_{10} \epsilon$ which is 0.43429. $k$ = 0.01. $kP(0)$ = the antilog of 0.9998 or 9.996. The desired initial population is equal to $kP(0)/k$ or 9.996/0.01 or 999.6.

If one uses the second formula and fits the regression line in the same manner the resulting equation is

$$C/U(t) = 10 - 0.01C(t)$$

In this case $k$ = 0.01 and $kP(0)$ = 10; so $P(0)$ = $kP(0)/k$ or 10/0.01 = 1000.

When $C/U$ is plotted against $C(t)$ the regression line if extrapolated cuts the $x$-axis at the size of the initial catchable population. This extrapolation gives a quick and convenient method for estimating graphically the initial catchable population or $Y_\infty$.

Two factors likely to cause trouble are variations in availability and competition between units of fishing effort. So far no way has been worked out for making allowance for changes in availability for this method.

The determination of the degree of competition between units of fishing effort was worked out by Rounsefell (1949) for the Fraser River sockeye salmon fishery. However, as it is not at present applicable to fisheries in general a discussion of the method is omitted.

### 7·14  Estimation of natural mortality

Natural mortalities have been estimated by various methods. One method is to determine the total mortality of a population at the very beginning of exploitation when practically all of it can be ascribed to natural mortality. However, natural mortality is much heavier in an unfished population than it is after exploitation.

Of course, with no fishing, $M$ equals $n$. When exploitation commences $M \neq n$ for $f + n = r$, but also $F + M - FM = r$. The expectation of a fish dying from natural causes $n$ is thus reduced by fishing, even though $M$, the rate of dying, may remain constant. There is a good probability, though, that $M$ itself may be reduced by fishing as there is more food and space available per fish.

It would appear that natural mortality is fairly low in most heavily exploited species. Thompson and Bell (1934) estimate it at 10 per cent for halibut, and Silliman (1943) calculated 13.3 per cent for the Pacific sardine.

When total mortality is high and natural mortality is low an error of a few per cent in estimating natural mortality will not seriously impair the use of population estimates for most management purposes.

### 7·15  Definition of symbols

Throughout this chapter the following symbols have been used with the defined meanings:

$t$ = any particular interval of time between $t_n$ and $t_{n+1}$

$t_x$ = any particular moment of time

$A$ = number of fish at any age, 1 to $n$

$C_t$ = catch in unit interval of time $t_n$ to $t_{n+1}$

$P = \sum\limits_{x=1}^{n} A_x$ = total available population in numbers when $x$ is youngest age taken by the fishing gear

$P_n = C_n + N_n + S_n$

$P_{t_1} = C_{(t=1)}/f$

$N$ = deaths from natural causes in time $t$

$D = C + N$ = deaths from fishing and natural causes in time $t$

$S = P - D$ = survival in time $t$

$U$ = standard units of fishing effort

$V$ = availability

$E = UV$ = effective fishing effort

$I_R = C/U$ = index of relative abundance, no allowance for $V$

$I_E = C/E$ = index of relative abundance, when $V$ is constant or is minimized

$f = C/P$ = ratio of deaths from fishing to population in time $t$

$n = N/P$ = ratio of deaths from natural causes to population in time $t$

$F = 1 - \epsilon^{-Z} = 1 - 1/\epsilon^{Z}$ = rate of deaths from fishing in time $t$

$M = 1 - \epsilon^{-\Lambda} = 1 - 1/\epsilon^{\Lambda}$ = rate of deaths from natural causes in time $t$

$r = D/P = f + n = F + M - FM = 1 - \epsilon^{-\Delta} = 1 - 1/\epsilon^{\Delta}$
$= 1 - s$ = ratio of all deaths to population in time $t$, also equals the rate of deaths from all causes in time $t$

$s = 1 - r = \epsilon^{-\Delta} = 1/\epsilon^{\Delta}$ = rate of survival in time $t$

$Z = \Delta - \Lambda = \Delta f/r = \log_\epsilon (1/1 - F) = 2.303 \log_{10} (1/1 - F)$
= the instantaneous rate of deaths from fishing in time $t$

$\Lambda = \Delta - Z = \Delta n/r = \log_\epsilon (1/1 - M) = 2.303 \log_{10} (1/1 - M)$
= the instantaneous rate of deaths from natural causes in time $t$

$\Delta = Z + \Lambda = \log_\epsilon (1/1 - r) = 2.303 \log_{10} (1/1 - r)$ = the instantaneous rate of deaths from all causes in time $t$

$Z/f = \Lambda/n = \Delta/r$

$C_{(t=n)} = C_{(t=n-1)} \epsilon^{-(Z+\Lambda)t} = C_{(t=n-1)}/\epsilon^{\Delta t}$

$C_{(t=n-1)} = C_{(t=n)} \epsilon^{(Z+\Lambda)t}$

$C_{(t=n-1)} = C_{(t=n)}(1 + r)^n$

$Y$ = total yield of a fishery in time $t$

$$\lim_{t \to \infty} Y = \sum_{t=0}^{\infty} C = \frac{C_0}{r} = \frac{ZP_0}{\Delta}$$

$$\lim_{t \to n} Y = \sum_{t=0}^{n} C = \frac{C_0}{r(1 - s^n)} = \frac{ZP_0}{\Delta(1 - \epsilon^{-\Delta n})} = \frac{ZP_0}{\Delta(1 - 1/\epsilon^{\Delta n})}$$

$R$ = number of recruits to the population in time $t$

## References

DeLury, D. B.
1947. On the estimation of biological populations. *Biometrics 3* (4):145–167.
Fisher, Irving
1922. *The making of index numbers; a study of the varieties, tests, and reliability*. Houghton Mifflin: 538 pp., Boston.
Mottley, Charles M.
1949. The statistical analysis of creel-census data. *Trans. Am. Fish. Soc. 76:* 290–300.
Ricker, William E.
1940. Relation of "catch per unit effort" to abundance and rate of exploitation. *J. Fish. Res. Bd. Canada 5* (1):43–70.
1944. Further notes on fishing mortality and effort. *Copeia,* 1944 (1):23–44.
1948. Methods of estimating vital statistics of fish populations. *Indiana Univ. Publ., Sci. Ser. 15:* 101 pp.
Rounsefell, George A.
1949. Methods of estimating total runs and escapements of salmon. *Biometrics 5* (2):115–126.
Rounsefell, George A., and George B. Kelez
1938. The salmon and salmon fisheries of Swiftsure Bank, Puget Sound, and the Fraser River. *Bull. U. S. Bur. Fish. 49* (27):693–823.
Schnabel, Z. E.
1938. The estimation of the total fish population in a lake. *Am. Math. Monthly 45* (6):348–352.
Silliman, Ralph P.
1943. Studies of the Pacific pilchard or sardine (*Sardinops caerulea*). 5. A method of computing mortalities and replacements. *U. S. Fish and Wildl. Serv., Spec. Sci. Rept. 24:* 10 pp.
Thompson, W. F., and F. Heward Bell
1934. Biological statistics of the Pacific halibut fishery. (2) Effect of changes in intensity upon total yield and yield per unit of gear. *Rept. Int. Fish. Comm. 8:* 49 pp.

# PART III · FISH PONDS

# 8 · CONSTRUCTION AND STOCKING
# OF FISH PONDS

## 8·1  Introduction

Fish ponds have gained in popularity during the last few years primarily as a result of the enthusiastic publicity given the farm pond program. A farm pond producing 100 to 200 pounds of fish per acre easily equals the production of beef from an acre of land. Various persons have estimated the number of farm ponds at over 1 million. About 8000 ponds with a total area of 40,000 acres had been constructed before 1935 according to Swingle (1949) who estimated that by 1949 there were approximately 1,111,000 ponds with a total area of 530,000 acres, indicating that during the past 15 years 100 times as many ponds had been built as during the preceding two centuries.

Fishery workers are sometimes prone to forget that many of these ponds are not constructed entirely for the fishing that may result. Water for irrigation, livestock, flood control, prevention of silting, ice, waterfowl, fur animals, and general recreation may be more important to the owner. Fish play a secondary role for example in the irrigation ponds which may be drawn down to one half or one third of the pool capacity during the day and then permitted to refill during the night.

Pond culture of fish is actually one of the oldest agricultural practices in use today. Unfortunately the desire for food has been a stronger motive than the desire for scientific investigation, and we find that the facts surrounding the biology of the ponds have lagged considerably behind other aspects. From the viewpoint of fishery management the populations of fish in the average farm pond are frequently "out of balance." Overpopulation, with first one species and then another dominating, is a common difficulty in farm fish pond management. Another serious difficulty is the emphasis that is being placed on one factor rather than the interaction of several variables which may be responsible for the optimum return from the fish ponds. Perhaps an appreciation of the roles of colloid chemistry, microbiology, biochemistry, and the thermodynamics of aquatic environments will lead to better management.

Much necessary information concerning the management of fish ponds is being obtained in the southeastern United States, largely through the efforts of H. S. Swingle and E. V. Smith, biologists of the Agricultural Experiment Station of the Alabama Polytechnic Institute at Auburn, Alabama. Unfortunately, successful management practices in one locality, though they may suggest the general pattern for management in another, usually cannot be applied without further investigation. Local conditions such as fertility of the soil, length of the growing season, and endemic species of fish are only a few of the variables that must be determined for different regions. However, where areas are deficient in fishing water the small artificial lake is the best and most practical means of bringing good fishing to the angler.

## 8·2  Pond sites

An adequate water supply must be provided and excessive silting prevented if the fish pond is to be successful. The best water supply is a spring or springs. Besides providing an adequate, steady, and dependable source of water they may furnish a possible spawning site for trout. Normally, springs are easily controlled and do not provide enough water to cause too great a movement of water through the pond.

Streams may be used as a source of water if some method of controlling the flow is available. Generally if a stream is used the pond is built on one side of, rather than across, the stream valley. In this way the volume of water admitted to the pond can be checked, and during floods there is not so much danger of losing the dam and destroying the pond. Too great a flow through a pond becomes a problem as most of the effects of fertilization are lost through the outlet.

Terrace water ponds or "runoff" ponds depend for water on drainage from the watershed. Here again the problem is year-round control as there must be enough water to keep the pond sufficiently filled throughout the year and yet not enough at any one time to cause serious flooding. Size of drainage area is important. Keeping it down to the minimum requirements is one way to prevent excessive silting. The drainage area should be kept in permanent vegetal cover. In general 10 to 50 acres of watershed are required to support one acre of pond.

Soil impervious to water for the pond bottom and dam core is a second important consideration in determining the pond site. The proper type of soil can be worked and squeezed into a tight ball. Samples of the soil should be taken from the surface to a depth of 1 to 2 feet. Gravelly and sandy soils or limestone and shale areas should be avoided. If suitable watertight soil cannot be found it is possible to use commercial sealing compounds such as bentonite. The bottom soil of the pond must be pulverized and the bentonite particles distributed evenly through it. A sheepsfoot roller is then used to compact the bottom. One pond losing 750 gallons of water a minute was reported watertight after such a treatment.

Topography of the site is important not only from the consideration of economy of actual construction but also from the standpoint of cost of future maintenance. The ideal site would be surrounded on three sides by small hills with a narrow outlet on the fourth, providing for a minimum amount of excavating both for proper depth and for the dam itself. After the site is tentatively chosen a topographic survey should be made with the aid of a simple hand level to determine the boundaries of the area to be flooded, the proposed depths, and the most suitable location for the dam site. Maximum depth should vary from 6 to 12 feet depending on the severity of the winters. Runoff ponds should have about one quarter of the pond at least 10 feet deep to allow for periods of low water.

If the pond is to be used as a source of water, proximity to buildings may influence choice of location. Pollution of course should be avoided. Controlled pollution is common in some areas of the world in providing fertilization of fish ponds. This practice is not prevalent in North America where the ponds are constructed almost entirely as multipurpose water areas.

## 8·3    Construction

Knowledge of construction techniques of the small fish pond is far ahead of the understanding of management of the fish populations introduced after the pond is completed. Publications on the design of the pond and construction of the dam are numerous and complete. An excellent and easily followed account of building the pond can be found in the book, *Fish Ponds for the Farm*, by Frank C. Edminster. Edminster includes a clear description together with many diagrams and charts and tables of value to the biologist and owner of the proposed pond.

The first step in construction is the removal of all trees and brush from the area to be flowed, both to improve the appearance of the pond and to prevent the later decay of large amounts of organic material on the pond bottom.

Topsoil should be removed at the base of the dam until impervious soil is reached. This may mean removal of a few inches to several feet but is necessary if the dam is to be watertight. The height of the dam should be 3 to 5 feet above the level of the pond at flood stage making allowance for settling. The slope of the dam depends on the quality of the fill. If the soil is good-quality clay then the slope can be 2 to 1. With exceptionally large dams it may be desirable to decrease the slope of the dam even though the quality of the fill is con-

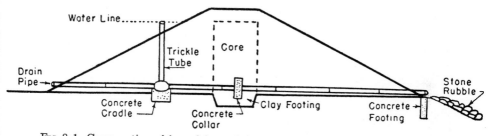

FIG. 8·1  Cross section of farm fish pond dam. (Credit: Frank C. Edminster, *Fish Ponds for the Farm,* Scribner's)

sidered good. If the fill is good a core of clay may not be necessary. However, if the fill is poor then a clay core may be necessary and the slope of the dam may have to be decreased to a 3-to-1 ratio. For dams up to 15 feet in height the width at the top should be 5 feet. For dams higher than 15 feet the width at the top should equal one third of the dam height.

Construction plans should include provision for handling of normal overflow and make proper allowance for complete drainage. Many ponds have been and are being constructed without any means of drainage, and this questionable practice will hamper later successful management of the pond. Figure 8·1 shows a cross section of a dam with core and trickle tube and drain pipe. The drain pipe can serve both purposes if installed properly. Size of the drain pipe may be 4 to 6 inches for ponds up to 3 acres and 6 to 12 inches for ponds up to 15 or 20 acres. Concrete collars should be placed around the pipes to support and to prevent leakage around the pipe. Drainage may be controlled by a valve or by an ell which can be pushed down to bottom when drainage is desired. Piping should be of solid construction.

An emergency spillway should be provided around one end of the dam. The spillway should not be part of the dam unless it is made of concrete.  The spillway will take care of flood waters from intensive rain or snow runoff.  Usual construction is such that when the water level in the pond is 6 inches over the trickle tube the spillway begins to function.  A wide, shallow spillway is desirable since a deep, narrow one will require a higher dam and will cause a greater loss of fish.

Since modern methods of management call for little or no shallow water areas along the banks the ponds should be graded sufficiently steep to hold the soil and yet not provide any extensive areas to encourage the growth of plants.

For ponds with a drainage tube, construction of catchment basins aids in collecting the fish.  The catchment basins are depressions from 6 to 8 feet square located near the outlet.

As a final step in completing a pond exposed banks should be seeded to prevent erosion, to add strength, and to beautify the area.  A fence may be necessary to prevent livestock from trampling the banks and muddying the water.

## 8·4   Species of fish

Choosing the proper species of fish with which to stock the pond after construction is completed is one of the most difficult and important decisions facing the owner and biologist.  Particularly is this true in the northeastern United States where the growing season is relatively short and few actual quantitative researches are available as guides.  Great variation in fishing success in lakes containing many species has led to trials of a single species or a very simple combination of species.  The best simple combination in general use today is the bluegill–bass combination and the best single species is the eastern brook trout.  The success of a species depends largely on its ability to survive and reproduce in the environment and its ability to compete with other species for food and space.  Balance of the pond fish populations is important since too few or too many replacements will affect the annual harvest and will usually result in overpopulation of one or another species if a combination is used.

The combination that has given the highest returns to anglers is the bluegill–largemouth bass.  However, in the Northeast returns have been below expectation and more investigation is needed.  In northern Maine many farm ponds are supporting good populations of brook trout.  There are at present no figures as to annual yield to the angler.  Various combinations of other species have been tested.  A consideration of some of these species and the results, meager as they are, may prove helpful.

**Largemouth bass** (*Micropterus salmoides*). Largemouth bass thrive in small, artificial lakes, feeding on young fish, crayfish, and aquatic and terrestrial insects. A temperature of 70° F is required before spawning begins and a temperature of 80° F before any noticeable growth is produced. They do not thrive well in muddy waters.

**Bluegill** (*Lepomis macrochirus*). The bluegills do well in small, artificial lakes and are considered game fish in many sections of the country. They feed primarily on entomostraca, midge larvae, and algae. The bluegill require a temperature of 80° F to spawn and, providing that temperature is maintained and the pond is in balance, will spawn throughout the summer. The resulting young provide forage fish for the piscivorous fish living in the same water. A temperature of 60° to 80° F is necessary for growth, and clear water is preferred.

**Redear sunfish** (*Lepomis microlophus*). These fish have been used in combination with the bluegill and the largemouth bass. They cannot be used alone with the bass since the redear, even when conditions permit spawning both in spring and fall, cannot produce enough young to keep the population in balance. They make their best growth in temperatures of 75° F. Apparently the redear sunfish is very susceptible to sudden changes in temperature.

**White crappie** (*Pomoxis annularis*) **and black crappie** (*Pomoxis nigromaculatus*). These two closely related fish make their best growth in large lakes which reach a temperature of 75° F. They spawn at temperatures around 65° F. Crappies will supposedly tolerate muddy water. Although they have been used in the bluegill–bass combination, about the only thing they add is variety in species taken by the angler.

**Warmouth** (*Chaenobryttus coronarius*). Inadequate testing of this species indicates a very low production.

**Round flier** (*Centrarchus macropterus*). The round flier reproduces earlier than the bass and may prove advantageous in colder ponds.

**Rock bass** (*Ambloplites rupestris*) **and pumpkinseed** (*Lepomis gibbosus*). Although investigations are being conducted with these species no results are available as yet.

**Yellow perch** (*Perca flavescens*). Much work needs to be done with this species, although it may be successful in colder ponds to replace the largemouth bass as the piscivorous fish.

**Eastern brook trout** (*Salvelinus fontinalis*). In cold-water ponds the brook trout has given good results. No controlled experiments have been run so that little is known as to actual production or the size or number to stock. Northern Maine farm ponds appear to have thriving populations of brook trout which spawn successfully in springs or the tiny spring tributaries which drain into the ponds.

**Rainbow trout** (*Salmo gairdneri*) **and brown trout** (*Salmo trutta*). Very little actual investigation has been carried on with these species, but indications are that they will not do well in ponds and will require annual restocking.

**Pickerel** (*Esox niger*). The pickerel has been suggested as a possible substitute for the largemouth bass as the piscivorous species in the bass–bluegill combination.

**Channel catfish** (*Ictalurus punctatus*). These fish are unable to spawn in the small fish pond and exhibit slow growth.

**Brown bullhead** (*Ameiurus nebulosus*). This species has not been successful either in combination with a predaceous fish or by itself. As a result of the many stunted bullheads the pond is soon out of balance.

**Gizzard shad** (*Dorosoma cepedianum*). When these fish were used in the bluegill–bass combination large shad accumulated in the pond and reduced the growth of adult bluegill with which they were competing for food. The gizzard shad will not take a lure or bait, and so the adults cannot be controlled by angling. The bass yield was not increased enough to justify leaving out the bluegills. The shad grew so rapidly that in 1 to 2 years they became too large for the bass to eat and so overpopulated the pond that they curtailed their own survival rate.

**Mullet** (*Mugil cephalus*). These fish feed on littoral diatoms and blue-green algae. Together with the next two species they make up the three most important market fish in Hawaiian fish ponds.

**Milkfish** (*Chanos chanos*). Milkfish feed on unicellular and other minute algae as young fish. Larger fish feed on increasingly greater amounts of large filamentous algae.

**Tenpounder** (*Elops saurus*). The tenpounder feeds on mosquito fish and shrimps.

**Goldfish** (*Carassius auratus*). Goldfish feed primarily on insects, plant material, and plankton and, as a forage fish, for a short while have produced large yields of largemouth bass. However, as they rapidly grow too large for bass to eat the pond becomes overpopulated with large, adult goldfish. Bluegills in combination may retard the production of the goldfish by eating the goldfish eggs.

**Golden shiner** (*Notemigonus crysoleucas*). The golden shiner competes directly with the bluegill for food, and large shiners have been known to eat small fish. They are unable to maintain their numbers when used alone or in some combination with the bluegill as a forage fish. Slow growth and a spawning period limited to the spring are largely responsible for this. They may continue in a pond for 1 to 3 years but eventually even the brood stock is consumed by the bass.

**Gambusia** (*Gambusia affinis*). Small size of the adult fish prevents their maintaining themselves in combination with the largemouth bass. They have been almost entirely eliminated in a few months in attempts to use them with the largemouth bass.

Generally where the bluegill–bass combination has been used improved fishing has resulted, for several reasons. Fortunately many sections of the country consider both fish as game fish, which provides some control over the adult forage fish when they become too large for the piscivorous fish to eat. Many forage fish cannot be used because there is no way to control the adults, and overpopulation results. The bluegill spawns throughout the summer (May to first of October in Alabama). This continuous crop of small fish provides a ready source of food for the bass during their growing season. In over 10 years of experimentation in Alabama the bluegill–bass combination has yielded an annual catch of 175 to 200 pounds of fish per acre. The bass have made up 20 to 61 pounds of this catch in different ponds receiving the same treatment. Bluegills and bass will maintain their numbers under intensive fishing pressure. In experiments conducted in Alabama paid fishermen could only deplete the pond populations about 50 per cent at which time the catch per unit of effort fell so low that fishing was useless. Actually underfishing is one of the chief causes of many ponds being out of balance and may necessitate the destruction of many bluegill nests to reduce the numbers and prevent overpopulation and stunting of the fish. The efficiency of angling devices is low and patience of the fishermen short. Long before the population of selected species (warm water) has been reduced to the danger point below which it cannot maintain itself, the fishing for that species has become so poor that fishing is greatly reduced or even stopped.

## 8·5   Stocking rate

Most recommendations for the stocking of small fish ponds call for 100 largemouth bass and 1000 bluegill sunfish per acre. From Texas to Georgia the general recommendation is 100 largemouth bass and 800 to 1500 bluegill sunfish, stocked as fingerlings at an average length of 2 inches. Such a recommendation is made on the assumption that the bass will reach maturity and spawn the following spring. This does not hold in many localities in the northern part of the United States where the bass never spawn until they have spent two full seasons and often three in the pond. The bluegills spawn during their first year and so are at least one whole brood ahead of the bass. It follows that the pond becomes overstocked with bluegills before enough bass are raised to control them. Stocking of adult bluegills and adult bass rather than the fry or fingerlings helps this situation.

For best survival, fish should be planted in the ponds in the spring when the water is cool and contains plenty of oxygen and food is at an optimum level. Small bluegills are hard to transport so that too early a planting of bluegill fry is almost impossible. Investigation is necessary to determine the best procedure for stocking trouts. It is suggested that 300 trout fingerlings be planted per acre.

The observation has been made that the survival of stocked fish in small fish ponds is much higher than could ordinarily be expected in streams or already established lakes.

## 8·6   Growth

Just as most of the quantitative work has been done on the bluegill–largemouth bass combination so most of the growth data concern those species. Bass may mature at 2 to 3 years in the northern states and in 10 to 12 months in the South. Bluegills mature as early as 1 year in the North and 4 to 12 months in the South.

Records from Illinois indicate that from June 23, 1938, to October 1938 bass grew from 0.87 to 6.45 inches. During a period from June 1938 to March 1939 bluegills increased as much as three times in weight. Bluegills 3.5 inches in March were 6.5 inches in October (Bennett 1948). In West Virginia bass fry were $1\frac{1}{2}$ inches 30 days after hatching (Surber 1949), and bluegills averaged 2.0 to 2.7 inches in $2\frac{1}{2}$ months (Surber 1948).

One-year-old bluegills should average about 3.5 inches in length, 2-year-old bluegills about 5.5 inches, 3-year-olds about 6.6 inches, and 4-year-olds about 8.0 inches.

In Michigan under favorable conditions of little competition and ample food bluegills matured in 12 months and averaged a total length of 6 inches in 17 months (Krumholz 1949). Little growth is exhibited by either bluegills or largemouths during the winter months.

## 8·7   Production

The production of large numbers of moderate-sized fish is the goal of fish pond management. Table 8·1 gives figures on the standing crop as reported by a few authors.

TABLE 8·1

POUNDS OF FISH PER ACRE OF POND

| Pounds per Acre | Locality | Authority |
|---|---|---|
| 138 (28–370) | Iowa | Fessler 1950 |
| 100–200 | Virginia | Surber 1948 |
| 71–1145 | Illinois | Bennett 1946 |
| 45 (game fish); 100–300 (coarse) | Indiana | Ricker 1945 |
| 657 (fertilized); 100–300 (unfertilized) | Alabama | Swingle 1949 |
| 17–36 | Nova Scotia | Smith 1948 |

Actually the table is of little value when it is considered that Carlander (1950) lists standing crop per acre ranging from 5 to 2799 pounds. Location of the pond, species, and method of determining production are some of the factors that influence these figures.

Not a little of the difficulty in regard to pond fish populations has resulted from the use of several terms in reference to the total weight of a fish population. Clarke (1946) and Krumholz (1948) have attempted to define productivity, fish production, carrying capacity, standing crop, yield, and other terms. Productivity should be used as a general term embracing all the concepts of the dynamics of production. Krumholz (*op. cit.*) suggests that carrying capacity should indicate the upper limit of weight of species or combination of species that can be supported by a body of water over an extended period of time. The above authors are in agreement in defining the standing crop as "the total weight of all the fishes present in the area at the time of observation." Yield refers to the weight of fish removed during a definite period of time.

**References**

Bennett, G. W.
  1946. Fertilizers in fish pond management. *Ill. Nat. Hist. Surv.* 2 pp. mimeo.
  1948. The bass-bluegill combination in a small artificial lake. *Ill. Nat. Hist. Surv. 24* (3):377–412.
Carlander, K. O.
  1950. *Handbook of freshwater fishery biology.* W. C. Brown Co.: 281 pp., Dubuque, Iowa.
Clarke, G. L.
  1946. Dynamics of production in a marine area. *Ecol. Mono. 16:* 321–335.
Edminster, Frank C.
  1947. *Fish ponds for the farm.* Charles Scribner's Sons: xii + 114, New York.
Fessler, F. R.
  1950. Fish populations in some Iowa farm ponds. *Prog. Fish-Cult. 12* (1):3–11.

Krumholz, L. A.
  1948.  Variations in size and composition of fish populations in recently stocked ponds. *Ecology 29* (4):401–414.
  1949.  Rates of survival and growth of bluegill yolk fry stocked at different intensities in hatchery ponds. *Trans. Am. Fish. Soc. 76:* 190–203.
Ricker, William E.
  1945.  Abundance, exploitation, and mortality of the fish in two lakes. *Invest. Ind. Lakes and Streams 2* (17):345–448.
Smith, M. W.
  1948.  Improved trout angling in a small lake after poisoning undesirable fish. *Can. Fish. Cult. 3* (4):3–6.
Surber, E. W.
  1948.  Increasing production of bluegill sunfish for farm pond stocking. *Prog. Fish-Cult. 10* (4):199–203.
  1949.  Control of aquatic plants in ponds and lakes. *U. S. Fish and Wildl. Serv., Fish. Leaf. 344:* 20 pp.
Swingle, H. S.
  1949a.  Experiments with combinations of largemouth black bass, bluegill and minnow in ponds. *Trans. Am. Fish. Soc. 76:* 46–62.
  1949b.  Some recent developments in pond management. *14 N. Am. Wildl. Conf.:* 295–310.

# 9 · FERTILIZATION AND MANAGEMENT
# OF FISH PONDS

## 9·1 Fertilization of ponds

All fish are dependent either directly or indirectly on plankton for food. Some species use phytoplankton directly; others feed on zooplankton and the immature stages of various insects. These larger food organisms subsist either on phytoplankton or on the bacteria that decompose phytoplankton and other organic matter. Some species of fish feed on entomostraca when young but on other fish, crayfish, frogs, and larger animals as they grow larger. As the food chain progresses from the bacteria and phytoplankton up to the carnivorous fish the number of organisms making up each group decreases. Thus there are fewer zooplankton than phytoplankton and fewer piscivorous fish than forage fish.

The mere addition of fertilizer to a pond or lake will not necessarily produce better fishing and in fact may sometimes ruin the waters for recreational purposes. Fish require proteins, fats, carbohydrates, and mineral salts which they obtain from insects, worms, crustaceans, and other zooplankton. The latter in turn derive their nourishment from bacteria and microscopic plant organisms, the development of which depends upon utilization of carbon, oxygen, phosphorus, and various mineral salts. Sunlight and warmth are important in plankton metabolism. In northern regions with less light and lower temperatures the results are poorer. Low productivity is usually found in lakes with water of high acidity, rocky or sand bottom, and a small littoral zone. Higher productivity results from shallow, alkaline lakes with silt or calcareous bottoms.

Fertilization of small fish ponds is supposed to heighten productivity by increasing the nutrients available to the lower portions of the food chain, especially the bacteria and phytoplankton. This in turn provides more food for higher organisms resulting finally in a higher return of fish from a unit area of water. Unfortunately, in common with many other studies which require simultaneous consideration of many variables, pond fertilization does not lend itself readily to neat or decisive experiments. Investigators have usually placed

121

too much importance on a single factor with the result that recommendations and conclusions concerning pond fertilization vary without reason, and the process reverts to trial and error in different localities. An acceptable fertilizer has been described as one that should increase the yield of fish and that must improve the fishability of the water by discouraging the growth of both filamentous algae and waterweeds, and by imparting to the water a cloudiness which increases the frequency of biting.

As programs of fertilization continue the disadvantages of large-scale fertilization become more and more evident. Frequently, under warm-water conditions, instead of a water bloom, large mats of algae are formed which float on the surface, spoiling the fishing, swimming, and recreational qualities of the pond. As these mats of vegetation die and fall to the bottom they may seriously change the chemical composition of the water. Fertilization of a lake may lead to the development of conditions suitable only for forage fish or undesirable species of larger fish. Organic substances may increase until the oxygen supply is lowered beyond safe limits.

Extensive fertilization of lakes may lead to their eutrophication and early extinction. Hasler (1947) mentions the eutrophication of certain lakes in Europe by the entrance of domestic sewage high in phosphorus and nitrogen which has changed the chemistry of the water, making the lakes unfit for recreation and changing the fish fauna from game species to coarse fish. It is certain that fertilization will hasten the extinction of lakes unless some method can be discovered to oxidize a large proportion of the additional deposit created by the fertilizers. More rapid deposition of sediments on a lake bottom may cause a deficiency of oxygen in the cooler hypolimnion available to trout during the summer months with the result that trout soon disappear. Fishermen may learn to dislike the effects of fertilization if it begins to damage the little remaining trout water.

Fertilizer added to shallow lakes in areas where winters are severe may, by increasing the organic content, cause winterkills. Several cases of this have been reported. Fertilization of a body of water increases the entire biomass, whereas fertilizer as it is applied to the land is usually meant for a single crop.

Inorganic fertilizers are customarily expressed as percentages of available nitrogen (N), phosphoric acid ($P_2O_5$), and potash ($K_2O$). Thus 6% N, 8% $P_2O_5$, and 4% $K_2O$ would be written 6-8-4. Sodium nitrate for increased N is frequently added when waters are neutral or acid and ammonium sulfate when waters are alkaline. The major fertilizing elements are nitrogen, phosphorus, potassium, and calcium.

Minor elements are manganese, boron, sulfur, iron, magnesium, copper, and zinc. It may be found as more research is completed that the so-called minor elements are of vital importance. For example, fertilization with manganese at 0.1 ppm gave good water bloom with the heavier bloom correlated with the increased application (Henderson 1949). One of the most important contributions to the fish pond program was the realization by H. S. Swingle and E. V. Smith of the Alabama Polytechnic Institute that inorganic fertilizers are more valuable than organic fertilizers. Inorganic fertilizers can be prepared with accurate amounts of desired elements, they are cleaner, and they provide a more desirable pond as they can be more easily applied. Organic fertilizers are unpredictable of results, ruin the aesthetic value of a pond, and are liable to transmit parasites and diseases, such as liver fluke and Bang's disease. Larger amounts of organic fertilizer must be employed to give results comparable to those achieved with the inorganic; one ton of manure equals roughly 100 pounds of 10-5-10.

One major obstacle to the proper fertilization of ponds is the fact that the chemical requirements are little known, but the analysis of pond bottoms and pond waters may eventually provide the key. Pond owners are frequently advised to use the same type of fertilizer that they are using on their lands, the logic being that the water draining off the land would likely be deficient in the same elements as the land itself. The mineral composition of pond water is a reflection of the mineral composition of the soils of the bottom and the surrounding basin—alkaline waters may result from calcium-rich soil. Soluble nutrient elements may be absorbed by the pond bottom. Addition of fertilizers may enrich the pond by disturbing the balance and causing the bottom to release previously absorbed nutrients. The pond bottom should be neither too absorptive nor too inactive, should be loose and well aerated to permit rapid oxidizing, should have buffer qualities, and should provide a suitable medium for the growth of bottom organisms.

Lime ($CaO$) is frequently added to a pond to create an alkaline reaction and to act as a buffer because it is generally believed that a slightly alkaline water grows the most fish. The calcium tends to displace certain other fertilizing substances, making potassium and phosphorus available in greater amounts. The acid-buffering capacity of lime also increases the ability of the water to store carbon dioxide.

The role of some of the other fertilizer ingredients is apparently open to question. The stabilized economy of phosphorus in a lake makes phosphorus fertilization schemes appear wasteful if the bulk of the phosphorus enters the sediments never to participate again in the so-called phosphorus cycle. Phosphorus has gained the reputation of being the most important single fertilizer. Yet no one knows for certain what a phosphorus deficiency is and so far only the bottom areas contain significant quantities of phosphorus in solution. Hayes (1949) suggests that phosphorus might be capable of stimulating nitrogen synthesis or liberation from bottom mud. Doubt is expressed however that such a procedure would be practicable.

Nitrogen can apparently be dispensed with since there is no correlation between yield and nitrogen application.

Despite these pessimistic views fertilization to increase fish production in small fish ponds is successful, and procedures have been established that give results in some sections of the country. Fertilization of large bodies of water has not however proved successful and in many cases has actually been harmful. During the recent conflict an attempt was made to fertilize arms of the sea in Scotland. Though an increased yield was reported the inefficiency and cost of the program made it impractical. On the basis of cost ($11) per surface acre it would require $350,000 to fertilize Norris Reservoir. Efforts to fertilize northern cold trout waters to increase their productivity have proved unsuccessful. Further research is necessary.

The established routine for pond fertilizations is to determine the formula for the fertilizer from an analysis of the soil in the drainage area. After the formula is determined the fertilizer is applied at the rate of 100 pounds per surface acre (tests with increased amounts have not shown a correlated increase in production). The first application is usually made in the early spring, and fertilization may be continued into the late fall. Fertilization of ponds during the winter months, even in the deep South, is not warranted since the growth of the fish during that period is very slight. A pond should be fertilized until a sufficiently dense water bloom is obtained to cause a turbidity that makes a Secchi disk disappear 18 inches below the surface. A rough test is to extend the forearm into the water up to the elbow. If the fist is not visible then the pond is fertilized properly.

Costs of fertilizing ponds vary, but a few figures may be helpful as an indication. The cost of fertilizing a 40-acre lake with 3000 pounds of soybean meal was $150. The cost of fertilization will range from about $11 to $20 per acre on small ponds with a maximum depth of 6 feet. Cost per acre of fertilizing a lake using 6-8-4 plus 10 pounds of nitrate of soda was $10 the first year and $15 the second year.

## 9·2  Results of fertilization

Fertilization is known to enhance the growth of algae by adding appropriate plant nutrients. A greater population of bottom animals has been found to exist directly underneath the nomad "lake highways" which stretch across the ice of lakes in Sweden than in other areas of the same lakes, as the droppings from the reindeer and the nomads fertilized the bottom when the ice melted.

Fertilization of four lakes in Ontario resulted in a marked increase in the net phytoplankton in 3 weeks to a month after the first application of fertilizer (Langford 1950). Diatoms and flagellates showed the greatest increment. The rise of zooplankton organisms was relatively less than that of phytoplankton although the rotifer population did increase in all lakes. A rapid decline followed the maximum abundance and subsequent applications failed to increase the numbers.

Inorganic fertilizer (10-6-4) was applied at 3-week intervals to a trout lake of 4.3 acres and a warm-water lake of 27.5 acres in Michigan (Ball 1950). A total of 400 pounds was placed in the trout lake and 2800 pounds in the warm-water lake. The bloom in neither lake reached the level recommended by Swingle and Smith and was always on the wane before the next application. No bloom was observed in the trout lake. During the second winter the fish populations in both lakes were winterkilled.

In Alabama fertilizers increased the carrying capacity of ponds from 300 to 400 per cent. The average over a 5-year period in unfertilized ponds was 19.2 pounds of fish per acre while the fertilized ponds produced 188.1 pounds per acre. In some instances increasing the volume of fish food results in a concomitant increase in the number of young fish surviving with the result that a stunted population is often created.

When the weight of bottom organisms was increased from 5 to 9 grams per square meter the weight of bass increased from 48 pounds to 105 pounds (Howell 1942).

Surber (1948) using 14 ponds (0.2 to 0.62 acre) tested the production of bluegills, using different concentrations of the same organic fertilizer (10-5-5). Two unfertilized ponds were used as controls. There was no clear-cut correlation between the amount of fertilizer and yield. The unfertilized ponds produced 86 pounds, ponds fertilized with 100 pounds per application produced 133 pounds, 200 pounds per application produced 127 pounds of bluegills, and 300 pounds per application produced 104 pounds of bluegills.

In rearing bass, ponds are fertilized before being filled and fertilized again after being filled, as often as needed to increase the amount of food present for the small bass. A greater number of Daphnia and insects are produced if the ponds are fertilized.

Large populations of insects are found in ponds 3 to 3½ months after filling but they are more abundant in the fertilized ponds. Addition of fertilizer may more than treble the average dry weight of these bottom organisms (Ball 1949).

## 9·3   Control of aquatic vegetation

Aquatic vegetation, in excessive amounts, is one of the major causes of pond fish populations becoming out of balance. The aquatic plants

Fig. 9·1   Spraying a pond with sodium arsenite to control aquatic vegetation at the Tishomingo, Oklahoma, fish-cultural station. (Credit: E. P. Haddon, U. S. Fish and Wildlife Service)

provide the small fish with too much protection and lead to a stunted population. They tend to harbor mosquitoes and snakes and as a source of irritation to fishermen lessen the aesthetic value of the pond. It is possible that dense mats of aquatic vegetation form traps for zooplankton during periods of extremely low oxygen.

Manual methods of weed control are expensive and laborious. Dragging with chains and cables, raking and hoeing, dredging, and using firehoses to wash the roots loose are some of the common methods employed. When these methods are used, the weeds frequently return within a period of 3 weeks. Drying the pond keeps down the aquatic vegetation for about one month.

Inefficiency of manual methods of weed control has led to the use of chemical methods. Copper sulfate has been proved unsuccessful and too dangerous to employ. Sodium arsenite can be used locally, but its results are of brief duration, and it is of course a deadly poison to mammals. If sodium arsenite is used, then the spring and early summer appear to be the best season.

Most popular at present is the chemical dichlorophenoxyacetic acid known popularly, fortunately, as 2,4-D. Most susceptible to its killing action are the broad-leaved, succulent type of weed (Snow 1949). Weeds with roots and submerged stems may survive until several applications have been made. Death usually occurs in 1 to 4 weeks. Grasses are resistant to 2,4-D. The chemical is harmless to mammals in small amounts. A high concentration will kill pond-fish. Dichlorophenoxyacetic acid is most effective at temperatures of 70° F or higher during the earlier stages of the plant growth. Moisture, temperature, stage of development, or the plant's period of greatest susceptibility may determine success of spraying.

The chemical is available in powder form as a salt of 2,4-D and in the liquid form as an ester of 2,4-D. Water must be used with the powder form. The powder forms are considerably cheaper, but best results have been obtained with the liquid forms when mixed with Diesel fuel or kerosene because more complete coverage is obtained, application is faster, less spray solution is needed, and there is less loss through runoff. For example, if water is used 100 to 400 gallons must be used per acre. If oil, 50 to 100 gallons are necessary. Pellets have not proved successful to date.

In the preparation of 2,4-D for spraying one must first dissolve it in a cosolvent and then dilute it with the carrier liquid after which the whole is thoroughly mixed. Esters directly miscible with oil are known but are not readily obtained. Solubility in water is about 3%, providing either ammonium hydroxide or washing soda (sodium carbonate) is used to aid in dissolving it. A 5% solution of 2,4-D is ordinarily satisfactory, but higher percentages may be used in unusual circumstances. Cosolvents commonly used are tributylphosphate (TBP) (15 ppm toxic to fish) and triethanolamine (TEA). Cost of 2,4-D is about $1.00 per pound with TBP at $0.50 a pound and TEA about $0.75 a quart. Water or oil will suffice for the carrier liquid. Twenty gallons per acre of 5½% 2,4-D dissolved in TBP killed nearly all foliage. The following table (Surber et al. 1947) gives the composition of two possible spray solutions:

| Solution No. | 2,4-D Weight, % Pounds | | Cosolvent Name | Volume, Quarts | Carrier to Make 5 Gallons |
|---|---|---|---|---|---|
| 1 | 5 | 2 | TBP | 2 | kerosene |
| 2 | 5 | 2 | TEA | 1 | water |

The following data (Surber et al. 1947) may prove helpful for application to various aquatic plants:

**Cattail** (*Typha latifolia*). Five per cent 2,4-D with TBP as the cosolvent and kerosene as carrier proved most effective. Only a single spraying was necessary if used before the spikes flowered. Twenty gallons of the solution were applied per acre.

**Spikerush** (*Eleocharis*). This plant is particularly hard to control manually because it is only 6 inches high on an average and cannot be raked or cut satisfactorily. Applications of 2,4-D proved very effective.

**Round-stem bulrush** (*Scirpus validus*). A 5% solution of 2,4-D in tributylphosphate (TBP) killed down to the roots. More than one application is necessary.

**Burreed** (*Sparganium americanum*). A single treatment of 15% 2,4-D in TEA and water, or even more effective was a 5% 2,4-D in TBP and kerosene.

**Willow** (*Salix*). Five per cent 2,4-D in TBP and kerosene provide a quick and easy means of control.

Submerged plants present a little tougher problem.

**Waterweed** (*Anacharis canadensis*). Thus far 2,4-D at 10 pounds per acre has only succeeded in arresting the growth in some ponds. It has many different ways of reproducing itself which make it hard to control by cutting or raking.

**Potamogeton.** Adequate control is furnished with 2,4-D in TBP.

**Water lily** (*Nymphaea*). Spraying on leaves with 5% 2,4-D in TBP and kerosene was ineffective. A second spraying after the pond was drained was very much more successful with only a few plants reappearing.

Chlorinated hydrocarbons having high specific gravities and low solubility in water have been tried. The action is confined to local areas as the chemicals sink to the bottom. They are not dangerous to mammals. Trichlorbenzene at 5 ppm was found to kill both the fish and weeds. However, in the process of killing the fish it gave them a disagreeable taste. Orthodichlorbenzene is the safest and most effective of this type. Forty per cent of one pond was treated without affecting the fish or the taste of the water. The chemical should be sprayed under water to be effective. A dosage of 20 to 40 gallons per acre is recommended for *Potamogeton*. These chemicals kill by destroying the chlorophyll and are also absorbed into the roots. Within a few hours weeds treated in this manner turn white and in from 1 to 4 weeks drop to the bottom. Results last from a few months to years. Average cost is 9 to 12 cents per pound or $1.00 to $1.40 per gallon. Cost per acre to apply is $25 to $50 (Eicher 1949).

Ammate (ammonium sulfamate) is applied at the rate of 15% or ¾ pound per gallon of water. It is reasonably economical. Best results are obtained when the plant is fruiting.

Chlorophenyl allyl carbonate dissolved in kerosene was 95% effective in controlling giant cutgrass when sprayed in 2% concentration. Equivalent success was obtained on cattails with a 4% concentration.

Submerged plants may be controlled by proper fertilization. The submerged plants must have sunlight in order to grow. Consequently, if fertilization is begun in the early spring, by the time plant growth begins the water will be colored and little or no sunlight will be available for plant growth.

## 9·4  Fish pond populations

The Alabama Agricultural Experiment Station under the direction of H. S. Swingle has been gathering information for the last 15 years on well-established fish populations. A recent bulletin (Swingle 1950) presenting data on balanced and unbalanced fish populations is based on information from 89 separate fish populations which had been established from 2 to 30 years. Eighty-five of these populations were determined by draining the ponds, to insure an accurate count of the standing crop. Four of the populations were determined by poisoning with rotenone. Many of the relationships will prove of value as standards for the comparison of fish populations. Much of the information in this section has been taken from the bulletin cited above.

Quoting Swingle,

. . . The interrelationships in fish populations are satisfactory if the populations yield, year after year, crops of harvestable fish that are satisfactory in amount when the basic fertilities of the bodies of water containing these populations are considered.

Such populations are considered to be "balanced populations" and the species within such a population are "in balance." What then are some of the criteria of a balanced population? If an annual crop of harvestable fish is to be produced then the species in the balanced population must be capable of reproducing within the environment.

The extravagance of nature evidenced in the high reproductive capacity of fishes results in the production of far greater numbers of young than can be grown to a harvestable size. Thus the second criterion of a balanced population is the control of the numbers of young fish by a predatory species. In the ideal balanced population a certain poundage of fish removed in one year is replaced by the correct number of fish to provide a like harvest in succeeding years. Too many replacements will result in an unsatisfactory size, and too few replacements will not utilize the productive capacities of the water.

The following example is given to illustrate the factors involved in the simple bluegill–bass combination. Bluegills are stocked at the rate of 1500 per acre of which approximately 1000 will survive to reach a harvestable size of 4 ounces within one year. In subsequent years 4-ounce bluegills can be harvested only if the number of young are reduced until by the time they reach 4 ounces they equal the number of old fish removed from the population by angling or natural causes. Each pair of adult bluegills produces an average of 5000 young. If both adult parents are lost there is then room in the population for two of the original 5000 progeny. Thus in the bluegill–bass combination the predator bass and natural mortality must remove 4998. This reduction may take place over a period of 1 to 5 years giving rise to several age classes and size groups below the size of the harvestable fish in a population. These smaller fish serve as food for the piscivorous species and as replacements for the adult stock. Thus a balanced population is composed of three groups consisting of the adult fish satisfactory for harvesting, intermediate fish too small for harvesting and too large for food, and small fish of a size readily available to the predatory species.

Unbalanced populations are unable to produce annual crops of fish year after year. Although this may be due to the failure to provide sufficient recruits it is more commonly the result of overcrowding because too many individuals have survived.

In his efforts to provide some quantitative method of comparing populations, Swingle has utilized several ratios. Three of these are discussed in detail. Investigation of pond fish populations in the North has not yet reached the point where this information can be applied except as an indication. The $F/C$ ratio is the ratio of the total weight of all forage fishes ($F$) to the total weight of all carnivorous or piscivorous fishes ($C$) in a population. The following lists of so-called $C$ and $F$ species have been taken from the text of the Alabama Agricultural Experiment Station Bulletin (*op. cit.*).

## C Species

Largemouth black bass, *Micropterus salmoides*
White crappie, *Pomoxis annularis* (above 4 ounces in weight)
Black crappie, *Pomoxis nigromaculatus*
Chain pickerel, *Esox niger*
Longnose gar, *Lepisosteus osseus*
Spotted black bass, *Micropterus punctulatus*
Bowfin, *Amia calva*

## F Species

White crappie, *Pomoxis annularis* (under 4 ounces)
Black crappie, *Pomoxis nigromaculatus* (under 4 ounces)
Bluegill, *Lepomis macrochirus*
Spotted sunfish, *Lepomis punctatus*
Redear sunfish, *Lepomis microlophus*
Green sunfish, *Lepomis cyanellus*
Longear sunfish, *Lepomis megalotis*
Orangespotted sunfish, *Lepomis humilis*
Warmouth, *Chaenobryttus coronarius*
Yellow bullhead, *Ameiurus natalis*
Southern brown bullhead, *Ameiurus nebulosus marmoratus*
Golden shiner, *Notemigonus crysoleucas*
Chubsucker, *Erimyzon sucetta*
Gizzard shad, *Dorosoma cepedianum*
Goldfish, *Carassius auratus*
Gambusia, *Gambusia affinis*
Smallmouth buffalo, *Ictiobus bubalus*
Spotted sucker, *Minytrema melanops*
Carp, *Cyprinus carpio*
American eel, *Anguilla rostrata*

The following example of the fish population of a pond will illustrate the calculation of the $F/C$ ratio:

|  | Pounds |
|---|---|
| 43 large largemouth bass | 53.9 |
| 68 small largemouth bass | 2.8 |
| 41 large black crappie | 12.6 |
| 4,196 intermediate black crappie | 275.4 |
| 318 small black crappie | 4.7 |
| 724 intermediate bluegills | 57.8 |
| 13,860 small bluegills | 219.0 |
| Total | 626.2 |

Weight of the bluegills plus the weight of the small and intermediate black crappie equals the weight of *F* species:

$$219.0 + 57.8 + 4.7 + 275.4 = 556.9 \text{ pounds}$$

while the weight of all the bass plus the weight of all crappie weighing more than 4 ounces equals the $C$ value or weight of the $C$ species:

$$53.9 + 2.8 + 12.6 = 69.3 \text{ pounds}$$

The $F/C$ ratio is therefore

$$\frac{F}{C} = \frac{F \text{ value}}{C \text{ value}} = \frac{556.9}{69.3} = \frac{8.0}{1.0} = 8.0$$

Isolated ratios would be of little value except for comparison with other ratios from known populations.

The values for the various $F/C$ ratios are interesting to interpret. The range in balanced populations was 1.4 to 10.0, and 94.3 per cent were within the range of 1.4 to 6.8. Unbalanced populations had a range of 0.06 to 65.1. In balanced populations the ratio was most frequently between 3 and 4, and in the unbalanced populations the mode occurred in the interval of 7 to 8. Considerable overlapping of ratio values resulted. All populations with $F/C$ ratios in excess of 10 were unbalanced. Values of the ratio from 1 to 3 indicated, in general, that the population was somewhat overcrowded with $C$ species.

Although insufficient data are available it appears that, where the fertility remains relatively constant, as a result of uniform fertilization, and the cover remains constant, the $F/C$ ratios remain constant in spite of great variations in the ratio between the harvested $F$ and $C$ species. It also appears that in older populations there is a tendency for the $F/C$ ratio to be low, resulting in a poor catch, because it indicates low abundance. It is entirely possible that such a course of events is responsible for the decline in fishing as impoundments become older. Figure 9·2 presents interpretations of the $F/C$ ratios.

It has been suggested that, once the poundage a certain area can produce is known, the $F/C$ ratio could be used in determining the number of fish to stock. If it is found that a pond will support 100 pounds of bluegills or similar fish the number of bluegills and bass required for stocking may be figured as follows (choosing an $F/C$ ratio of 4 as being desirable). If this ratio is to be achieved, the weight of bluegills after 1 year will be

$$4/5 \times 100 = 80 \text{ pounds}$$

Bluegills will reach a size of 4 ounces in one year so that it will be necessary to stock $80 \times 4$ or 320 bluegills. Although only 75 per cent of the bluegills will survive since they spawn the first year, the loss due to mortality will be filled by young fish. The weight of the largemouth bass stocked will be

$$1/5 \times 100 = 20 \text{ pounds}$$

In the case of the bass that do not spawn the first summer it is necessary to include survival figures when calculating number to stock.

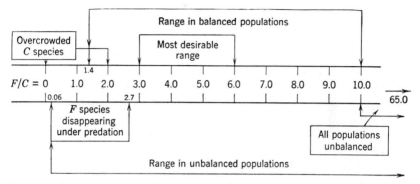

FIG. 9·2 Conditions in populations indicated by $F/C$ ratios. (Modified slightly after Swingle)

Seventy per cent of the bass will be alive one year later according to figures of the Alabama Agricultural Experiment Station. Thus $100\% = 100/70 \times 20 = 29$ advanced fry or fingerling bass which should be planted.

*The $Y/C$ ratio* equals the $Y$ value, or the total weight in pounds of all those individuals in the $F$ group that are small enough to be eaten by the average-sized adult in the $C$ group, divided by the $C$ value, or total weight in pounds of the $C$ group. This ratio emphasizes the importance of the small fish. Many poisoning experiments in the past have neglected to determine the weight of the small fish. A $Y/C$ ratio above 5.0 will indicate unbalance. Figure 9·3 presents the conditions indicated by $Y/C$ ratios and the overlapping that may occur between the balanced and unbalanced populations. Values for this ratio should be least in the spring just before the spawning of the $F$ species and should increase after the young hatch. The greatest importance comes from the influence of the young on the production of $C$ species on which many waters are judged.

*The $A_T$ value* (total availability value) is the percentage of the total weight of a fish population composed of fish of harvestable size.

It is necessary to select arbitrarily minimum weights or lengths for the so-called harvestable size. The total availability value may be further divided into that portion composed of species that are normally harvested $(A_T{}^H)$ and that portion composed of unharvested species $(A_T{}^N)$. The range of $A_T$ values for the balanced populations was 33 to 90, and the range for the unbalanced populations was 0 to 40. There was a narrow band of overlap from 33 to 40, but outside of this the $A_T$ value appeared to be a dependable indicator of the remainder of the population. The most desirable range was between 60 and 85.

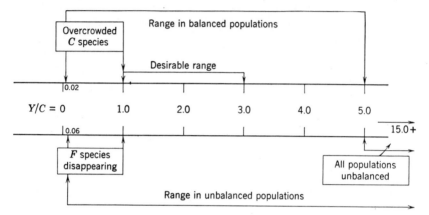

Fig. 9·3   Conditions in populations indicated by $Y/C$ ratios. (After Swingle)

$A_T$ values above 85 indicated ponds overcrowded with predator species, and values below 40 indicated too large a percentage of small and intermediate fish.

This value is credited by Swingle as the most useful indicator of balance and a measure of the efficiency of a population in production of harvestable fish. The value may also be used in determining the numbers to stock. The following example is given. Enough fish must be stocked so that 1 year later their weight will make up more than 33 per cent (minimum $A_T$ value) of the total weight of the population. If the pond is capable of producing 400 pounds of fish and is stocked with only 100 bass fingerlings plus 100 bluegill fingerlings, the following may be expected 1 year later:

70% survival of 100 stocked bass          70 bass
75% survival of 100 stocked bluegills     75 bluegills

The population composition at the age of 1 year would be:

|                                          | Pounds |
|------------------------------------------|--------|
| 70 large bass                            | 70     |
| 75 large bluegills                       | 25     |
| Total small and intermediate fishes      | 305    |
| Total                                    | 400    |

The $A_T$ value would be

$$\frac{70 + 25}{400} \times 100 = 23.8$$

It is interesting to note that if an $A_T$ value equal to 70 is desired the stocking rate would be 100 bass plus 1120 bluegills or almost exactly the so-called 1-to-10 ratio recommended in southern United States. The number of bass was kept constant at 100 per acre since experiments have shown that approximately 100 bass per acre is the maximum number that will reach a 1-pound average size in 1 year. It is figures such as these that are lacking in northern United States. Figure 9·4 presents the various $A_T$ values and the conditions they indicate.

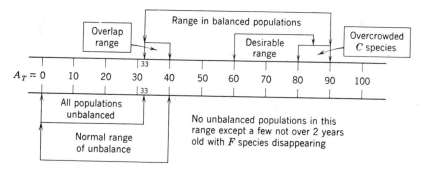

FIG. 9·4  Conditions in fish populations indicated by various $A_T$ values. (Modified slightly after Swingle)

The $E$ value of a species or group is the percentage of weight of the entire population composed of that species or group. It is in a sense the measure of the survival potential but is of importance only if a large percentage of the individuals that survive reach a desirable size year after year in the form of an annual harvestable crop. This situation can only occur in a balanced population. Consistently low $E$ values for a species in a balanced population would indicate that it was of little value from the standpoint of harvestable crop. For simple combinations such as the bluegill–bass the $E$ values for the two species can be calculated from the range of $F/C$ ratios given in Fig. 9·2.

## References

Ball, R. C.
   1949. Experimental use of fertilizer in the production of fish-food organisms and fish. *Mich. State Coll., Tech. Bull. 210.*
   1950. Fertilization of natural lakes in Michigan. *Trans. Am. Fish. Soc. 78:* 145–155.
Eicher, George J., Jr.
   1949. Localized weed control in management of gamefish. *Trans. Am. Fish. Soc. 76:* 177–182.
Hasler, Arthur D.
   1947. Eutrophication of lakes by domestic drainage. *Ecology 28* (4):383–395.
Hayes, Ronald F.
   1949. Lake fertilization experiment. *Nova Scotia, Rept. Consultant on Inland Fisheries, IV.*
Henderson, C.
   1949. Manganese for increased production of water-bloom algae in ponds. *Prog. Fish-Cult. 11* (3):157–159.
Howell, H. H.
   1942. Bottom organisms in fertilized and unfertilized fish ponds in Alabama. *Trans. Am. Fish. Soc. 71:* 165–179.
Landford, R. R.
   1950. Fertilization of lakes in Algonquin Park, Ontario. *Trans. Am. Fish. Soc. 78:* 133–144.
Snow, J. R.
   1949. Control of pondweeds with 2,4-D. *Prog. Fish-Cult. 11* (2):105–108.
Surber, E. W.
   1948. Fertilization of a recreational lake to control submerged plants. *Prog. Fish-Cult. 10* (2):53–58.
Surber, E. W., C. E. Minarik, and W. B. Farni, Jr.
   1947. The control of aquatic plants with phenoxyacetic compounds. *Prog. Fish-Cult. 9* (3):143–150.
Swingle, H. S.
   1950. Relationships and dynamics of balanced and unbalanced fish populations. *Alabama Agr. Exp. Sta. Bull. 274:* 74 pp.
Symposium
   1952. Farm fish ponds and management (12 papers). *J. Wildl. Management 16* (3):233–288.

# 10 · TYPES OF FISHING GEAR AND THEIR USE

## 10·1  Introduction

In order to manage fisheries intelligently it is necessary to have some knowledge of types of fishing gear.  There is great divergence in the efficiency of different forms of gear, in their adaptability to certain conditions, and in their desirability from the standpoint of conservation.  In a report by the Fish and Wildlife Service (1945) is tabulated the average prewar catch of 82,000 fishermen who took the nation's toll of 4400 million pounds of fish and shellfish.  This is adapted as shown in Table 10·1.

### TABLE 10·1

| Gear Type | Number of Fishermen | Catch in Millions of Pounds | Catch per Fisherman in Pounds |
|---|---|---|---|
| Purse seines | 13,000 | 2100 | 161,000 |
| Pound nets | 6,000 | 400 | 66,700 |
| Otter trawls | 11,000 | 700 | 63,500 |
| Lines | 24,000 | 500 | 20,800 |
| Gill nets | 19,000 | 200 | 10,500 |
| Other | 19,000 | 500 | 26,300 |
| All types | 82,000 | 4400 | 53,800 |

Thus, although it would take several volumes to describe the various types of fishing gear and their modifications, it is obvious that comparatively few types take the major share of the catch.  This chapter is necessarily a mere outline of fishing gear and no attempt has been made to include all minor types although a few such are included because they are important to some particular fishery, because they exhibit some stage in the development of a modern gear, or because they have historical interest.

## 10·2    Impaling gear

This is any form of gear by means of which a fish is impaled on a sharp shaft.  In general it 'can only be employed when the fish are plainly visible.

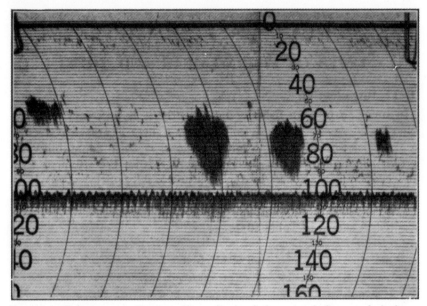

FIG. 10·1  Echogram on the recording roll of a fathometer (echo sounder) showing the water surface, the bottom, and schools of menhaden at middepths. Depths shown on echogram are in feet.  (Credit: Ernest Miles, U. S. Fish and Wildlife Service)

**Spear or gaff.**  This is a very ancient gear used where fish, especially large ones, are concentrated in a small area.  Thus, it is used to capture freshwater and anadromous fish on their spawning beds or when they are handicapped while negotiating stretches of swift water.  It is often used to spear fish through holes in the ice or while resting in stream eddies.  It may consist of a metal head of one to several tines or points, usually barbed, on a long handle.  Against larger fish the head usually slips onto a socket on the end of the handle from which it becomes detached as soon as the fish is struck.  The head may be attached to the handle by a short line, or it may become entirely detached but have a long line with which the fish is landed. The gaff is a modified form of spear, consisting usually, but not invariably, of a single recurved tine.  The tine is seldom barbed as dependence is placed on the recurved angle to prevent escape.  As used by the northwest Indian tribes it is fished with a long handle and a detachable head as just described for the spear. It is very effective against salmon held up by obstructions, but many injured fish escape. A gaff attached firmly to a short handle is widely used to finally land rod and reel fish as they are brought to boat or to the shore.

Spears are used extensively in taking fish among coral reefs and are the weapon employed in the popular sport of shallow diving with a head helmet.

**Harpoon.** The harpoon is a spear modified for throwing. The rear end of the harpoon or "lily iron" has two broad thin "barbs" or blades. They differ from actual barbs in that the rear edges are dull and they are not only broad but also curve at a slight angle from the head. The line is attached in front of these rear blades. Thus when a fisherman, standing in the "pulpit" protruding past the prow of his vessel, strikes deeply into a tuna or a swordfish, the backward pull of the line turns the back end of the lily iron into the flesh and anchors it securely. Large fish are often played by throwing overboard a keg or other float to which the end of the line is attached. This tires the fish without pulling with enough force to dislodge the iron. We will not discuss the intricate harpoon guns, etc., of the modern whale-killer vessel. The harpoon accounts for the largest share of the swordfish catch. They are approached by the vessel while lying motionless or playing slowly about on the surface.

**Bow and arrow.** This is a primitive gear only mentioned for its unique interest.

**Herring rake.** This is a very specialized gear developed by the northwest Indians but used extensively by salmon trollers to secure small quantities of bait herring. It consists of a long handle with a long very thin blade at each end and looks like a double-bladed oar. On one edge of each blade is set a closely spaced row of extremely sharp points. Each point is about an inch and a half in length and the size of about 14-gage wire. These rakes are handmade so the dimensions vary to suit the individual.

The usual method of fishing is to kneel in the bow of a light row-boat and quietly approach a small school of herring as they "boil" in a tiderip. Then the fisherman sweeps downward and backward alternately with each end of the rake, allowing the impaled herring to fall into the boat behind him at the end of each stroke.

## 10·3  Hook-and-line gear

Notwithstanding the fact that hook-and-line gear in its various forms is used in many modern fisheries, it is very ancient in origin and was probably used by practically all primitive peoples. The primitive hooks were usually made of combinations of pieces of shell, hardwood, or bone. The various forms of this gear are:

**Jig.** This consists of one to several bare hooks attached, usually by short lines or gangings, to a weighted line. Sometimes the hooks are attached to a wire frame. The jig is fished by jerking it up and down in the water. Some species, i.e., mackerel, are snagged as they strike at the bare hooks; some are caught because the jig passes through a dense school and the fish do not avoid the hooks.

**Baited hook.** This consists essentially of one or more simple hooks attached to various types and arrangements of lines and fished with bait as an attraction.

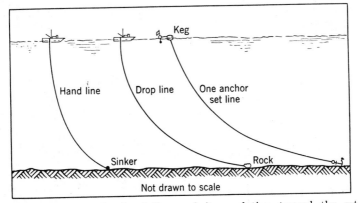

Fig. 10·2 Illustrating the hand line and its evolution toward the set line. (Credit: California Department of Fish and Game)

*Hand line.* This is a single line with one or several baited hooks attached. As fishing gear has become more complex and more efficient, the use of the hand line has decreased. It is employed to take snappers (*Lutjanus* sp.) and groupers (*Epinephelus* sp.) in the Caribbean Sea (Whiteleather and Brown 1945). For this fishery each line uses about 21 hooks each fastened to the main line by a line or ganging about 3 feet in length. A 12-pound lead is attached to the end. Much of the fishing is in water 30 to 80 fathoms in depth. About 8 to 10 hand lines are fished over the side of the vessel as it drifts over the grounds.

Many hand lines have the lead and the gangings attached to the main line by swivels to prevent excessive fouling and kinking of the line. Usually lines are hauled in over rollers on the side of the vessel. They are still used to a slight extent on the Atlantic Coast for cod, tautog, and mackerel, and on the Pacific Coast for mackerel, flatfish, ling cod (*Ophiodon*), rockfish (*Sebastodes*), and other species. They are used chiefly when fishing for benthic species on reefs and very rough grounds that are difficult to fish with long lines.

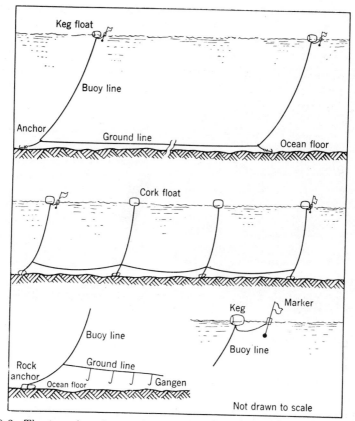

Fig. 10·3  The top view shows a set line (or long line) fishing on the bottom. In the next view the gear has been modified by intermediate surface floats to fish somewhat above the bottom. (Credit: California Department of Fish and Game)

*Long line, trot line, flag line, or line trawl.* This is an adaptation of the older hand line in which the main line or ground line is horizontal and carries many short vertical gangings, each with its baited hook.

In fishing this gear it may be anchored or drifted. For bottom-feeding species it is usually anchored. First a float is thrown overboard and sufficient anchor line is payed out to reach the bottom, allowing some extra anchor line for changes in tide levels and to prevent dragging. A small anchor or grapnel is then attached. The float is usually a keg, a cork, or a mesh-enclosed glass float, although some floats are very elaborate. The float often carries a tall bamboo pole bearing a red or white flag, and in some fisheries it usually carries a lantern. A main line is then attached to the anchor and the line payed

Fig. 10·4  Deck view of the *Marjorie Parker* showing the dory trawling gear that is fast giving way to the otter trawl. In 1952 only two large vessels were still line-trawling out of Boston. Note the nested dories with their heavy manila loading slings, the small buoys and kedge anchors, the riding sail, and the empty tubs waiting to take the coils of gear that are drying on deck.

out, with its baited hooks spaced on short gangings, as the vessel moves ahead. As the end of each "line" is reached another is attached until a long string of gear often several miles in length and holding thousands of baited hooks has been set. For such long strings an extra float on a buoy line is attached at intervals depending on tide, weather, and the roughness of the bottom, to aid in finding the gear and in retrieving it if the main line is broken in hauling. The end of the string is also anchored and buoyed.

Such a string of gear is usually called a long line on the Pacific Coast and a line trawl in the North Atlantic. It is also called a set line, and in inland waters the term trot line is more usual.

FIG. 10·5 A combination lobster and line trawl boat popular in New England. Note the six tubs of baited line trawl on the aft deck. The fisherman is setting a tub of gear as the boat moves ahead.

FIG. 10·6 Setting a tub of line trawl for haddock off Mount Desert Island. The gear is set with the boat moving ahead about half speed, and it takes experience and skill to flip the baited hooks out of the tub.

FIG. 10·7  Hauling back the line trawl. The ground line is hauled over the small gurdy with the vessel moving slowly ahead.

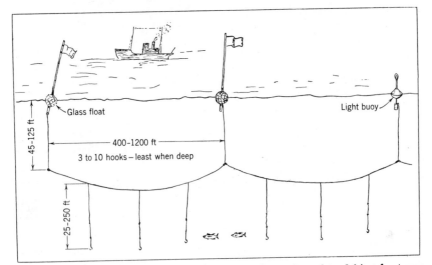

FIG. 10·8  Flag line, a form of drift line or long line, adapted to fishing for tunas below the surface in midocean.

The lines composing a string are usually coiled in half barrels or tubs, sometimes in shallow baskets, and in the halibut fisheries on pieces of canvas called a "skate."

By shortening the buoy lines of the floats the line may be fished at any desired depth.

The long line may be fished without being anchored. This is called a drift line. It is extensively employed by the Japanese (Kask and Hiyama 1947) for fishing tuna. Each float bears a flag whence the term "flag line." In fishing tuna one end is attached to the vessel, and smaller boats are used to overhaul the line.

**Trolling gear.** Trolling consists in towing hook-and-line gear through the water. The hook may be baited or may be part of an artificial lure.

In trolling for salmon or albacore the boats use several lines. One or two lines may be fished over the stern of the vessel, and the others are attached to outrigger poles. In a regular trolling vessel each line is led through small blocks to its own small gurdy or reel. These reels are arranged along a shaft which is kept turning by the vessel's engine. Each gurdy has its own clutch so that each line may be reeled in individually. The depth of trolling is controlled by the vessel's speed, and by the weight of the lead sinker.

Usually a boat fishes with lines at different depths, and with different lures until fish start striking. All lines are then fished as close to the depth at which the fish are biting as can be accomplished without fouling the lines, and the lure is used that the fish are striking.

The gear is rigged in various ways to suit the individual fisherman. Usually a heavy spring or a short length of heavy rubber is attached to the outrigger. To the end of this is attached a small running block through which the heavy cotton line is run to a gurdy. To the end of the line are fastened a heavy swivel and then a sinker. The sinker varies in shape and may be keeled to keep it from turning in the water. Next follows a split ring or another swivel and then a length of bronze, stainless steel, or piano wire to which the lure is attached.

Hooks used in trolling are rarely offset, and the point is usually long. Lures are of many types: hooks baited with a whole small fish, hooks baited with a fillet from the side of a fish, metal spoons, metal spinners, feathered jigs, plugs, etc. The type of lure used varies with the species, the season, the locality, and the whim of the fisherman. Artificial lures are preferred when the fish will strike them well since they can be more quickly taken from the fish, they save time in rebaiting, and are less costly than bait which is sometimes difficult to obtain in suitable variety or quantity.

For small boats using only one or two lines a "spreader" is sometimes used on the end of the line. This is merely a piece of very stiff wire (at the least no. 10) bent with two arms and fastened at the apex of the arms to a swivel in the end of the line. To one arm is attached the lead followed by a short line, leader, and lure. The second arm is fitted in the same manner but with no lead. The two arms should be of unequal length to prevent fouling. Trolling is used extensively in taking chinook and silver salmon and albacore (*Germo alalunga*) on the Pacific Coast. It is used almost universally in taking many species of fish for sport purposes, such as tuna, mackerel, and trout.

**Pole and line gear.** This is merely the elaboration of the original hand line. It ranges from the tuna pole to the expensive rod and reel of the angler.

Most of the tremendous catch of yellowfin tuna (*Neothunnus macropterus*), and skipjack or oceanic bonito (*Katsuwonus vagans*), is made by pole fishing. This is well described by Godsil (1938).

The bamboo poles used are between 8 and 9 feet in length, about 2 inches at the base and ¾ to 1 inch at the tip. A heavy linen loop is seized to the tip of the pole. In this loop is fastened a 2½- to 3-foot heavy cotton line. To this is fastened a 2-foot piano wire leader (size 18 to 22) bearing the lure. For live bait a plain barbless hook is used. The other lure, called a squid or striker, is a similar hook with the shank embedded in tubular brass filled with lead, with white feathers projecting beyond the hook.

When the fish range in size from 20 to 30 pounds, each fisherman fishes individually with his own pole and line. For larger fish a single leader is attached to the lines from two poles. For fish over 50 to 60 pounds three lines are united to a single ring to which is attached a swivel, leader, and single lure. Very large tuna sometimes require four and even five poles. Swinging these huge fish aboard requires the utmost co-ordination of the men involved.

On sighting a school of tuna the vessel slows down, and live bait is tossed overboard. If tuna strike the bait the boat stops and the fishermen line up on racks hung over the side of the vessel. The squid is used whenever the fish will take it as it saves much time in rebaiting and the hook usually falls out as the fish come aboard.

The pole and line has been standard angling gear for so long that it needs no detailed description.

## 10·4 Maze or barricade

The maze or barricade principle of taking fish consists essentially in leading fish into a situation or enclosure from which they cannot escape, or from which the avenue of escape is not readily apparent. It includes many varieties of fish pots, fyke nets, pound nets, tidal weirs and stream racks.

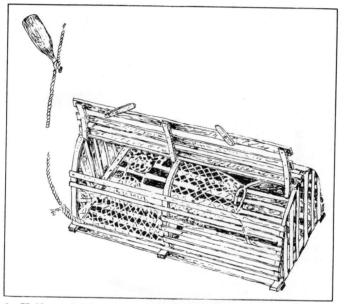

FIG. 10·9  Half-round lobster pot. (Redrawn from sketch by Boris O. Knake, *Fish. Leaf. 64, U. S. Fish and Wildlife Service*)

**Pot gear.**  These are small portable traps that fish enter, usually through a small opening, and with or without enticement by bait. They are used very extensively to capture lobsters, spiny lobsters, crabs, sea bass, eels, catfish (*Ictalurus* sp.), octopi, carp, and live bait for angling.

Pots are most effective in capturing slow-moving creatures that move about on or just above the sea or lake bottom. They are usually small enough so that a large number can be piled on the deck of a small boat, and light enough so that they can be readily hauled aboard or set out in choppy weather.

For lobsters fishermen prefer either the half-round or the rectangular pot. The half-round pot is about 32 inches long by 27 inches wide and about 18 inches high. A half-round bow is used at each end, and in the center. The trap is built of laths, usually about 1⅛ inches wide by ⅜ inch thick spaced about the width of a lath apart. A curved door to permit removal of the catch is made of three laths running the length of the trap, and nailed to three curved cleats. It is hinged with strips of leather or rubber, and fastens down with two wooden buttons.

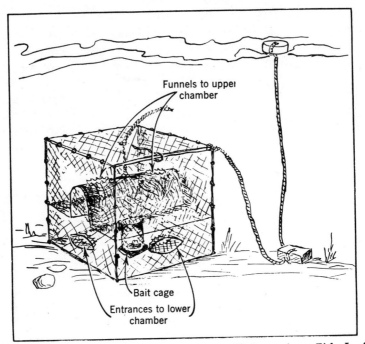

Fig. 10·10   Crab pot used in Chesapeake Bay. (Redrawn from *Fish. Leaf. 262,* *U. S. Fish and Wildlife Service*)

The center bow is placed a little off center from the middle of the trap, making two compartments called the "chamber" and the "parlor."

The shorter section, the chamber, usually has an entrance on both sides of the trap. Each opening between the laths is usually about 8 inches high by 13 inches wide, and the bottom of the opening is about 2½ inches above the floor of the pot. Each has a tunnel of netting about 7 inches deep ending in a ring 4 inches to 6 inches in diameter. The tunnels from opposite sides are tied together with brace lines to keep the netting taut.

From this chamber the inner portion, or parlor, is entered by a longer tunnel or "head" of netting that has its base lashed to the center bow and extends lengthwise of the pot into the parlor.

The completed trap is weighted with a few bricks, concrete, or flat stones, and the buoy line is attached to a lower corner at the chamber end.  Bait is kept on a hook or in a mesh bag attached to the center bow so that it hangs in the parlor entrance.

These traps may vary from 28 inches to 48 inches in length.  Tunnels may be made of laths, and sometimes the parlor tunnel is replaced by a vertical self-closing lath door so that lobsters cannot escape.

The rectangular lobster pot is easier to make, to store, and to repair and is therefore becoming more popular.  It is made about 30 to 40 inches in length, with the top usually about 4 inches narrower than the bottom.

The buoy line has a small float attached about a fathom from the pot to keep the lines from becoming cut or entangled on the rocky bottom.  The surface end of the line is attached to a small buoy that usually has a spindle through it, to aid both in finding it and in retrieving the buoy from the boat.

Pots are often fished in long strings, trawl fashion.  About 10 to 15 traps are fastened by ganging lines about two fathoms long to a heavier trawl line.  Pots are spaced about 5 to 10 fathoms apart.

Crabs are often fished with pots, and although they can be taken in lobster pots special types are also used.  Thus in Chesapeake Bay a trap 2 feet square is made of 1½-inch mesh, doubly galvanized, 18-gage poultry wire.  If 1-inch mesh is used the pots are also effective for large eels.  A horizontal wire partition 8 inches off the bottom divides the trap into an upper and a lower chamber.  The lower chamber is entered from all four sides through small wire tunnels.  The partition bulges upward in a fold about 8 inches high for about one third of its width.  In the top of this fold are two small openings that give access to the upper chamber.

Spiny lobsters can be taken in pots similar to those used for lobsters, but they are also taken by leaving old ice-making molds on the bottom, into which they retreat to hide.  When the mold is hauled they cannot climb the sides to escape.  Similarly the Japanese use large terra cotta vases which octopi enter in seeking a convenient shelter.

Cylindrical pots are used extensively for capturing eels, and in Chesapeake Bay they take the largest share of the catfish.

Eel pots can be made of almost any material but wire is the most easily obtainable.  A typical pot is 30 inches long and 9 to 11 inches in diameter.  Three ⅜-inch stock metal rings are covered with 16-gage, ½-inch, galvanized wire netting.  Two flat iron bars each 30 inches long, 1¼ inches wide, and ¼ inch thick are used for reinforcement.

The center ring is 10 inches from one end so that the first chamber is 10 inches long, the second 20 inches long.  The first chamber is entered through a knit web tunnel about 3 inches in depth with an opening of 4 inches attached to a metal ring.  The second tunnel is about 7 inches deep, and the opening only 2 inches in diameter.  This opening is sometimes made larger and then stretched into an oval shape.  The catch is removed through an end opening in the larger chamber.  They are fished in a manner similar to that of lobster pots.  Bait is suspended in front of the second tunnel.

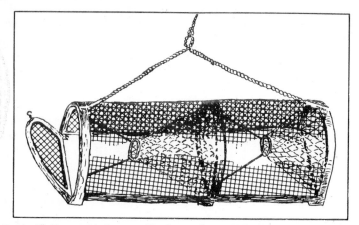

Fig. 10·11   Half-round eel pot.  (Redrawn from *Fish. Leaf. 127, U. S. Fish and Wildlife Service*)

Many eel pots are much smaller for ease in handling, and some are made of oak splints.  These lighter pots are often fished trawl fashion, about 25 pots on 10-foot gangings fastened about 10 feet apart.

Rectangular and half-round wire eel pots are also in use.  One form of rectangular pot is about 30 inches long, 12 inches wide, and 8 inches high and is fished with only one long funnel in one end.

Catfish traps are usually larger, about 3 to 4 feet in length and 18 to 20 inches in diameter, but they are similar to the cylindrical eel pot.

Various types of pots of all shapes and sizes are used in different localities.  In the tropics they are used extensively for taking reef fishes.  Called basket traps, they are usually made of split bamboo, wood, or vines, but wire is also used.

**Fyke net.**  The fyke net is essentially a shallow water gear owing to the difficulty of setting it effectively in deep water.  The fyke net is used extensively in some river fisheries, as it is best adapted for use in a fair current, and under such conditions it is sometimes used without any wings or leader.

The simplest form of fyke is merely a long net bag with a rectangular opening, each side of the opening being lashed to a stake. If there is a current flowing into the opening such a net may take some species, especially shrimps and prawns.

The typical fyke net is a long bag mounted on one to several hoops. The hoops serve a double purpose; they keep the net from collapsing,

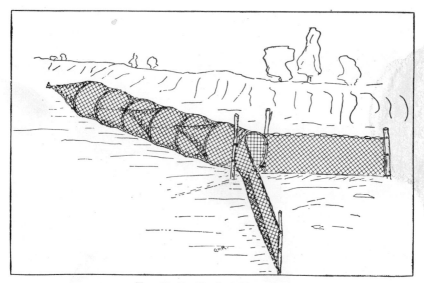

FIG. 10·12 Typical fyke net.

and they form the attachment for the base of net funnels which prevent the fish from escaping readily. The catch is removed from the last pocket. The fyke usually has short, vertical, net wings set obliquely on either side of the mouth of the bag. As fish moving with the current strike these wings they are deflected toward the mouth of the net. In the catfish (*Ictalurus catus*) fishery in the Sacramento River fykes 25 feet long with hoops 5 feet in diameter are used.

In swift currents the wings are necessarily short and the bag very long so as not to offer too much resistance to the water. However, fykes are used in many shore fisheries, especially for taking flounders and other bottom fishes. In such situations very long wings can be used as the currents are fairly slow. These wings are heavily leaded on the bottom and have cork or glass floats on top. Instead of stakes the net is set with anchors.

**Pound net or trap.**  This is a very effective form of gear for migratory species that tend to follow the shoreline.  There are scores of designs and variations, but the basic principle is the same for all. Fish moving along the shore encounter a lead of brush, netting, or wire. They follow this lead in an attempt to get past it and are led into one or more enclosures from which they find it difficult to escape.  Sometimes the lead is placed on a fishing bank offshore, and either an enclosure is placed at each end or one end terminates in a huge rounded

FIG. 10·13  A herring pound on Whidbey Island, Washington, for taking spawning herring in early spring to use for halibut bait.

hook or "jigger" which tends to shunt fish back in the direction from whence they came.

The simplest type is the brush weirs used in the Maine sardine fishery.  They are built of wooden stakes and saplings driven into the bottom in shallow waters.  The young herring encounter the leader which they follow toward deeper water, finally passing into an enclosure of brush or netting.  The passage into the enclosure may be provided with a net apron that the fisherman lowers after a school has entered the enclosure or pound to prevent their escape.  The fish concentrated there may then be removed with a small seine.

A variation of this type is the tidal weir, which takes advantage of shallow bars or flats. Fish enter the trap at high stages of the tide over a considerable area. As the tide falls, this portion is exposed first, and the fish are concentrated in a deeper portion, but escape is cut off by a barricade. Such weirs, built of stones or bamboo, are also used in the islands of the Pacific.

The typical pound net used in the Great Lakes and along the Atlantic Seaboard is built of wire or cotton netting (the mesh size varying with locality and species sought), except for the final enclosure which is usually of tarred cotton webbing. Piling is driven into the bottom in depths up to 80 feet or more, and the netting is hung from these piles.

The most elaborate traps or pound nets are those used in the Pacific salmon fisheries. They are of two kinds, pile and floating. Pile traps often have a lead of half a mile or more. It is absorbing to watch schools of salmon moving with the tide, as they encounter the wire lead. They hesitate and sometimes sound, looking for a deep opening. Usually they start toward deep water following the wire at a distance of 10 to 20 feet. This leads the school into the huge funnel formed by the end of the lead and the top of the "heart." The entrance to the heart is a wide opening usually 10 to 16 feet across. Traps located where the flood and ebb tides flow in opposite directions usually have an opening into the heart from both sides of the lead, but if they are in a tidal eddy the single opening is on the uptide side. The heart has no bottom, but the tunnel from the point of the heart into the next chamber or "pot" extends only part of the way to the bottom and has a floor. The pot, also usually made of wire, has a bottom. The wire tunnel from the heart to the pot has a narrow mouth about 18 to 30 inches in width. The pot itself is about 40 feet square.

The salmon are now led from the pot into a similar square chamber called a "spiller," usually made of heavily tarred cotton web, although some have web sides and a wire bottom. The spiller is placed alongside the pot and is connected by a web tunnel with a narrow opening, usually 6 to 12 inches in width. The opening is adjustable and may be entirely closed. The salmon enter the trap with the tide, but after being confined they commence to swim continually against the tide. Thus in a tidal eddy the spiller must be located on the uptide side of the pot and in other situations the connecting tunnel is alternately opened and closed as the current changes direction. In exceptionally favorable locations traps are provided with two spillers to prevent overcrowding during the peak of the run.

The four corners of the spiller are held down by ropes running through the ring of a "downhaul" which is a chain that slips down the corner piling. To remove the fish the four corners of the bottom are hauled close to the surface by hand windlasses. The web is overhauled by men on a large skiff or small scow inside the spiller until the salmon are confined in a bag made by one side of the spiller. They are then

FIG. 10·14  Lifting the bottom of the spiller in a pile-driven salmon trap onto a pot scow to confine the catch in a pocket for brailing. Note the stiffness of the heavily tarred cotton web.

removed by lowering the webbing on the outside of the spiller low enough to fasten it to the side of the transporting scow or vessel. A "brail" or apron, consisting of a rectangular piece of webbing, has one end fastened to the scow. The other end is fastened to a heavy pipe that is lowered into the "bag" of heavily concentrated fish. The pipe end of the brail is then hoisted by a power winch. Each time it is hoisted, hundreds of struggling salmon are dumped into the scow.

Because of the difficulty or impossibility of driving piling in many favorable fishing locations with hard or rocky bottom the *floating* trap was evolved. In this trap the heart, pot, and spiller are hung from a floating framework of huge logs anchored in position by heavy wire cables to huge anchors made of concrete. The lead is supported by a cable stretched over floats.

The deep trap net, also sometimes termed a "submarine pound net," was developed in the Great Lakes (Van Oosten, Hile, and Jobes 1946). It differs from the typical pound net held by stakes or pilings and from the floating trap which has a rigid floating framework, by being held in position and in shape entirely by anchors and buoys, and by having a top of webbing on all but the heart. It can thus be fished in

FIG. 10·15  Brailing the salmon out of the spiller into the cannery scow. The top of the brail (usually a two-inch pipe) is hoisted from the boom of the cannery tender moored alongside the scow. Note the heavy construction of the trap.

water of considerable depth, regardless of the hardness of the bottom, and can be readily taken up and shifted to a new location in order to follow the concentrations of fish. Because of this ability to follow the fish concentrations, it has proved very effective for whitefish and can catch them during periods when they are too deep to be available to pound nets.

The deep trap nets observed by Van Oosten et al. had leaders 40 to 80 rods long and 20 to 47½ feet deep. The hearts were of the same depth as the leaders with a spread of about 100 feet at the tips and a length of about 45 feet. In some nets the outside walls of the hearts were extended about 24 feet as single thicknesses of netting known as wings. The "hood" or "breast" connecting the heart with the tunnel had both a top and bottom and a length varying from 24 to 27 feet.

The tunnel, varying from 45 to 75 feet in length, tapered from the same depth as the heart to form a 3-foot square opening extending inside the pot or crib. The pots were roughly cubical, varying from 18 to 47½ feet in depth and 30 to 40 feet in length.

In lifting the nets the main anchor line is brought to the surface and the vessel worked under or alongside the pot from which the fish are removed through laced openings in the bottom.

**Chinese shrimp nets.** The Chinese shrimp net is a highly specialized form of gear used only for taking shrimp (Bonnot 1932). It resembles a multiple fyke net but has no throat or constriction. Each net is a large handmade bag of hemp or fiber in the form of a cone 40 feet long. The mouth of the net forms a rectangle 4 feet high by 30 feet wide. The last 8 to 10 feet of the small end is a cylinder about 18 inches in diameter. The handwoven mesh is about 3½ inches at the mouth, diminishing gradually to 1 inch where the cylinder is attached. All of the cylinder is 1-inch mesh.

These nets are fished in San Francisco Bay in groups; each group is called a bed. The method of fishing these nets is so unique that we quote from Bonnot (1932):

The shrimp beds are laid out at right angles to the tide flow in from 6 to 10 fathoms of water. Anchor pins are driven into the mud 30 feet apart. At each end of the string of anchors another is driven, in line with the string and spaced 90 feet from the last at that end. The anchor pins are driven by a long wooden pole which has at its larger end a length of iron pipe. The pins are driven some distance into the mud. From each anchor a rope runs to a brail. The length of rope varies with the depth of water (8 fathoms of water, 180 feet of rope). Each brail is slung to its anchor line by a bridle, 28 feet long (included in the 180 feet). The brails are tied together by a rope which is clove-hitched to their centers. Anothr rope runs along the string of brails half way between the top and center, being looped and pinned to each and attached to a keg buoy at each end. The nets are fastened to the bottom rings of the brails by slip knots and to the top rings by loops and wooden pins. The pins are connected to each other by a quarter-inch rope which is attached at each end to the buoy line. The reason for this will appear later.

The most efficient bed is laid out at an exact right angle to the tide flow. If the angle of the flood tide varies from that of the ebb, due, perhaps, to an outthrust of the shore line, the bed must be made to compromise between the two, or if the angle is too great, it can be used for one tide only. In a clear channel where the tide runs back and forth on the same line a bed will fish both tides. The ground tackle, anchors, ropes and brails are left down

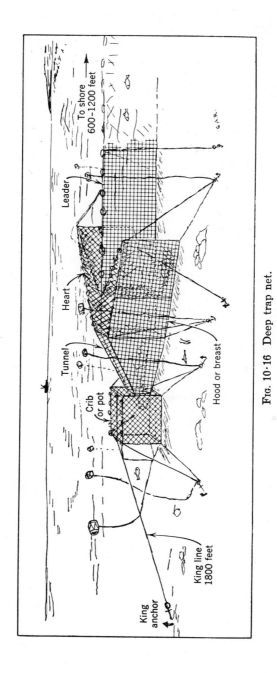

FIG. 10·16 Deep trap net.

for the season, and, though the brails and anchors are reclaimed, the rope is left on the bottom or picked up and thrown away. The rope used is three-quarter-inch manila, and a bed to accommodate 50 or 60 nets represents several miles of rope which is used only one season.

The nets are set at slack water. The first brail is lifted by bringing in the buoy line with the winch. One side of the net is attached, the next brail is brought in and the other side of the net attached and one side of the next net. The whole string is run in this manner. The brails and the attached nets are let down on one side of the boat while the brails are brought up on the other side. When picking up the nets the same procedure is used. The pins which attach the nets to the top rings are important in lifting the nets. The lifting is started before the tide has stopped running. As it would be difficult to raise the nets with the mouths wide open to the force of the tide, after the brail has been lifted from the bottom a jerk on the quarter-inch line pulls out the wooden pin and releases the top of the net and the rectangular opening collapses. The net is attached only to the bottom rings and so comes up flattened out. A pull on the slip knot and the net is free to be pulled in by several men. If the catch is heavy the small end of the net will be stretched into the shape of a large ball. When too heavy to be lifted by hand a tackle is used. A cord is wound about the small end and tied with a slip knot. A pull on this and the catch is dumped into the shrimp bin or into baskets. The nets are left down for the entire run of the tide, five to eight hours, as it would be impossible to lift them when the tide is running strong. The nets must be lifted at each change of the tide. The ground tackle can swing around and face either tide but the nets would become tangled. Five or six men are necessary to handle a large number of nets as the time in which they can be set or lifted is limited.

**Stream weirs.** The catching of fish by the blocking of a stream with a weir or fence was a popular and effective method of fishing among primitive peoples. Thus Moser (1899) describes the barricades used by the Thlinget Indians in southeast Alaska to take adult salmon migrating upstream to spawn, and McLean (1932) describes the brush and stake entanglements constructed by the Indians near Stuart Lake on the upper Fraser River in 1830 to take salmon in wicker baskets as they swam through the openings. Babcock (1903) describes the building by the Indians of a dam of rocks and brush across a stream in the form of a great funnel with a basket trap at the lower end to catch the young sockeye salmon on their seaward migrations. Besides those caught many thousands were destroyed by becoming entangled in the brush.

Stream weirs are used in the North Atlantic to take the hordes of alewives that pass upstream in the spring. They are also placed across many streams in the late summer and fall, especially below lakes, to catch adult eels descending toward the sea on their spawning journey to the ocean depths off Bermuda.

Except under special circumstances and close supervision this type of fishing can be destructive to species other than the one sought.

## 10·5  Entangling nets

Entangling nets are used to take a great variety of fishes: salmon, cod, mackerel, pollock, herring, whitefish, smelt, crabs, sharks, etc. In some countries they are also used for tuna, sardines, and spiny lobsters. There are two main types of entangling nets, the gill net and the trammel net. In the gill net the fish becomes caught by the mesh of the net in trying to swim through. Usually, if the mesh is the correct size for the size of fish sought, the fish is able to get its head through a mesh but its body is too large, and when the fish attempts to free itself the twine slips under the gill cover preventing escape. Many fish will be caught around the middle of the body, and some may be caught by the twine entangling the maxillary bone of the jaw or the teeth. In the trammel net the fish pushes a loose bight of a small-meshed net through one of the very large meshes of a second wall of netting. The fish is then enclosed in a bag.

**Gill net.**  Gill nets vary in size of mesh in accordance with the size of the individual or species sought. The twine also varies in size and strength although in general the larger-sized mesh is made of heavier twine. Gill nets are usually made of cotton or linen but nylon is becoming popular. Linen is more expensive than cotton but is preferred, as it is much stronger for its size, and twine of small diameter is more effective in entangling fish.

The ordinary gill net consists of a single wall of webbing kept vertical in the water with sinkers and floats. The webbing is hung to a cork line at the top and a lead line at the bottom. At least 50 per cent more net is used than the length of these lines so that the net will hang full. A loosely hung net is more efficient.

A drift net may be fished in either of two ways—at the surface or in midwater, always suspended vertically with a cork line on the top edge and a lead line on the bottom. In fishing below the surface, the size and number of floats and weights are adjusted so that the net will sink; the desired fishing depth is maintained by lines fastened at intervals from the cork line to large surface buoys.

A stake net is fished by attaching the net to driven stakes. It is used principally in shallow bays and estuaries.

A diver net, used often in salmon rivers, drifts on the bottom, the weights applied being a little less than needed to stop the net from dragging. Trammel nets are often fished in this manner.

A sink or anchor gill net is set in a stationary position on the bottom by anchors. It is also referred to as a set net.

Circle gill netting consists in setting the gill net around a school of fish usually in water sufficiently shallow for the net to reach the bottom,

Fig. 10·17   Hauling a salmon drift gill net in Bristol Bay, Alaska.

and then scaring the fish so that they rush the net and become gilled.

As gill nets are not so effective when the fish can see the net, they are usually fished at night; but in rivers the turbidity of the water often renders them effective in daylight. When there are many phosphorescent organisms in the water gill nets sometimes will not fish effectively when it is dark but may take fish in twilight.

When the species sought may be off the bottom, the fishermen sometimes set a gill net obliquely from the bottom toward the surface until they discover the depth being frequented.

Drift gill nets are used principally for pelagic species such as herring and salmon. When used on large bodies of water or at sea they are set in long strings or gangs with lighted buoys at intervals. One string may be several miles long. Modern vessels usually employ a special net puller which consists essentially of a smooth curved metal chute and a large revolving metal drum set vertically.

When drifted in midwater they are used for lake trout, whitefish, cod, and other species that, though usually dwelling somewhat below the surface, are often found some distance above the bottom.

Anchored gill nets may also be fished off the bottom merely by employing sufficiently light weights on the lead line with heavier weights on lines at intervals. Anchor or sink gill nets are used in the North Atlantic for capturing cod and other bottom fish.

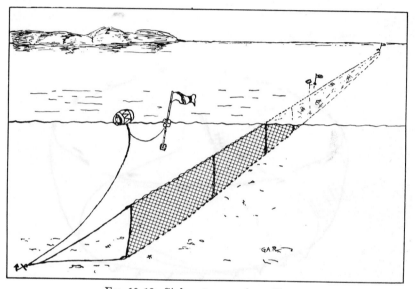

Fig. 10·18 Sink, set, or anchor gill net.

Circle gill netting is used in California for capturing jack smelt (*Atherinopsis californiensis*) and bay smelt (*Atherinops affinis*). It is sometimes employed for taking mackerel (*Pneumatophorus diego*).

Gill nets set on the bottom are used extensively on the Pacific Coast for taking crabs.

**Trammel net.** A trammel net consists of two or often three vertical walls of netting united at the top to a cork or float line and at the bottom to a lead line. One wall (or walls) of netting, of large mesh and heavy twine, is hung quite tight. The other wall, of fine mesh and light twine, is hung very loosely. Fish push a bag of the fine net through one of the large meshes of the coarse net and find it impossible to extricate themselves.

Trammel nets have never been so popular as the simple gill net because they are more costly and require greater time and care both in handling and in extricating the fish. Gill nets are very selective in their fishing, each size of mesh tending to catch chiefly fish in a narrow size range. Trammel nets take fish over a wide range of sizes. They are used principally in taking high-priced fish, especially the chinook salmon of the Columbia River.

## 10·6   Encircling nets

This includes all types of nets used to capture fish by placing a mobile net either completely around them or so as to block their escape. They can be classified according to the method of fishing them as shore landing, vessel landing, and blocking.

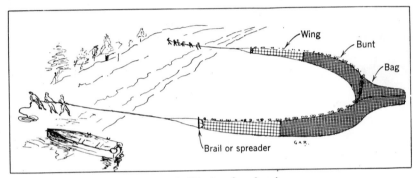

Fig. 10·19   Haul or beach seine.

**Haul seine or beach seine.** This gear was undoubtedly the forerunner of both the purse seine and the otter trawl. Once used extensively, it became unprofitable for general use and is now employed only in special fisheries. Thus it was at first one of the principal gears in the Pacific salmon fisheries but is now used in only a few localities. At the mouth of the Columbia River a few large seines are pulled in over the shallows by teams of horses. A large seine is operated by power at the mouth of the Karluk River in Alaska. A few large haul seines operate along the South Atlantic Coast, and they are used for shad in the lower reaches of the Connecticut River. Largely though, the haul seine is used sparingly.

Essentially a haul seine is a strip of strong netting hung to a stout cork line at the top and a strong very heavily weighted lead line on the bottom. On muddy bottoms the lead line may require little weight. The wings of the net are often of larger mesh than the middle portion or bunt. The wings may taper so that they are shallower on the ends. The bunt sometimes has the center portion of the netting formed into a bag to aid in confining the fish. At the ends of the wings the cork and lead lines are often fastened on each end of a short stout pole or brail. The hauling lines are then attached to the top and bottom of the brail by a short bridle.

The usual method of fishing is to load the net onto a boat. One end of one of the hauling lines is left on the shore and the boat leaves the shore paying out the line until the other end of the line is reached. The boat changes direction and lays out the net parallel to the beach. When the net is all in the water the boat brings the end of the second hauling line ashore.

Sometimes, especially when fishing for pelagic or schooling species the net is left in this position until fish are sighted between the net and the shore; then hauling commences. When it is known that fish are traveling along the beach in a certain direction one end of the net may be hauled in first so as to form a hook against the beach. As soon as a school of fish enters the area the second line is hauled. In fishing for nonschooling fish both ends of the net are usually hauled in at once.

**Stop seine.** In this method of fishing the fishermen must wait, sometimes for weeks, until a large school of fish enters a small cove or bight. Immediately a deep seine is placed across the opening, confining the fish. When the bay is large it may require several seines lashed together to close the opening. Once the fish are thus impounded they are removed as needed with a small seine. This method has been used for centuries in the Norwegian spring fishery for adult herring and is one method used in Maine to take young herring for the sardine canneries.

**Purse seine.** This form of gear accounts for the major share of our fish harvest. It is very efficient for taking pelagic schooling species. The recent use of various types of modern sounding devices, such as echo sounding, radar, and sonar, in locating schools of fish beneath the surface is already increasing its effectiveness.

There are several forms of the vessel-landing seine. The lampara, adopted from a Mediterranean net, was used extensively for sardines in California. The wings are of coarse mesh while the center is of fine mesh and shaped like a scoop. The two wings of coarse mesh are both hauled in at once onto the stern of the vessel. This elongates the circle and brings the lead lines under the center portion close together, preventing the fish from diving under the net. It has very largely given way to other forms of nets, except for the capture of live bait.

The lampara was later changed by adding rings along the lead line of the bag and a purse line that was attached a few fathoms along

the wings. When the wings were hauled in as far as the end of the
purse line the net was pursed immediately. There were various modifications as pursing often necessitated using smaller meshes in the
wings. This transition type of net has also largely given way to the
modern purse seine which was meanwhile fully developed in the
Northwest and Alaska for herring and salmon.

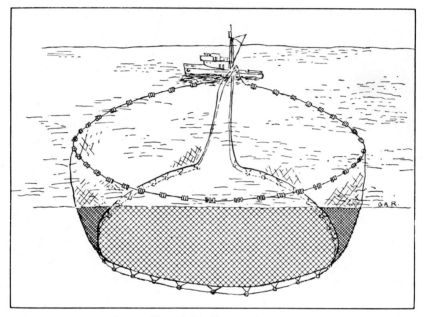

Fig. 10·20  Purse seine.

The purse seine has certain advantages. Because of the strength
imparted by its fine mesh and weight it is more suitable in rough
weather or when the catch is large. The fine mesh prevents the escape
of fish while the net is being pursed, and it can be pursed more rapidly
than the other forms. The purse seine is a continuous deep ribbon
of web with corks on one side and leads on the other. Rings are
fastened at intervals, each by two short ropes, to the lead line. A
purse line runs completely around the net through these rings. The
net is piled on to a turntable on the stern of the vessel. The end of
the net is fastened by a short rope to a skiff that is towed behind the
vessel. As soon as a school of fish of the proper size and species is
located the net is set around it, an attempt being made to set the net
across their path if they are moving. As the skiff is fastened to the
end of the net it acts as a drag as soon as it is cast off from the vessel.

The vessel sets the net in a circle while cruising at full speed. As soon as both ends are brought together the purse line is hauled aboard as the net is being hauled from one end. Usually the turntable is swung so that the net is taken in from one side. Most vessels use a steel cable for a purse line. It is hauled by taking a turn around a "gypsy" powered by a shaft from the vessel's main engine. The roller

FIG. 10·21 Setting a purse seine. The net is running out over the roller on the turntable. With the net partially circled the captain is watching for an approaching school before completing the set.

on the margin of the turntable also may be powered to aid in hauling in the heavy net, but today the net is usually hauled in from the boom. When all of the purse line and most of the net is aboard the fish are safely confined in a bag formed by the fine meshed net from which they are brailed by a large dip net swung from the boom.

Purse seines vary in size according to the size of the vessel, the size of the mesh, the species sought, and the depth to be fished. The length runs from 30 or 40 fathoms up to 360 fathoms—only occasional seines are longer. The webbing is manufactured in strips 3½ fathoms deep. The number of strips used is governed by the depth. In deep water 10 to 11 strips are about the maximum used, but in fishing in shallow bays, where the net may take bottom and tear, less depth is desirable and as few as 4 or 5 strips may be used.

Some of the species taken are salmon, herring, sardines, mackerel, bluefin tuna, barracuda, jack mackerel (*Trachurus symmetricus*), and anchovies.

FIG. 10·22   The seine has been pursed, the turntable has been turned with the roller to port, and the net is being hauled.

## 10·7   Towed nets

These are forms of gear in which the water is strained through the meshes of a moving net, leaving the fish in the bag.   There are several main types of trawls with many minor modifications of each.   The first trawls probably were an offshoot from the beach or haul seine. This is illustrated by the sailing trawls and by the snurrevard or Danish seine used extensively in Europe, but so far only slightly in America.   The chief forms of trawls are as follows:

**Sailing trawl.**   This trawl is used in Japan by small sailing vessels. It resembles a haul seine, except that the wings are short, and the bag is boxlike.   It is dragged along the bottom by sailing vessels moving sidewise, and the wings are kept apart by being attached to the end of long poles projecting from each end of the vessel.   It is used only in shallow water (4 to 10 fathoms).   The hauling ropes or "warps" are of manila about 60 fathoms in length.   The catch consists chiefly of shrimp, flatfish, crabs, and other shellfish.   The net itself is about 90 feet long including the bag or "cod end" which is about 21 feet. The mesh varies in size from about 1½ inches in the anterior part of the wings to 1 inch in the cod end.

**Danish seine or snurrevard.** Although called a seine, this net is really a trawl as it is dragged through the water. The Danish seine usually is towed in the direction of the current. When the seine is being set, the end of the portside tow rope is shackled to a buoy (generally a 55-gallon drum) which is lowered into the water. The ship then sails on a course at 140 to 150 degrees from the current, paying out the warp. When the warp has been cast in the water, the

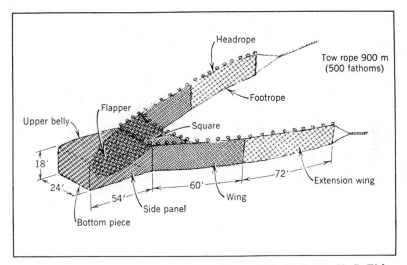

Fɪɢ. 10·23  Danish seine. The one shown (From *Fish. Leaf. 389, U. S. Fish and Wildlife Service*) is a Japanese modification with a flapper.

ship sails across the current, casting in succession the ground rope, the portside wing of the net, the belly, and the starboard wing and ground rope. When this is done, the ship sails toward the buoy and picks it up after all the warp has been paid out. Both the lines are then made fast, and the ship tows the net with the current. The ground ropes and the wings close slowly, chasing the fish toward the belly; when the tow ropes become parallel, they are hauled in with the help of the engine.

**Paranzella or two-boat trawl.** This net is dragged by two vessels that keep the correct distance apart to spread the two wings properly. Two-boat trawls are used in both Japan and the Philippines. Those employed in the California fisheries were introduced from Italy about 1877. The nets vary in size according to the power of the vessels. The forward end of each wing is attached to a vertical pole or "spreader." The towing warp is attached to the spreader by two short bridle ropes. It was for many years the only trawl used in California. The chief catch was flatfish. The true paranzella has been replaced by the otter trawl.

**Beam trawl.** There is some question as to whether the ancestor of the otter trawl was the paranzella, the Danish seine, or the beam trawl. The beam trawl is restricted both in the width of the swath it covers on the bottom and the height of the headrope (the top of the opening) above the bottom.

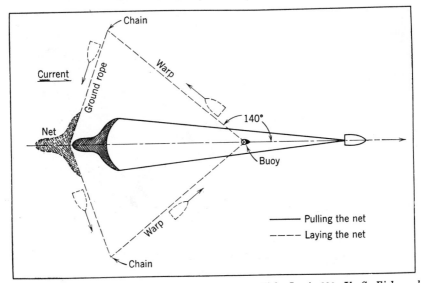

Fɪɢ. 10·24   Operation of Danish seine.   (From *Fish. Leaf. 389, U. S. Fish and Wildlife Service*)

The headrope of the net is lashed to a heavy spar, seldom over 35 to 40 feet in length. This is held 3 or 4 feet off the bottom at each end by heavy metal frames, the bottom of which are the shoes or runners which run along the floor of the sea. The sides of the net are lashed to these frames. The footrope is much longer than the headrope and is dragged along the bottom in a loop, the center of the footrope usually being as far behind the beam as the length of the beam. The whole net is about twice as long as the beam. The small end of the net, of smaller mesh, is called a cod end. The lower side of the cod end is protected from the bottom by "chafing gear," usually a bull hide. Some beam trawls have one or more net funnels in the bag just in front of the cod end to prevent fish from swimming out of the slow-moving net.

Beam trawls were once the principal trawling gear of western Europe and New England, but they were replaced by otter trawls early in the century. Beam trawls are still used in a few localities. Thus they are used in Alaska to take shrimp.

**Otter trawl.** The otter trawl differs from the beam trawl and the paranzella in the method of keeping the net open. The forward end of each wing is attached to an "otter board." The otter board is a large board roughly rectangular in shape. It is usually 4 to 8 feet

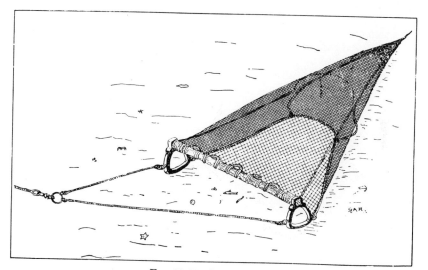

Fig. 10·25  Beam trawl.

long, 3 to 5 feet high, and 2 to 4 inches thick. Made of oak with heavy iron strapping, it has one long edge heavily shod with an iron runner to slide over the bottom. The front edge is usually rounded on the bottom to aid in bouncing over obstructions.

The towing bridle or warp is attached to the board by four heavy chains or short heavy rods. The two forward rods are shorter so that when towed the board sheers to the side. As the two boards sheer in opposite directions, they keep the mouth of the net open. At first the otter boards were attached directly to each wing of the net. In the Vigneron-Dahl modification known as the V-D trawl each wing was attached to a short brail or spreader, the headrope to the upper end and the footrope to the lower end. The spreader was attached by a short bridle to one long ground cable which led to the lower after edge of the otter board. This arrangement kept the otter boards farther apart, and it would appear that many of the fish disturbed by the groundline eventually were caught in the net, since this form of trawl was considerably more effective than its predecessor.

The original V-D gear, like its predecessor, did not fish far off the bottom, for in spite of floats (chiefly glass or metal balls, rubber or cork floats) along the headrope the outward pressure kept the headrope low. This was a big disadvantage in fishing for many species that are not always close to the bottom. The New England trawlers

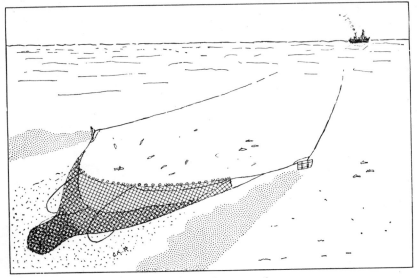

Fig. 10·26   Otter trawl.

discarded the spreader and used two long ground cables to each otter board. One went from the lower edge of the otter board to the footrope and the other from the upper edge of the otter board to the headrope. The wing was made higher, and the new method of attachment permitted the headrope to arch upward, greatly increasing the height of the net. Later the cables from the upper and lower edges of the wing, called "leg wires," were joined a little distance in front of the net into a single ground wire that was attached to the upper edge of the otter board. This tended to keep the net from digging into the bottom.

The footrope, which constitutes the lower edge of the net, is made in various fashions. For small trawls it may be merely a heavy manila hawser, weighted with lead and perhaps, for chafing gear, wrapped in burlap lashed on with rope yarn. In large trawls it is usually a heavy steel cable. In New England the trawlers fished at first only on smooth bottom to avoid tearing the net or having the footrope hang up on heavy boulders or ledges. However, the best fishing was often on rough ground where tear-ups were frequent. Soon the fishermen largely overcame this difficulty by using "rollers."

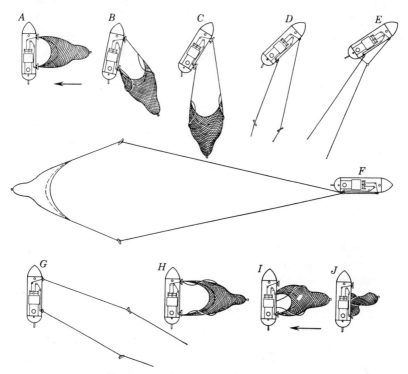

FIG. 10·27 Operation of otter trawl.

1. Laying otter trawl: *A*. The ship is stopped; the net is laid on the windward side. *B*. The ground ropes are paid out; the ship circles to windward to clear the net. *C*. The ship continues circling; all the ground ropes are paid out. *D*. The otter boards are dropped; both warps are paid out. *E*. The messenger hook brings the warps to the hookup block. *F*. Beginning the tow.

2. Hauling in otter trawl: *G*. End of the tow. The hookup block is tripped; the ship is stopped and swings across the wind. *H*. The warps are hauled in, the otter boards are shackled to the gallows, and the ground ropes are hauled in. *I*. The starboard wing is shifted from the forward gallows to a bracket at the forward corner of the wheelhouse. *J*. The quarter ropes are hauled in. The cod end is hoisted on board with a sling and tackle.

Rollers are wooden disks 7 to 8 inches thick and either 8 or 20 inches in diameter. They are strung like beads on a cable, first a 20-inch roller, than two 8-inch rollers, then a 20-inch roller, etc. This cable is attached to the footrope by short roller chains, one chain between each pair of small rollers. On a typical large trawl there are 16 rollers for the belly section—6 large, with 5 pairs of small rollers between them. Sometimes only these "bosom" rollers are used, but for rougher bottom they are sometimes used along the half of each lower wing next to the belly. Each side takes 13 rollers, 4 large, with 3 sets of 3 small rollers between them.

All but the very early otter trawls are towed by two warps, one to each otter board, as this permits the net to spread properly. The winches on most trawlers are provided with two drums, one for each cable.

The small inshore otter-trawl vessels, known in New England as "draggers," often use small trawls 30 to 50 feet or more in width. The trawl nets used by the larger vessels usually measure 78 feet along the headrope and 116 feet along the footrope for groundfish. The smaller-meshed trawls used for ocean perch are 60 feet on the headrope and 80 feet on the footrope.

Trawlers usually land their catch amidships. As the otter boards come in they are hauled up and attached to heavy metal frames shaped like an inverted V, called "gallows frames." One is placed well forward and the other just aft of amidships. Practically all New England trawlers have two gallows frames on each side of the vessel so that they can fish on either the port or starboard side. If a net is sufficiently torn to require some time for mending, a different net is set on the opposite side of the vessel so that fishing can continue while the first net is being repaired. Most Pacific Coast trawlers set the nets off the stern and have one gallows frame well aft on each side.

Midwater trawls using subsidiary otter boards to spread the net mouth vertically as well as horizontally have been tried experimentally but are not in commercial use in North America. Otter trawls, one of the principal forms of modern gear, are in use throughout the world. They take any species that customarily lives on or near the sea bottom.

**Dredge.** A dredge resembles a beam trawl. It is used for taking scallops, oysters, quahogs, or other sedentary species. A dredge usually consists of a heavy metal frame that forms the mouth of an attached bag. The bag is usually shallow and made of heavy chain mesh.

The frames of the sea scallop dredges used in New England measure about 8 to 11 feet in width and about 16 to 18 inches in height. The bag is made of welded steel rings 3 inches in diameter of $5/16$-inch stock held together with iron links $1\frac{1}{8}$ inches in diameter, and also of $5/16$-inch stock. The top of the bag is made of sash cord and cord clips, both to lighten the total weight and to aid the dredge in falling top side up when lowered to the bottom. A standard 11-foot dredge weighs about 1000 pounds empty. The typical New England scallop vessel tows two dredges simultaneously, one off each side, from the forward gallows frames, and these are alternately brought up and the contents dumped on deck. The majority of the sea scallop fleet fish on Georges Bank in summer and in South Channel in winter so that only seaworthy vessels are used.

In the sheltered inland waterways of North Carolina small motor boats dredge for scallops on the shallow flats. They use very small dredges of about 2-bushel capacity. Each boat tows two to four dredges, each dredge usually being fastened by a short tow line to a pole placed crosswise of the boat.

Dredges used for oysters are narrower than the scallop dredges, usually about 4 to 6 feet wide; the bar across the mouth of the front frame has short teeth at intervals to scoop the oysters from the bottom or tear them loose if attached. Although usually pulled by power vessels, the dredge boats are restricted in some areas to sail. Thus in Chesapeake Bay only sail is permitted, except that when there is no wind the fishermen are allowed to push the dredge vessels by means of small blunt-nosed pusher boats powered with outboard motors.

The surf clam or skimmer (*Spisula solidissima*), especially abundant in New York waters, is taken chiefly by the jet dredge. This dredge is wider than most clam dredges, up to at least 4 feet across the mouth. The bar is flat as it relies for its digging action on a forced jet of water. A hose about 1½ inches in diameter runs from the vessel along the towing warp to the dredge. The water is pumped under pressure through the hose to a manifold that spreads the water into a narrow stream that hits the bottom just ahead of the bar, digging the clams loose. This dredge, lacking teeth, can be used on either hard or soft bottom. It is also used in Rhode Island waters to take the ocean quahog (*Arctica islandica*).

The quahog dredges, used especially in Rhode Island and Massachusetts waters, usually have 12 to 20 teeth spaced 2 inches or less apart. These teeth, about 7 inches long, dig the clams out of the soft bottom. A channel on the top of the runner on each side of the bottom of the dredge is weighted with lead, usually about 100 pounds in each channel, depending on the type of bottom and the power of the vessel. The bag is made of 2-inch chain rings and on a 20-tooth dredge may hold as high as 20 bushels of quahogs. These dredges are used both for the ocean quahog and for the common quahog or hard clam (*Venus mercenaria*).

## 10·8  Scooping nets

These are nets that take fish by being moved swiftly and lifting the fish clear of the water.

**Dip net or scoop net.** This is a small net on a rigid frame, with a long handle, employed almost universally in transferring fish from large nets into vessels and also used to capture fish. In California a considerable fishery for mackerel employs the scoop net. Small vessels, usually under 40 feet, and with a crew of one to three men use these long-handled dip nets which are a deep mesh bag on a spring steel hoop usually 28 inches in diameter. A mackerel school is brought to the boat by "chumming" with ground bait. Standing on a rack hanging over the side of the vessel the fishermen scoop up the mackerel as they rush at the cloud of "chum."

Dip nets are used for stream fishing. They were used by the Indians to take salmon and are still used in a few rivers, such as the Columbia and the Fraser, in places where the fish are impeded by rapids or falls so that they must pass upstream through a confined channel. The net is thrust into the water and swept rapidly downstream so as to keep the rim ahead of the bag in the fast current. At the end of the sweep the net is lifted quickly from the water with the handle and rim almost vertical so that any fish in the long bag are effectually trapped. The dip net is also used in taking alewives along the Atlantic Coast. The alewife fisherman, whenever the site permits, places a small board barrier at the lower end of the dipping channel. This impedes the escape of the fish as the frame of the net comes up against the boards.

**Fish wheel.** This is a highly specialized gear formerly used for shad on the Atlantic Coast and once used extensively for salmon on the Columbia River where it is now restricted by legislation. It is still used on the Yukon River in Alaska to take salmon for dog feed. The principle is very simple. It is a waterwheel with four wide vanes. Each vane terminates in a piece of netting with a slightly recurved edge. The current of the river keeps the wheel turning, and as the salmon migrate upstream the huge scoops on the ends of the vanes lift them from the water. On the lower side of each vane above the net is a small board chute running obliquely across the vane. As a vane rotates it scoops up a salmon; then as it continues to rise the salmon slides out of the net into the oblique chute down which it slides into a box placed at one side of the wheel.

**Reef net.** This gear originated among the Indians in the lower Gulf of Georgia and Juan de Fuca Strait, where it is used to take salmon, principally the sockeye (*Oncorhynchus nerka*) as it migrates through the salt-water channels en route to the Fraser River. The fishing sites are among the long reefs covered with the giant kelp. A channel is cut through the kelp to encourage the salmon to attempt to pass over the reef at the chosen site. The net is merely a flat blanket suspended in the water between two small boats. The Indians used canoes, but slim 30-foot boats are in use today. The down-channel edge of the net is deeper in the water. When a school of salmon enters the channel it encounters strands of rope near the bottom and is led upward until the fish are over the net, when it is quickly hoisted.

**Blanket net.** This is a flat or slightly concave net, usually nearly square, suspended horizontally in the water by the four corners. It may be suspended from a pier or from the boom of a vessel. Fish are enticed over the net in the daytime by ground bait or at night by a bright light. The net is hauled vertically. The principal use is for catching bait. In Japan large-sized blanket nets operated from either two or four boats are used to capture pelagic fishes.

## 10·9   Miscellaneous gear

In addition to the various types of gear described above there are many other kinds that do not readily conform to the established categories. Some of these types are:

**Tongs.** This is a pair of long poles fastened together near their extremities. The end of each pole has claws, and the two sets of claws are brought together by closing the handles together like a set of sugar tongs. The handles (or stales) are often lengthened by adding extra sections that fit into sockets but they are difficult to use in water over about 20 feet in depth. Tongs are used for gathering oysters and clams from reefs not exposed at low tide. Although most popular in the Middle and South Atlantic States, they are used as far north as Rhode Island and Massachusetts.

In Chesapeake Bay the depth at which tongs are practical has been increased by use of patent tongs. These have short handles and are lowered by a rope that runs through a block on the upper end of one handle, then across and through a block on the upper end of the opposite handle, down which it runs to the base. Pulling on the rope closes the tongs together.

**Rakes.** These rakes are large and long tined for taking scallops in shallow water or for sifting clams from bottoms not exposed to digging at low tide. They are worked from small boats. Very long-handled rakes are used in harvesting edible seaweeds.

**Torching.** This is a fishing method once used extensively in New England for taking herring. A blazing torch is projected forward from the prow of a dory or rowboat. While one man rows, a second man in the bow with a long-handled dip net scoops out the herring attracted by the strong light.

**Throw or casting net.** This is a method used to a limited extent throughout the South Pacific, Mexico, Japan, and Java. It is useful in taking reef fishes under surf and coral bottom conditions that are difficult for most forms of gear, and it is also quite effective in taking mullet (*Mugil*) in lagoons. A throw net is a light circular net somewhat bell-shaped and weighted around its perimeter. A man folds the net so that it can be thrown out over the water to land horizontally. When thrown over a school of fish the weighted edges sink rapidly. The net is retrieved by a line attached near the center. To prevent the fish from merely swimming out when the net is raised the circumference is recurved inward to form a pouch around the inner edge of the net.

**Suction dredge.** This is a method of harvesting oysters that sucks up the oysters as well as loose shells and other material on the bottom. The oysters are culled out and the other material returned or saved to use for oyster cultch during the season when young oysters are setting.

**Hoop net.** This is usually a circular frame with two or more hoops that form a net basket. It is used chiefly for crabs, and when it is hauled the crabs become so entangled in the netting that they cannot scramble over the edge before the net is hauled to the surface.

**Crab trot line.** This is a specialized form of gear used especially in Chesapeake Bay for taking the blue crab (*Callinectes sapidus*). The bait is tied to a long line laid along the bottom. The gear is fished without removal from the water merely by running the line over a roller projecting beyond the side of the vessel, as the vessel moves ahead. As the bait strike the roller the crabs fall off and are captured either by a short-handled dip net or by a special type of net fastened under and behind the roller.

**Dynamite.** This is almost wholly a poaching device.

**Diving suit.** Diving suits are used chiefly in the sponge, the pearl oyster, and the abalone fisheries.

**Poison.** Although employed as a management tool to eradicate fish, it is not a recognized method of fishing except in certain tropical countries. The most widely used poisons are cubé and derris root powders, cresol, and quicklime.

# TABLE 10·2

## Types of Usual Fishing Gear, Their Use and Fishing Characteristics

| General Type of Gear | Form of Gear | Catch in Pounds per Fisherman | Mobility | Examples of General Use |
|---|---|---|---|---|
| Impaling | Spear (gaff) | Low | High | Streams and through ice, also in goggle fishing |
|  | Harpoon | Low | High | Swordfish and tunas |
| Hook and line | Hand line | Low | High | Restricted |
|  | Long line (trot line, flagline) | Good | High | Bankfishes, as trot line for crabs and river fishes, as flagline for tunas |
|  | Trolling gear | Good | High | Salmon, tunas, sport |
|  | Pole and line | Good | High | Tunas, sport angling |
| Maze or barricade | Pot gear | Good | Fair | Lobsters, crabs, eels, catfish, octopi, reef fishes, bait |
|  | Fyke net | Good | Low | Flounders, river fishes |
|  | Pound net (trap) | Very high | Fixed | Salmon, shad, whiting, migrating shore species, Great Lakes fishes |
|  | Chinese shrimp net | Good | Fixed | Shrimp in San Francisco Bay, China, Sumatra, etc. |
|  | Stream weirs | Very high | Fixed | Eels, alewives |
| Entangling nets | Gill net (drift) | High | High | Pelagic marine species, lake trout, ciscoes, whitefish, etc. |
|  | Gill net (anchor) | High | Good | Cod, haddock, pollock, salmon |
|  | Gill net (circled) | Fair | High | Smelt, mackerel |
|  | Trammel net | High | High | Chiefly salmon |
| Encircling nets | Haul (beach) seine | Low | Low | Used to limited extent wherever beaches are suitable |
|  | Stop seine | Good | Good | Herring in Maine |
|  | Purse seine | Very high | High | Schooling species, tunas, sardines, herring, mackerel, anchovies, etc. |
| Towed nets | Danish seine | Good | High | Chiefly flatfish |
|  | Paranzella | Fair | High | Chiefly flatfish |
|  | Beam trawl | Fair | High | Shrimp and bankfishes |
|  | Otter trawl | Very high | High | Bankfishes, shrimp, and other varieties, when near the bottom |
|  | Dredge | Good | High | Oysters, quahogs, scallops |
| Scooping nets | Dip net | Fair | Varies | Salmon, alewives, mackerel |
|  | Fish wheel | Fair | Fixed | Salmon on a few rivers |
|  | Reef net | Good | Fixed | Salmon in Northwest |
|  | Blanket net | Low | Low | Chiefly for bait |
| Miscellaneous | Tongs | Low | Good | Chiefly for oysters |
|  | Rakes | Low | Good | Scallops and clams |
|  | Suction dredge | High | Good | Oysters |
|  | Throw net | Low | Fair | Reef fishes |
|  | Hoop net | Low | High | Chiefly crabs |
|  | Diving suit | Fair | Fair | Sponges, pearl oysters, abalones |

**Electric shock.** Electric shock has been in use for some time as a method for collecting fish for study purposes but has not yet been introduced commercially although attempts are being made by at least one foreign firm to patent an electric fishing method.

## 10·10 Summary

Although a great many different forms of gear have been touched upon, it is obvious that many of these contribute little to the annual yield of the fisheries. The reason for this is more clearly shown by Table 10·2 which shows the scale of catch per fisherman for different types. A few types with a low return in pounds per man, i.e., harpoon, tongs, persist because they take species of high monetary value. Some types with low returns persist because they are adapted to certain fishing conditions or because the gear itself is relatively inexpensive. Some fisheries are highly seasonal in nature so that, although the return per man may be low on an annual basis, the fishery is quite lucrative to farmers or others who can turn to fishing for a short period.

The mobility of fishing gear as well as its adaptability to different species is exceedingly important in all consideration of fishing regulations, as will be shown in Chapter 24. Often regulations designed to protect one species have merely thrown an additional fishing pressure on another species. This is especially evident in the fisheries of the Pacific Coast in which a large share of the modern vessels can be used with equal success for purse seining, long lining, or otter trawling.

### References

Babcock, John P.
1903. The spawning-beds of the Fraser River. In *Ann. Rept. Comm. of Fisheries (British Columbia)* for 1902. Victoria.

Bonnot, Paul
1932. The California shrimp industry. *Calif. Div. Fish and Game, Bur. Comm. Fish., Fish. Bull. 38:* 20 pp.

Bourgois, François
1951. Japanese offshore trawling. *U. S. Fish and Wildl. Serv., Fish. Leaf. 389,* also *Rept. 138, Nat. Resources Section,* Supreme Commander for the Allied Powers: 60 pp.

Firth, Frank E.
1951. American fishing gear and fishery methods. In *Marine Products of Commerce* by Donald K. Tressler and James McW. Lemon. 2d ed. Reinhold Publ. Co.: 234–281, New York.

Fish and Wildlife Service (L. A. Walford, ed.)
1945. Fishery resources of the United States. *U. S. Senate Doc. 51,* 79 Cong. 1st Sess., 1945: iv + 135.

Fry, Donald H., Jr.
1931.  The ring net, half ring net, or purse lampara in the fisheries of California. *Calif. Div. Fish and Game, Bur. Comm. Fish. 27:* 1–65.

Godsil, H. C.
1938.  The high seas tuna fishery of California. *Calif. Div. Fish and Game, Bur. Mar. Fish., Fish. Bull. 51:* 40 pp.

Kask, John L., and Yoshio Hiyama
1947.  Japanese fishing gear. *U. S. Fish and Wildl. Serv., Fish. Leaf. 234,* also *Rept. 71, Nat. Resources Section,* Supreme Commander for the Allied Powers: 107 pp.

McLean, John (W. S. Wallace, ed.)
1932.  *Notes of a twenty-five year's service in the Hudson's Bay Territory.* The Champlain Society, Toronto.

Moser, Jefferson F.
1899.  The salmon and salmon fisheries of Alaska. *Bull. U. S. Fish Comm. 18,* 1898 (1899): 178 pp.

Rostlund, Erhard
1952.  Freshwater fish and fishing in native North America. *Univ. Calif. Publ. Geog. 9:* x + 313.

Royce, William F.
1947.  Gear used in the sea scallop fishery. *U. S. Fish and Wildl. Serv., Fish. Leaf. 225:* 5 pp.

Scofield, W. Launce
1947.  Drift and set line fishing in California. *Calif. Div. Fish and Game, Bur. Mar. Fish., Fish. Bull. 66:* 38 pp.

1948.  Trawling gear in California. *Calif. Div. Fish and Game, Bur. Mar. Fish., Fish. Bull. 72:* 60 pp.

1951.  Purse seines and other roundhaul nets in California. *Calif. Div. Fish and Game, Bur. Mar. Fish., Fish. Bull. 81:* 83 pp.

Umali, Augustin F.
1950.  Guide to the classification of fishing gear in the Philippines. *U. S. Fish and Wildl. Serv., Res. Rept. 17:* 165 pp.

Van Oosten, John, Ralph Hile, and Frank Jobes
1946.  The whitefish fishery of Lakes Huron and Michigan with special reference to the deep-trap-net fishery. *U. S. Fish and Wildl. Serv., Fish. Bull. 50* (40):297–394.

Whiteleather, Richard T., and Herbert H. Brown
1945.  *An experimental fishery survey in Trinidad, Tobago, and British Guiana with recommended improvements in methods and gear.* Anglo-American Caribbean Commission: 130 pp., Washington.

# 11 · FISHWAYS

## 11·1 Where are fishways useful?

The purpose of a fishway is to provide for the upstream or downstream passage of fish past either a dam or a natural barrier. It consists of a water-filled lock, channel, or series of connected pools by means of which the fish may swim past the obstruction.

Anadromous fishes—sturgeon, salmon, alewives, smelt, sea-run trout, shad—must ascend streams to reach spawning grounds that are suitable and sufficiently extensive to accommodate them. Lacustrine anadromous species must reach a lake or pond large enough to rear the young. For certain fluvial anadromous species, such as the Atlantic salmon, in which the young spend some time in the stream before migrating seaward, large nursery areas in the streams are necessary; the same applies to adfluvial species which cannot reproduce successfully unless they can migrate out of a lake into suitable spawning areas. Failure to provide proper fishways has destroyed fine runs of all of these species.

The spawning requirements of certain species, especially most of the salmonoids, are rather strict. They require beds of coarse gravel or rubble in moving water to keep the buried eggs aerated during the long incubation period. Many lakes suitable for landlocked salmon and trouts are sparsely populated because tributary streams containing the needed spawning beds have impassable obstructions.

The need for fishways is not always so clear for many species of warm-water fishes that can grow and reproduce successfully without migration. Where resident fishes are the principal species each situation needs careful appraisal before a fishway is deemed necessary.

## 11·2 When should a fishway be constructed?

Fishways are often expensive to build and operate. The fishery administrator is too often placed in the uncomfortable position of having to decide, without adequate evidence for or against its desirability, whether or not a fishway should be built. The question of what constitutes damage and the responsibility involved is far from a simple matter. From the standpoint of some conservationists, all damage to a natural resource must be compensated for. From the practical side, however, this is clearly impossible, and not always desirable. Each case should actually be decided upon its merits.

When a dam blocks only a small area, the expense of a fishway may often be wholly disproportionate to the possible benefits. Regardless of who pays the bill it may be economically unsound to build such a fishway. In many states such situations have been recognized, and the owners of such an obstruction have been permitted to compensate for the damage incurred in other ways, such as by contributions toward artificial propagation.

When commercial fisheries are involved, evaluation of a fishery in order to estimate the damage caused by lack of a fishway can be accomplished quite readily, but for a sport fishery evaluations are somewhat more difficult (Kahn and Rounsefell 1947).

When the run of a species has already been destroyed by a dam that has been in existence for many years, the value of a fishway must be estimated on the potential value of the re-established run.

In general, the cost of a fishway should be weighed against the capitalized value of the present or potential resource that requires it. Thus, if it is found that the trout run depending on the spawning grounds above a proposed dam produces an annual benefit of $2000, the capitalized value of the run is $50,000 (using an interest rate of 4 per cent which is applicable to natural resources conserved by the taxpayer's money and is the same rate used by the Corps of Engineers in computing benefits from engineering projects). If an adequate fishway can be built for less than $50,000 the cost becomes a justifiable expenditure from the national viewpoint. What happens when the fishway cannot be built for the $50,000? On the theory that the owner of the dam must compensate for any damages incurred there are of course several lines of procedure indicated. It becomes a matter of policy whether or not a permanent fishery resource should be extinguished by a dam with an estimated useful life of 40 to 60 years. If both the fishery and the dam are of importance to the area then a more expensive fishway may be justified. This is exactly the line of reasoning adopted when many of the large public dams are constructed despite an unfavorable cost–benefit ratio. In other words, a resource is preserved at a monetary loss but is nonetheless preserved.

Evaluation of the requirements for a fishway at a natural obstruction should be made in the same manner as for a dam. There is one difference. A fishway at a natural obstruction, instead of preventing a loss, often results in the creation of a new resource.

## 11·3   Basic requirements of a fishway

There are certain basic requirements that should be met by any fishway. These are:

1. It should be suitable for and passable by all the migratory species in that particular stream.
2. It should operate at all water levels in the forebay and tailrace of a dam or above and below a natural obstruction.
3. It should operate at all volumes of stream flow.
4. Fish should ascend without injury or exertion of extreme effort.
5. Fish must find the entrance and enter without too much delay.

## 11·4   General types of fishways

Fishways have been in use since very ancient times. Many designs and types have been tried in various places. A few have been successful, some have had limited success, and the majority have failed. There are only a few general types of fishways:

**The simple sluice or inclined chute,** with or without some modification to decrease velocity and with or without resting pools.

**The pool type.** This widely used type is a succession of pools connected by short rapids or low falls. The pools may also be connected by a submerged orifice.

**The Denil type.** This is a narrow chute carrying a large volume of water at high velocity, especially on the surface. The force of this stream striking closely spaced baffles aids in maintaining a low velocity near the bottom.

**The fish lock.** This type requires mechanical gates and either an attendant or an automatic device to regulate the flow of water into and out of the lock.

**The deep-baffled channel.** This type is designed for a low gradient and is especially suitable to an extreme variation in flow and water level.

## 11·5   Selection of the type and design of a fishway

The final criterion of a fishway is its success in passing fish. Unless great care is observed in its design and location, its chances of success are greatly diminished.

Far too many fishways are built after a dam has been completed— and are merely attached to the lower side of the structure. To insure success a fishway should be an integral part of the dam structure; it should be built with the dam and if necessary go through the dam instead of going over or around it. When a fishway is built afterward the engineer is greatly handicapped, and the result is nearly always

FIG. 11·1 Pool-type fishway without submerged orifice. Note the extra long pool on the curve. (Credit: U. S. Fish and Wildlife Service)

FIG. 11·2 Same fishway as in preceding figure with correct amount of water flow for proper operation. Where it can be used this fishway is the most economical in its use of water. (Credit: U. S. Fish and Wildlife Service)

a poorer fishway at greater expense. Only by the enactment and rigid enforcement of adequate legislation can this handicap be overcome, as dam builders usually prefer to build without a fishway if there is any possibility of being able to avoid adding one later.

Because of the factors of terrain, height of dam, available funds, and the amount of spillway space that can be utilized, the fishway engineer frequently finds that his choice of location and design is strictly limited. Perhaps the best way to destroy a fish run is to

construct a fishway that is only partially successful. A poor fishway
is apt to be much worse than no fishway. This applies especially
where the law requires a dam owner to build an approved fishway.
If a dam owner builds an approved fishway and the fishway is unsuccessful he will not willingly build another. As long as there is no fish-

Fig. 11·3  Looking upstream inside a vertical baffle fishway of the same design
as those at Hell's Gate on the Fraser River. (Credit: International Pacific Salmon Fisheries Commission)

way there is a chance to build a successful one, but what happens to
the poor ones?

There are many situations in which one fishway is not adequate to
provide passage for fish over a dam. At the Rock Island dam of the
Puget Sound Power and Light Company on the Columbia River, large
fishways were built on both banks. Although they were successful
in passing salmon, a large number of fish injured themselves leaping
at the rock ledges in midstream. A third ladder was therefore constructed in the center of the dam. Most state fishway legislation
does not provide for adequate passage of fish but merely requires the
dam owner to build "a fishway." If he has complied with the state

law but fish are not passing the dam successfully, the run is on its way out.

On all dam projects licensed by the Federal Power Commission the fish-protective devices, including fishways, must be approved by the Secretary of the United States Department of the Interior. Since the enactment of the Federal Power Act of 1920, and subsequent amendments, an increasing number of dams, especially on larger streams, are being licensed by the Commission.

In most situations the pool type of fishway, with a flow over the weir between pools, and a submerged orifice through the weir, has proved quite successful for active fish.

The simple inclined chute or sluice is applicable in special cases. Perhaps the simplest is the "balk." This is merely a beam placed at an angle across the gradually sloping face of a low dam so as to form a trough of low gradient up which salmon can easily swim for a short distance (Menzies 1934). Few modern dams are built so low or with such a gradually sloping face as to permit the use of this simple method.

The inclined sluice is in very common use in passing alewives over low dams (see Figure 11·4). Despite all the theoretical objections that can be raised, this fishway, as developed, with a series of baffles, does work fairly well for alewives. It is too turbulent, it is very swift in places, it does not provide resting pools, and it does not operate satisfactorily on low flows, but the alewives scramble up somehow. When the water is too shallow, they turn on their sides and wriggle up amid great splashing. Although salmon are sometimes known to use these fishways, they are unsuitable for salmon because of their lack of depth and the many very sharp turns. The principle of this type of fishway is that it actually extends greatly the length of the stream by making a tortuous channel. The effective width of the channel is actually much less than the width of the sluice, and the many sharp turns cause cross currents that are very difficult, especially for large fish.

## 11·6  Locating the fishway entrance

The most important feature of any fishway is the entrance. If the entrance is located too far downstream from the obstruction it will be passed by the fish, which follow the main channel until stopped by a barrier. Such an entrance may be found by a very small proportion of the fish on their way upstream, or by some fish drifting downstream, exhausted or injured, after vainly leaping at the dam. A great many fishways that are added after the dam has been completed have their entrances too far downstream.

For a fishway to be successful the entrance should be located close
to the toe of the dam.   When a dam is built obliquely across a stream

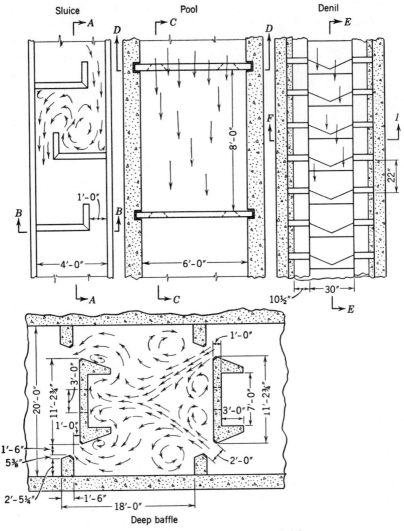

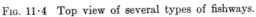

FIG. 11·4   Top view of several types of fishways.

it is usually best to locate the fishway at the upstream end.   The
primary requirement for attracting fish is that the entrance be located
so close to the main current from the spillway or tailrace that fish
following this current will be led to the fishway entrance.   Once the

fish are at the entrance they can usually be induced to enter if a sufficient amount of water is provided. The volume necessary depends to a large extent on the volume of the main stream.

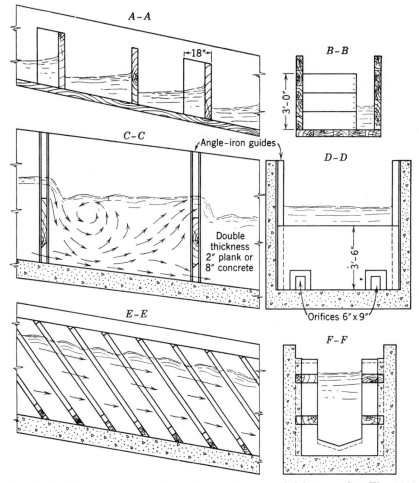

FIG. 11·5  Side and end elevations of several types of fishways. See Fig. 11·4 for location of sections.

Fish enter a fishway far more readily if the flow from the bottom pool issues in the same direction as the main flow of the stream.

Power dams present special difficulties because there may be extended periods when all or most of the flow passes through the turbines and issues from the tailrace. Often fishways are required both at the spillway and the tailrace. In special cases where the terrain and the directions of flow are correct, and the volumes involved are not excessive, fish may be diverted from a tailrace to pass upstream to a fishway at the spillway. When this is not practicable a second fishway at the powerhouse is indicated.

The Denil type of fishway (Denil 1938) works on a principle entirely different from that of the pool type. Whereas the pool type dissipates the energy of the falling water in each pool, the Denil type permits a very fast current. A portion of the energy generated by this fast current is dissipated against closely spaced marginal and bottom baffles with re-entrant angles. These angles cause small backward jets that slow the current along the bottom. The fish swim up this slower current that underlies the fast-moving surface. This type has been used experimentally in the United States (McLeod and Nemenyi 1941) on Mississippi River fishes with favorable results, and it is being tried for Pacific salmon. This type of fishway has the advantage of requiring less space and might be cheaper to construct than the pool type of fishway. It requires more water to operate than the pool type and there is some question concerning its durability where ice and heavy drift are encountered. However, recent simplified designs (Furuskog 1945) appear to have largely overcome the last objection.

The fish lock is suitable only for situations where the operation can be observed closely. The lock is adapted for sites that offer little space for a fishway or where the lift is so high as to preclude the use of a conventional fishway.

Actually, if enough space is available, it is easy to design a fishway that fish will ascend successfully, *if they enter it*. The problem of fishway entrances is applicable equally to all types and will be therefore discussed in a separate section.

The deep-baffled channel was designed by the engineers of the International Pacific Salmon Fisheries Commission to provide passage for salmon around swift rapids in narrow gorges subject to extreme fluctuations in water level. It is not designed for use at dams as the slope is very gradual, about 1 in 30 or 40.

## 11·7  Types of entrances

The type of entrance depends largely on its location in relation to the main current, and on the range of water levels. When the range of water levels is very slight no special provisions may be necessary. However, when the range is several feet it is obvious that the first few pools of the ladder will be submerged at the higher levels, which results in a slow unattractive flow from the entrance. One method of combating this is to introduce auxiliary water into the bottom few pools of the fishway. Water is usually conveyed through a large pipe or flume into a diffusion chamber under the floor of the pools from which it enters the pools through gratings at about 0.25 foot per second. This permits the addition of large quantities of water without preventing the fish from recognizing and following the main current leading up the fishway. Where auxiliary water cannot be added it will aid if the last weir of the fishway be extended vertically as high as the highest water levels expected. The entire height of this weir can then be provided with a slot so that the flow issuing from the ladder will be confined to a narrow width, thus increasing its velocity. This can be improved upon by providing a floating gate that will rise from the bottom as the water rises and thus control the depth of the open slot at all water levels. The confined flow is far more attractive to fish.

Fishway entrances at powerhouses present a special problem because the velocity of the water issuing from the draft tubes is much lower than that from a spillway. As a consequence fish are able to approach close to the powerhouse across the entire width of the stream. In many power installations on small streams the top of the draft tubes is practically at the surface of the water at low water levels, so that a fishway entrance necessarily must be placed at the sides of the powerhouse (Bair and Rounsefell 1951). At Bonneville Dam on the Columbia River the draft tubes are submerged sufficiently so that a special collecting device is employed. It is a long flume leading from the fishway entirely across the face of the powerhouse above the draft tubes. A number of entrances are provided so that fish approaching can enter the flume which leads to the fishway from whatever point they reach the powerhouse. Auxiliary water from a second flume behind and below the first flume enters the bottom of the collecting flume at intervals to maintain a directional flow. This is necessary as the water passing over each entrance weir of the collecting flume must be replaced to effect this condition.

## 11·8   Types of exits

The fishway exit has not been given sufficient attention. Too large a proportion of fishways function only within a narrow range of forebay levels because the exit is not properly designed. A fishway should be operable at all water levels; yet scores are built with only one exit and with no control of the heights of the upper weirs. When the differences in forebay level are only a few feet one entrance may suffice, but several of the top pools must have weirs adjustable in height. At highest water levels there will be a rise between every pool to the top of the fishway, but as the water falls, the weir of the top pool will be lowered; then it and the next weir will be lowered simultaneously, until at lowest water levels several pools will be at the same level. The actual exit itself may be either at the surface or submerged. When a ladder has a submerged exit but has no height control on the upper weirs, the exit becomes impassable at high water because of the great difference in elevation between the water surfaces of the forebay and the first pool. In such poorly designed fishways it is sometimes impossible to open the gate far enough to permit a fish to squeeze through without flooding the ladder because of the tremendous pressure. Under such conditions the fish seldom can overcome the high threshhold resistance at the gate even if the opening is enlarged.

In a properly designed ladder with adequate control of the height of the upper weirs, a submerged exit has certain advantages. It is less subject to plugging with drift, it is less likely to allow surges of water down the ladder, and it does not change the volume of water delivered down the fishway by as large an amount for any given change in the forebay level as does a surface exit.

The exit should be in water of sufficient depth, but should not be located at the crest of the spillway or very close to any water diversion. This protects the fish from being swept downstream as they leave the fishway exit.

Owing to the great variation in water level in storage dams the exit sometimes poses an extremely difficult problem. The usual solution is to provide a number of exits (these are usually ports with gates) that leave the fishway at various elevations and pierce the dam structure. Such a fishway is extremely costly if it has to be added after a dam has been constructed, and a fish lock may sometimes be the only solution.

Fishway exits should always be provided with some type of stout trash rack to prevent damage from ice or drift.

### 11·9   Fishway velocities

The water velocity permissible in a fishway is governed by several factors, but chiefly by the species and size of the fish, the total height of the dam, the distance between resting pools, and the size and type of the fishway. Most observations on the speed of fish are maximum speeds under ideal conditions over a comparatively short distance. Swimming against a current with its surges and eddies is quite different from swimming in quiet water.

A table of maximum velocities against which fish can swim is given by Frischholz (1924). His velocities in meters have been translated into feet. In a straight flume or sluiceway, in which the water flows without any baffles or obstructions, he found for distances over 33 feet that poor-swimming species could swim only 1.7 to 3.3 feet per second and good swimmers 3.3 to 5.0 feet. When the distance was reduced to less than 33 feet the poor swimmers could swim 3.3 to 5.0 feet per second and the good swimmers 6.6 to 8.3 feet.

In a fishway in which the flow is checked at intervals by baffles or partitions so that the points of maximum velocity are spaced at intervals, a much greater velocity can be tolerated at these particular points. He gives a maximum velocity of 3.3 to 6.6 feet per second for poor swimmers passing over five of these swift points and 6.6 to 9.8 for good swimmers. When less than five openings were to be negotiated the poor swimmers could face currents of 5.0 to 8.3 feet per second and good swimmers those of 13.1 to 16.4 feet per second. Of course these last-named swimming velocities are attained only with extreme exertion and for a very short distance. They are much too fast to consider in fishway construction.

The 6.6 to 8.3 feet per second for good swimmers in a straight flume less than 33 feet in length roughly coincides with the findings of McLeod and Nemenyi (1941). The best speed that trout (a good swimmer) could attain was 7 feet per second in flumes not over 10 feet in length.

In general, the velocities should be held to a maximum of less than 5 feet per second at any point in the fishway, except perhaps through sharp-edged submerged orifices, and if poor swimmers, such as perch, carp, whitefish, or catfish, are to make use of the passage the velocities should be somewhat less.

## 11·10   Fishway dimensions

The dimensions of a fishway depend on several factors: the size and speed of the species to be passed, the numbers of fish expected to use the fishway at any one time, the volume of water to be accommodated, and the total height of the ladder.

For a very small stream that is an important migration pathway for a species—such as a large alewife run ascending into a lake—it is often possible to furnish excellent passage over a low dam by utilizing the entire stream bed, turning it into a succession of pools connected by low falls or short rapids. These pools can usually be built of masonry, and the extra roughness is a great aid in dissipating the energy of the falling water.

When alewives or trout are the largest species involved, a pool-type fishway in which the pools are 6 feet long, 4 feet wide, and 3 feet deep will usually suffice. For salmon the pools should be at least 8 feet long and 6 feet wide with no depth less than 3 feet (see Figures 11·4 and 11·5). The maximum drop in water surface between pools should be between 8 and 10 inches for alewives and between 12 and 16 inches

FIG. 11·6  Pools in a successful alewife fishway at Somesville, Maine, designed by the senior author. A chute leads from the face of the rear wall of each pool into the pool above enabling the alewives to swim up without jumping. Difference in water levels is seven inches. (Credit: Stuart DeRoche, Maine Inland Fisheries and Game)

for salmon. The drop between pools cannot be measured by what the most vigorous fish can do, but should be measured by what drop can easily be passed by the average fish or by gravid fish arriving toward the end of the spawning migration when temperatures may be unfavorable.

The pool sizes given are for straight fishways. Turns are preferably gradual curves with the length of the pool measured on the inside of the turn. Fishways are built occasionally in which the pools are in two or three rows and the fish must ascend in a zigzag pattern. In such a ladder all pools in which the water changes its direction of flow should be full length in both directions. Thus for salmon such a pool should be at least 8 feet square.

The dimensions given may have to be increased for larger streams. Thus at Bonneville Dam on the Columbia River the fishways are 40 feet wide; the pools average about 16 feet long and over 5 feet deep. The senior author witnessed 34,000 chinook salmon ascending these

FIG. 11·7 Looking upstream in one of the fishways at Bonneville Dam, on the Columbia River. (Credit: U. S. Fish and Wildlife Service)

ladders in one day, and it was clear that small pools would have been entirely inadequate.

Whether or not the weirs between pools are notched to accommodate water depends somewhat on the volume of flow. Except where water is very scarce it should not usually be necessary. When weirs are notched the notch should be at least one-third the length of the weir and should have a horizontal bottom and vertical sides. The edges of the notch can be beveled with the slope downstream.

Many pool-type fishways are provided with a submerged orifice in each weir. These orifices are designed to facilitate the passage of species that object to swimming over the weir, but they are also used more readily than the surface overflow by most species. In many fishways these openings are too large for the size of the pools, thus causing great turbulence in the pools. This is especially true in the aforementioned zigzag ladders in which the change in direction combined with the turbulence is extremely confusing to the fish. For salmon an opening 6 inches wide by 9 inches high is usually sufficient. In the large fishways at Bonneville the submerged orifices are 2 feet square. The edges of these openings should be beveled, the sharp edges upstream. The beveling is an aid to the fish in overcoming the heavy threshhold resistance encountered in passing from one pool to the next as it confines the point of greatest resistance to a very narrow plane.

In the straight-run fishway there is no advantage to staggering the position of these orifices. If the pools are of the proper dimensions there will be practically no carryover of velocity from one pool to the next. If the orifices are in line a fish will often swim through several in one fast rush, but if they are staggered the fish must search for them. The cross currents created by staggering the orifices make each pool less of a resting pool. When no orifices are larger than 6 inches by 9 inches two orifices may be used in each weir in 6-foot-by-8-foot pools.

In Figures 11·4 and 11·5 are shown examples of typical fishway sections. The sluice is the type often used in New England for passing alewives. The pool type is a modern Cail fishway of the minimum size recommended for passing salmon on a small or medium-sized stream. The Denil is adapted from a successful Swedish fish ladder (Furuskog 1945). The deep baffle fishway is the type used on the Fraser River by the International Pacific Salmon Fisheries Commission for passing salmon over natural rapids.

## 11·11 Operation and maintenance of fishways

Whenever a fishway is built three points should be settled:

**Inspection.** Provision should be made for periodic mechanical inspection of every fishway. A fishway may be out of operation for months merely because no one person is made responsible for seeing that it is always in repair and that its requirements are anticipated. A report of each inspection date, the condition of the fishway, any minor repairs made, and any foreseeable needs should be filed.

**Maintenance.** It should be clearly understood where the responsibility lies for the maintenance of a fishway. This may seem unimportant, but fishways are built by many agencies and often the agency building the fishway is not responsible for its maintenance. Thus some fishways were built during the 1930's by the Civilian Conservation Corps and others were built with funds from the Works Progress Ad-

Fig. 11·8   A view of the main Hell's Gate fishways taken from cliffs above the left bank. Salmon enter each fishway through the various slots at the downstream end (left) of the fishways, and leave through the trashracks on the upstream (right) end. (Credit: International Pacific Salmon Fisheries Commission)

ministration and the Public Works Administration. Obviously these agencies were not responsible for their maintenance. Many fishways have fallen into bad repair from lack of adequate maintenance. Maintenance requires an outlay of funds, and few private dam owners are likely to keep a fishway in top condition unless their responsibility is clear and the condition of the fishway is checked periodically.

**Operation.** Even the most skillfully designed fishways will not pass fish unless they are open and properly regulated. They must be kept clean of debris and drift. The exit weirs and gate must be adjusted to allow for changes in forebay level. For larger installations auxiliary water controls need occasional adjustment, especially when there are shifts in tailwater level. At some dams the forebay level falls and rises every 24 hours as water is alternately used during the day and stored overnight. Usually the dam owner or his tenant is responsible for operation, but every warden or conservation officer should be coached by a fishway engineer or inspector so that he will know how a fishway should function. He should pass on his knowledge to the dam owner and should check occasionally and report on every fishway in his area. Each fishway is designed to operate best within a specified range of flows. Too little or too much water may hinder the proper passage of fish.

### References

Bair, Scott H., and George A. Rounsefell
  1951. An interim report on salmon restoration in the St. Croix, Aroostook, and St. John Rivers. *U. S. Fish and Wildl. Serv.:* 28 pp.
Denil, G.
  1938. La mécanique du poisson de rivière. Reprinted from *Annales des travaux publics de Belgique,* Aug.–Oct. 1936, Feb.–Dec. 1937, Feb.–Aug. 1938: 395 pp., Brussels.
Frischholz, Dr.
  1924. Anlage und Betrieb von Fischpässen. (Construction and operation of fishpasses.) *Handbuch der Binnenfischerei Mitteleuropas* (Handbook of the Central European freshwater fisheries) *6* (1):137 pp., Stuttgart.
Furuskog, Valter
  1945. En ny laxtrappa. (A new fishladder.) *Svensk Fiskeri-Tidskrift 11:* 236–239.
Kahn, Richard A., and George A. Rounsefell
  1947. Evaluation of fisheries in determining benefits and losses from engineering projects. *U. S. Fish and Wildl. Serv., Spec. Sci. Rept. 40:* 10 pp.
McLeod, A. M., and Paul Nemenyi
  1941. An investigation of fishways. *Univ. Iowa Stud. Eng., Bull. 24:* 63 pp., Iowa City.
Menzies, W. J. M.
  1934. Salmon passes—their design and construction. Fisheries, Scotland, *Salmon Fish.,* 1934 (1):29 pp., Edinburgh.
Nemenyi, Paul
  1941. An annotated bibliography of fishways. *Univ. Iowa Stud. Eng., Bull. 23:* 64 pp., Iowa City.
Pryce-Tannatt, T. E.
  1938. Fish passes. *The Buckland Lectures for 1937.* Edward Arnold and Co.: 108 pp., London.
Rounsefell, George A.
  1944. Fishways for small streams. *U. S. Fish and Wildl. Serv., Fish. Leaf. 92:* 5 pp.

# 12 · SCREENS AND RACKS

## 12·1   Purpose of screens and racks

The purposes for which screens and racks are constructed are important considerations in determining where they are needed, the types suitable for particular situations, and what costs are justified. The chief purposes are:

**Confinement.** Screens are often used to prevent fish from leaving a pond, lake, or other body of water.

**Protection from water diversions.** Screens are used to prevent fish moving downstream from entering water diversions that endanger them. This may apply to diversions for domestic and industrial water, irrigation, power, or other uses.

**Protection from blind channels.** Screens or racks are used to prevent fish migrating upstream from entering blind channels or especially tailraces of power plants and other diversion returns up which the fish cannot safely migrate or in which they will tarry instead of finding the main channel.

**Population control.** Racks and screens are used for trapping migratory fish to eradicate them or to control their numbers, i.e., the sea lamprey in the Great Lakes.

**Census.** Information of great value in solving problems of management is derived from counts of migratory fish tallied at racks.

## 12·2   Necessity for screens

In some areas screens have been placed at the outlet of many ponds and lakes to prevent the egress of fish, and especially hatchery-liberated fish. When for any of many possible reasons the fishing in a lake becomes poor a clamor is often raised for a screen. The reasoning runs something like this. Great(?) numbers of fish have been released in the lake. Everyone knows that these fish should grow up and produce good fishing. Fishing has not improved. Therefore it is obvious(?) that the liberated fish have left the lake. If these fish are prevented from leaving the lake good fishing is bound to occur.

197

This line of reasoning is often fostered by well-intentioned but unin-
formed hatcherymen who really believe that a very high proportion
of their liberated fish survive in the wild and that all that is necessary
to improve fishing is to treat each lake like an enlarged hatchery pond.

What are the facts? Actual scientific information on the effect of
such screening is meager. About as fast as a screen is installed to
revive fishing in one lake a screen is removed from another because
fishing did not show any improvement. It is hardly a scientific test
to screen only lakes with poor fishing because such lakes are likely to
improve anyway in the natural course of events. Biologically there is
little justification for such screens. If a lake provides a suitable environment for liberated fish they will be likely to remain. If a lake
is unsuitable nothing is gained by not permitting fish to escape, if any
happen to find their way out. When one stocks hatchery fish in a
lake without adequate knowledge of the size of the wild population
it often happens that they are merely a very small fraction of the
wild population already present. They cannot be expected to exert
any noticeable influence on abundance.

But what of the effects of screening on the wild fish populations
and on species other than that for which the screen was intended?
Screening of lakes has been responsible for ruining many runs of
alewives that formerly spawned in them. This has the effect of greatly
decreasing the supply of food available to the game fishes. The total
productivity of the lake is lowered. We have had fishermen tell us
quite seriously that the alewives should be eliminated because the
game fish had so much to eat they would not bite! In fact this is
probably the actual motive behind the installation of some screens
purported to be for keeping game fish in a lake. The screening of
lakes has undoubtedly been a factor in eliminating runs of anadromous
trout and Atlantic salmon from some streams, especially those in
which the chief riffle areas, which serve as nursery areas for the young,
are above the lake.

Some years ago there was a great fad in New England for planting
sea-run salmon of any species in screened lakes so that the smolts
could not descend to the sea at the proper time. Millions of chinook
salmon eggs (*Oncorhynchus tshawytscha*) were imported from the
Pacific Coast for this purpose. These salmon of course provided some
temporary angling and then disappeared. In several instances in
which flood waters took out screens, permitting smolts to escape downstream, large sea-run adults returned. This happened in the Royal,
Pemaquid, and Damariscotta Rivers of Maine and probably in others.
However, the eggs obtained from these sea-run adults were replanted

in screened lakes so that the great chinook salmon was never allowed to become established.

The screening of lakes has contributed to the reduction of the land-locked salmon. In lakes with inlet streams too small or'otherwise unsuitable for spawning it is natural for the landlocked salmon to spawn in the coarse stones and gravel of the outlet stream. When the outlet is barred by a screen, reproduction may be very poor and the run may be gradually or suddenly eliminated. The first thoughts of the average observer on seeing a number of adult salmon descending an outlet stream is that they are leaving the lake, never to return. He immediately becomes a screen convert.

There are two special cases in which a screen may be justified as a temporary expedient: (1) when there is an area of lethal pollution downstream, (2) when there is an impassable natural falls or dam without a fishway. In both cases, if the outlet stream is needed for spawning, the screen should be located as far as possible below the lake.

Screens to prevent fish from entering diversions which carry water for irrigation, city water supply, etc., are clearly beneficial and should be installed wherever substantial damage is occurring. For power diversions which return the water to the main river the amount of damage depends not only on the numbers of fish entering the diversion but also on the degree to which they are harmed.

A power diversion may harm fish in two ways, by pressure changes and by mechanical injury. If the fish have been close to the surface for some time before entering the penstock they will not be accommodated to high pressure. Such fish can undergo the pressure of the penstock and its sudden release with much less harm than fish that were accommodated to high pressure before entering the penstock.

Mechanical injury depends on the size, type, and speed of the turbines. The Kaplan or propeller type of turbine usually installed for large volumes of water at a fairly low head (i.e. at Bonneville) undoubtedly is far less harmful than the Francis type. In fact at Bonneville there may be some question as to whether the turbines are not a safer passage for smolts than the spillway. The spillway is gated, and as the smolts emerge under the gate a 50-foot pressure is instantly released. They then are hurled with terrific force down the face of the spillway. On the apron the water is thrown against two rows of huge concrete baffles designed to dissipate quickly the enormous amount of energy.

The damage caused to a run of migrating fish by a power diversion depends not only on the proportion of fish harmed by passage through the diversion, but also on the proportion of the total downstream migration that passes through it. Thus information on the season of downstream migration of a species plus seasonal data on the proportion of the total flow passing through the diversion will yield an estimate of the proportion of the run destroyed. For run-of-the-river power installations with little storage capacity, the damage is apt to be far less than for installations at dams with large storage capacity. In the latter case a much larger proportion of the total flow is utilizable, and the season of spill from the dam is apt to be more erratic.

The screening of diversions at points where they re-enter a main channel is often of great importance. On many rivers diversions re-enter the stream at some distance below the dam. Even when the river bed carries sufficient transportation water to enable the fish to pass upstream to the dam from the point where the tailrace re-enters the river, fish may enter the tailrace instead, especially when it has a volume comparable in size to or larger than the stream itself.

### 12·3   Rotary or drum screen

Several types of screens are in use. The design to be chosen depends on the volume and velocity of the water to be screened; the

FIG. 12·1  A rotary screen installation in a large irrigation diversion. Note that the canal is widened to slow the current as it approaches the screens. (Credit: U. S. Fish and Wildlife Service)

amount and type of drift; the size of the fish to be stopped; whether it is for upstream or downstream migrants; the depth and shape of the cross section of canal, stream, or lake where the screen is to be installed; the permanence of the installation; and the funds available.

The most satisfactory screen for canal diversions, such as those for irrigation, is the *self-cleaning rotary drum*. It is shown in Figures 12·1 to 12·3. Note that the canal must be widened to decrease the velocity. The current should approach in a straight course; avoid placing one too close to a turn, or sediment will pile up on one side

FIG. 12·2  A closeup, looking upstream, of a dry canal with the rotary screens raised for overhauling. These screens are power-operated. (Credit: U. S. Fish and Wildlife Service)

of the channel. The velocity of the water should not exceed 1½ feet per second for fish under 3 inches in length, and slower rates are desirable. To prevent small fish from being carried over the screen, about one fourth of the drum should be above the surface.

The drum is most often covered with screen of 3 meshes to the inch of 12-gage wire, galvanized *after* weaving. To keep self-cleaning, the drum normally rotates from about 0.10 to 0.15 revolution per minute. The drums can be driven by paddle wheels or by electric motors. Both types are in successful operation.

The bypass is absolutely essential as small fish will not swim back up the ditch. The bypass returns the fish to the main river. The rotary screens are adaptable to small ditches as well as to huge ditches carrying over 2000 cubic feet of water per second.

Fig. 12·3   Closeup of paddlewheel-driven rotary screens in a small diversion.
(Credit: U. S. Fish and Wildlife Service)

## 12·4   Self-cleaning bar screen

A specially designed bar screen that is self-cleaning is used extensively in California (Wales 1948). It is installed with the bottom edge of the screen upstream and sloping back very gradually. A paddle wheel downstream from the screen operates a continuous chain on each side of the screen (Figure 12·4). Between the two chains are a succession of wipers that travel downstream up the face of the screen and push the debris over the screen. The screen bars are parallel to the stream course, and each bar is wedge-shaped. The thick edge of the wedge is against the current so that stones or debris small enough to fit between the bars continue on through instead of clogging. The wipers pass through a rubber seal at the bottom of the channel, but it is difficult to keep fish from passing through the seal. It is designed for use in small irrigation canals, but is often replaced either by the more efficient rotary drum screen or the new perforated plate screen.

## 12·5   Simple bar screen

The simple bar screen with no provision for cleaning except manual raking is employed very extensively. Parallel bars are used instead of a square mesh because the latter clogs more easily and is much harder to clean. At sites where sufficient screen area can be installed to permit the water to approach the screen with a very low velocity, it can be used successfully if the drift is not excessive. Thus, when the area of screen is large enough so that a large proportion must be clogged before the flow of water is impeded, it need be cleaned only at fairly long intervals. The water should never have to approach the screen at more than one-half foot per second. The screens are usually made in removable panels so that single panels may be taken out for cleaning or repair. A bar screen should always be provided with a walkway to facilitate cleaning (Figure 12·5).

Fig. 12·4  A self-cleaning bar screen. (Credit: U. S. Fish and Wildlife Service)

Bar screens are made usually of narrow iron bars. Wedge-shaped bars can be obtained of stock size, and they do not clog quite so easily as the bar with a rectangular cross section. A great many of these screens are made of hardwood slats fastened together with iron bolts.

Where a screen is placed in water that is not very deep and the area is not very large in proportion to the water flow (a condition often unavoidable in streams) there is danger of it being carried away because the screen acts like a dam as it becomes clogged. In such situations the structure holding the screens must be very strong to withstand the pressure of high water behind it; provision should always be made so that water can spill over the screens without harming them.

For stopping very small fish a wire mesh screen is almost necessary. To be practical without excessive costs for cleaning, such screens should be built so that a clean screen panel may be easily slipped into place behind or in front of a dirty screen. The dirty screen can then be removed and reversed in another place and the current will aid in cleaning.

The parallel bar screen is most successful for stopping fish when placed in lakes, or reservoirs above the outlet of a diversion, where the water is fairly deep and the screen can be made sufficiently long to give a large straining area. At lake outlets we have seen numerous screens that were placed across the narrow outlet, possibly to save

FIG. 12·5 A bar screen at lake outlet showing walkway for cleaning. (Credit: U. S. Fish and Wildlife Service)

costs. Unless closely attended, such screens soon clog and form low dams that raise the lake, overflowing outlying land. They do not prevent fish from moving downstream when water flows over or around them.

To stop or divert adult fish moving upstream the bar screen or rack is successful (Figure 12·6). Because of the size of the adult fish the bars, or the more usual wooden pickets, can be spaced farther apart to facilitate cleaning. For salmon the openings between pickets can be as much as 1¾ inches, and smaller debris and algae are only occasionally a problem.

A rack used to divert salmon or other upstream-migrating fish from entering a tailrace or other unsuitable tributary should be placed obliquely across the outlet of the tributary, and more or less parallel to the course of the main stream. This will discourage fish from tarrying behind the rack, leading them to the upstream end where they are more easily attracted into the river channel.

Fig. 12·6 Showing rack for counting adult salmon on their upstream spawning migration in Babine River, British Columbia. (Credit: R. Earle Foerster, Fisheries Research Board, Canada)

## 12·6   Belt screen

This type is suitable only for major installations. It consists of a succession of metal frames, screen-covered, that form a belt the width of the watercourse. The belt runs over sprockets, and the rising part of the screen is washed by streams of water as it emerges from the surface. It is only practicable for deep narrow canals where a few units will suffice. One difficulty in using this type for stopping downstream migrating young fish is that of providing an adequate bypass close to the screen.

## 12·7   Murphey perforated plate screen

This is a new type of screen developed in California, especially for irrigation diversions (Leitritz 1952). It is shown in Figure 12·7 (redrawn from *California Fish and Game*). Leitritz says of this screen:

This perforated plate screen with mechanical wiper bar is the latest development in fish screens in California. It has been experimented with for over three years and offers great promise. It is designed for and is being used primarily in irrigation diversions. Basically, this screen consists of a perforated metal plate with circular openings of ⁵⁄₃₂ inch diameter. The plate, having about 46 percent open area, is placed in the screen box at an angle of approximately 32 degrees. A wiper bar travels up and down over the surface of the plate much like the blades on a windshield wiper, except that

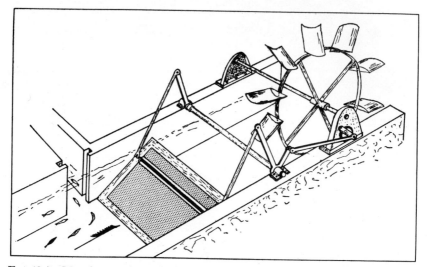

Fɪɢ. 12·7   Murphey perforated plate screen. (After Leitritz, California Fish and Game)

the blades do not swing in an arc, but rather move up and down the full length of the plate. Power for operating the wiper bar is usually obtained from a large diameter paddle-wheel set behind the plate. Several different types of driving mechanisms have been developed. A direct drive from the crank arm on the paddle-wheel is practical for small irrigation ditches, while a more powerful drive using a reduction gear is better suited for large diversions. If desirable, the wiper bar may be operated directly by an electric motor. At one installation, a hydraulic drive using a double-action hydraulic cylinder driven by a one-quarter horsepower motor is used. This small motor and hydraulic cylinder operate wiper bars over three perforated plates, each plate being 5½ feet wide and 12 feet long. A revolutionary feature of this new screen is the wiper bar, which has a hard sharp edge and is designed to cut underneath the debris on both the upstroke and the downstroke. It has been found that this bar when pushed down across the face of the plate carries the debris ahead of it until it reaches the unperforated margin along the lower edge of the plate.

There is no current through this unperforated edge, and the flowing water strikes it, sweeping up and over the cleaner bar, carrying the debris with it. The material is then swept onto the upper edge of the cleaner bar, and when the bar is pulled back up against it, the debris is carried over the top of the

Fig. 12·8  Inclined plane trap for counting salmon smolts descending to the sea in Six-Mile Creek, upper Babine River, British Columbia. (Credit: R. Earle Foerster, Fisheries Research Board, Canada)

plate. By using the perforated plate with this type of cleaner, it is possible to seal the bottom edge as well as the sides of the plate so that no fish are able to get under or around the plate.

## 12·8  Inclined plane screen

This is a recent innovation in screens used for collecting downstream-migrating fish so that their numbers may be estimated for management purposes. It is especially useful and perhaps the only solution for collecting very small fish in situations where a considerable volume of water containing large amounts of debris must be strained. Scott H. Bair and Harlan B. Holmes of the U. S. Fish and Wildlife Service devised in 1945 an efficient inclined plane trap for collecting fingerling salmon migrating downstream through a narrow bypass in Bonneville Dam.

Ferris Neave of the Fisheries Research Board of Canada was the first to apply this principle to collecting fish in a natural situation. In 1948 a fence for collecting the very small downstream-migrating fry of pink and chum salmon was constructed in Port John Creek, British Columbia. Ph. Wolf (1951) had used the same principle previously in Sweden for collecting fish food organisms but not for collecting fish. The principle is to chute water a short distance onto a sloping fine mesh screen. The water falls through the screen while the fish and debris slide down the screen into a trough at the bottom. The height of the drop and the angle of the screen vary with the size of the screen mesh and the volume of water. The screen should be adjustable so that the angle of slope can be regulated.

Dr. Neave used Monel metal screen 12 meshes to the inch, 24 gage (0.023-inch apertures). For the trap at the bottom he used 24-gage galvanized wire, 6 meshes to the inch (0.095-inch apertures). His dam, about 3½ feet high to the spillway crest, dropped the water about 8 inches onto a screen about 3½ feet long and sloping about 10 degrees. He estimated that the screens could strain a maximum of almost 4 cubic feet per second for each foot of spillway width.

## 12·9  Electric screen

Electric fish screens of various designs, using various types of electric impulses, have been tried for over 30 years (Holmes 1948). So far they have met with very limited success. Although perhaps they may serve to keep resident fish from leaving an area, they have not proved successful in most cases in stopping migratory fish. This is especially true of fish migrating downstream.

There is some evidence that an electric fish screen sometimes may be successful for upstream migrating fish if used merely as a diverter to prevent fish from entering a side channel or tributary. The screen must be across the mouth of the side channel, and it should be more or less parallel to the main stream. Thus the fish will approach it at an angle, and any deflection tends to keep them in the main channel.

The "screen" is in reality a double row of electrodes. In one system a single closely spaced row of suspended small rods or chains forms one electrode, and a small pipe or similar metal conductor resting on the bottom parallel to the suspended row forms the other electrode. In the second system the electrodes consist of two rows of well-spaced, large, cylindrical electrodes, vertical in the water, with all electrodes in each of the two rows connected in parallel. The electric current flows between the two rows. The first design is sometimes referred to as a "grounded" system as one electrode rests on the bottom; the second system, with the electrodes contacting only the water, is sometimes called an "insulated" system.

The first system produces a high potential gradient around each electrode owing to their small size. In either design the portion of the field that the fish encounter before they reach the first row of electrodes determines the success of the screen. Thus, the electric conductivity of the water and of the bottom and sides of the channel greatly influence the breadth of this electric field, as in both cases the bottom really acts as an electrode.

The severity of the shock the fish receives depends both on the direction of the electric current and the thickness or length of the fish. The greater the length of fish parallel to the direction of the current the greater the shock. This is one reason why it is difficult to stop very small fish and why an impulse sufficient to stop small fish may severely injure large fish.

Both alternating and direct current have been used. However, sixty-cycle alternating current is near the optimum frequency for efficiency in causing muscular tetanus. This summation of muscular contraction may cause severe injury such as torn muscles and broken bones to any fish that penetrate far into the electric field. Muscular tetanus prevents fish from swimming so that if they are coming downstream they are carried through the screen by the current. For these reasons alternating current is not widely used for screens. Capacitor-discharge impulses have been used and are superior to continuously applied alternating current. These intermittent impulses if over one-tenth second apart allow the muscle to respond independently to each stimulus. The fish is able to swim and tetanus does not occur.

Water velocities at an electric screen should be much less than at a mechanical screen when used to stop downstream migrants, because the fish must be able to stop and change direction before drifting into the electric field. The velocity should certainly be less than one foot per second.

**References**

Holmes, Harlan B.
  1948.  History, development, and problems of electric fish screen.  *U. S. Fish and Wildl. Serv., Spec. Sci. Rept. 53:* 62 pp.
Leitritz, Earl
  1952.  Stopping them: the development of fish screens in California.  *Calif. Fish and Game 38* (1):53–62.
McMillan, F. O.
  1928.  Electric fish screen.  *Bull. U. S. Bur. Fish. 44:* 97–128.
Wales, J. H.
  1948.  California's fish screen program.  *Calif. Fish and Game 34* (2):45–51.
Wolf, Ph.
  1951.  A trap for the capture of fish and other organisms moving downstream.  *Trans. Am. Fish. Soc. 80:* 41–45.

# 13 · POLLUTION

## 13·1  Introduction

Fish are vitally affected by the media in which they live; they have adapted themselves to live in various types of natural waters ranging from pure snow-fed brooks to the complex known as sea water. Some species have even adapted themselves to exist in hot springs. In considering pollution we are especially concerned with changes wrought by man in the chemical, physical, and biological properties of natural waters. The methods of detailed chemical analysis used in determining water quality are far beyond the scope of this book; for these methods we refer to American Public Health Association (1938) and Ellis, Westfall, and Ellis (1946). Rather we shall concern ourselves with the manner in which the problems of pollution may be attacked and resolved.

## 13·2  Types of water pollution

Pollutants may be roughly classified under several main headings:

1. Sewage, including storm water and street drainage.
2. Industrial wastes.
3. Mining wastes, including tailings.
4. Silt from soil erosion.

Only the effect on aquatic organisms will be considered. Sewage, for example, may be a menace to public health in concentrations too dilute to harm fish or bottom fauna.

**Sewage.**  The National Resources Committee (1939) estimated that sewage systems in the United States serve 73 million people; this represents about 95% of the population that might be served at practicable cost. These sewers had an estimated daily output of 5¾ billion gallons per day or about one half of 1 per cent of the average flow of all streams of the United States. Of this total 1½ billion gallons received only primary treatment (allowed to settle or treated in some other way to remove part of the solids); another 1¾ billion gallons received secondary treatment; that is, in addition to the primary treatment the sewage was subjected to some other process or processes to reduce further the bacteria and organic content. Forty-four per cent of the population not served by sewers is located chiefly in small villages, the outskirts of larger towns and cities, and on farms. Much of this sewage is not discharged into bodies of water, and in most instances the amounts are too small to create hazards, and so treatment might not be necessary from the standpoint of aquatic life.

**Industrial wastes.** Industrial wastes are extremely varied in their composition; their effect also varies with the volume of the bodies of water into which they discharge, so that the damage cannot be easily estimated by either volume or type of effluent. The chief groupings, roughly in order of their dollar values, are:

1. Food and beverages.
2. Textiles.
3. Ferrous metals.
4. Petroleum refining.
5. Chemicals.
6. Paper manufacture.
7. Rubber manufacture.
8. Nonferrous metals.
9. Gas manufacture.

**Mining wastes.** There are three major sources of pollution from mining:

1. Acid drainage and culm from coal mines, especially in the fields east of the Mississippi River.
2. Brines and crude petroleum from oil wells.
3. Debris from hydraulic mining of metals, especially in California.

The National Resources Committee estimated that in 1938 before the policy of sealing of abandoned mines was inaugurated the annual output of sulfuric acid from the oxidation of iron pyrites in the bituminous coal fields was 2,700,000 tons of 100% acid. This situation has been greatly improved in recent years by active campaigns of mine sealing, a technique which eliminates or reduces oxidation by either flooding the mines or cutting off the circulation of air.

Streams receive "wash water" from the anthracite mines, culm (the fine coal and refuse particles from eroding waste piles), and acid from the operating mines.

LAKE TROUT

SMALLMOUTH BLACK BASS

LANDLOCKED SALMON

BROWN TROUT

RAINBOW TROUT

BLUEBACK TROUT

Tremendous quantities of brine are produced by the oil fields, often a barrel of brine for every barrel of oil.  In areas where no large streams are available special disposal means must be provided, such as surface disposal or pumping into abandoned wells.  In coastal areas large quantities are piped directly to coastal waters.

When oil wells are first blown there is sometimes a large discharge of crude petroleum, which is highly toxic to aquatic life.  Occasionally such discharges are caught by earthen dikes.  When the well is not diked or is located in shallow water, the oil will, if not immediately controlled, tend to spread over a large area, killing fish, shellfish, and waterfowl.  One method of localizing the damage is to spray the oil slick with carbonized sand by means of air pressure (Chipman and Galtsoff 1949).  The carbonized sand retains the oil, and, although the submerged oil is toxic, this treatment prevents the damage from spreading.  This method is useful in harbors and around docks in preventing escaped oil from floating away into more productive waters.

The heavy silting of stream channels by hydraulic mining has been to a large extent alleviated by levees, debris dams, and other works.

**Soil erosion.**  The silting of streams by soil erosion is part of a national problem that is being attacked vigorously.  Thus in many sections of the southeastern United States one easily can observe from the air that entire counties are practicing contour plowing, terracing, and damming of eroded gullies.

## 13·3   How pollutants affect aquatic organisms

Pollutants may affect aquatic organisms in several ways, either directly or indirectly.  Some of these effects are produced by:

1. An increase in the osmotic pressure.
2. An increase in acidity.
3. A decrease in oxygen content of the water.
4. Specific toxic ingredients.
5. Destruction of food organisms.
6. Destruction of spawning grounds.
7. Mechanical injury to gills from silt or other suspended material.
8. Blocking of migration channels.
9. Rendering organisms unfit for food.
10. Accelerated aging of lakes and ponds.

The effect of osmotic pressure was tested on goldfish by Ellis (1937) using sodium chloride.  They survived indefinitely at concentrations of 5 parts or less per thousand but succumbed in 4 to 7 days at 10 parts per thousand. Ellis states that ". . . the predicted maximal nonlethal concentration of sodium chloride on the basis of osmotic pressure alone in terms of the osmotic pressure of fish blood would be approximately 7,000 p.p.m." [7 parts per thousand]. He concludes that ". . . any effluent as long as its osmotic pressure is greater than 6 atmospheres (or approximately 7,000 p.p.m.) may be expected to be lethal to freshwater fishes regardless of any specific toxic properties." However, Rawson and Moore (see Section 3·5) found many freshwater species living in lakes with salinities approaching 10 parts per thousand or above; both whitefish and pike-perch did well in lakes up to 15 parts per thousand, and one species existed in lakes with a salinity of 20 parts per thousand. This would seem to refute the notion that all freshwater fish are unable to survive in osmotic pressures higher than that of their blood.

Although the specific toxic effect varies between acids, all are lethal when more acid than $pH$ 4.0. Acids that kill at concentrations of $pH$ 5.0 or less are lethal because of some other factor in addition to the acidity itself.

The effects of low oxygen content are discussed in Section 3·6.

Specific toxic substances may injure the gills and other external structures, causing death from anoxemia. Some substances cause death after absorption through the gills, the mouth lining or other external surface. Still other substances kill after being taken into the body in water swallowed by the fish.

The destruction of food organisms on which the fish must depend can be a very serious consequence of pollution. Even when a pollutant does not kill or seriously harm fish, the changing of their biological environment, either by destruction of their habitual food or the causing of a marked change in the types of organisms present, may lower their abundance. This is noted for instance in streams polluted by sawdust, shavings, bark, or other wood waste. Though the fish may not be harmed directly, the covering of the bottom by a coating of waste greatly reduces their food supply.

The destruction of spawning grounds can be serious for species that require special locations or special types of bottom for successful reproduction. Thus the eggs of salmon and trout can be smothered during incubation by silt from soil erosion or by fine mine tailings (Shaw and Maga 1943). Setting of oyster spat is likewise reduced when the cultch is quickly coated by silt.

Mechanical injury to the gills from suspended materials such as silt and sawdust is usually unimportant in healthy fish, but, when these materials are accompanied by any pollutant that may interfere with the flow of mucus or may itself injure the gills, mechanical injury may be greatly increased.

Fish that must perform long migrations during some phase of their life history may be adversely affected by highly localized pollution. Thus the spring run of chinook salmon (*O. tshawytscha*) in the Willamette River in Oregon must pass the city of Portland during the warm months of the year when, under the prevailing seasonal conditions of low water flow and high temperatures, the sewage robs the water of most of its oxygen. The great reduction in the run has resulted in remedial measures being taken.

In citing the harmful effects of pollution, another aspect is the effect of pollution on the food value or salability of aquatic products. Thus the shellfish industry has suffered losses in millions of dollars from the legal closure of shellfish beds because of contamination by sewage. Although the sewage may have no effect whatever on the growth or food value of the shellfish, their harvesting and sale are prohibited because of the danger of their carrying typhoid, or other bacteria harmful to humans. Fish from certain areas in the Great Lakes Region are low in value because of the taste imparted to the flesh by pollutants.

In general, sewage pollution in small quantities is not harmful to aquatic life. Even small quantities, however, over a period of years may change the character of an aquatic environment. Thus the gradual process of aging, in which deep, clear, oligotrophic lakes fill with sediment, becoming mesotrophic, then eutrophic, and eventually turning into bogs, is accelerated by the fertilizing effect of sewage which encourages the growth of plankton, algae, and higher plants. There is danger, for instance, that small lakes suitable for trout, if subjected to continuous pollution, may gradually become unsuitable for the species (see Section 9·1).

### 13·4  Where is pollution found?

Some degree of pollution is found in practically all waters in well-populated areas. In mountainous regions the headwater streams are usually relatively pure. As they reach the first habitations they commence to receive their burden, but, where the volume of water is large in relation to the volume of the pollutants, harmful effects tend to be minimized.

The areas of heavy pollution, except for petroleum and mining wastes, and some industrial establishments, coincide in general with the areas of heavy population. The zone of greatest pollution runs from southern Maine down the Atlantic Seaboard to Norfolk, Virginia, and extends eastward from those points to Chicago, forming a great triangle. However, pollution is heavy in localized areas throughout the United States. The fruit and vegetable canning industries have plants widely scattered throughout the Midwest, California, the Northwest, the Middle Atlantic States, and sections of Florida and Texas. Butter and other milk products plants are scattered everywhere but are especially numerous in Wisconsin, Minnesota, Michigan, and the Northwest. In recent years heavy industries have grown rapidly on the Pacific Coast, in Texas, in the Tennessee Valley, and along the South Atlantic Coast.

Pollution is not confined to inland waters. Along the entire Atlantic Coast the shellfish industries have suffered from sewage pollution of oyster and clam beds. Shellfish in many localities have been injured by industrial pollution, especially wastes from pulp and paper plants, although other industrial pollution has also contributed. On Long Island the oyster and clam beds have been threatened by heavy pollution from duck farms.

## 13·5   Determination of effect of pollution

The exact determination of the effect of pollution is difficult and complex. One orthodox method is to determine the effect of various concentrations of a pollutant on fish or other aquatic organisms in a laboratory. This has both advantages and disadvantages. When it is a question of determining the expected effect of a future pollutant this method is obviously indicated. The greatest disadvantage lies in the fact that in actual practice many industrial effluents vary considerably from time to time both in volume and in composition. Laboratory experiments give valuable guidance, however, in setting the minimum concentrations that will seriously affect fish under laboratory conditions.

In a stream or other body of water, the effect of any particular effluent is often changed for better or worse by interaction with other effluents or with varying amounts of silt. Therefore, any laboratory determinations of the effect of pollutants should, if at all possible, be checked against actual field observations.

Because of the varying composition of industrial effluents from the same plant it is usually insufficient to synthesize an effluent for use in laboratory tests. It is better to collect effluents at various times and various stages, and particularly to collect the composite effluent that is discharged when all processes are in operation.

The concentration of an effluent at any given distance from the point of discharge usually will vary considerably from time to time. Statements concerning the average concentration of an effluent based on the volume of discharge and the volume of a stream over any period of time may be meaningless, therefore, in terms of damage. A heavy discharge for a short time may cause the concentration to rise far above the average. Because of these various complications, laboratory tests are usually not sufficient to give a realistic picture of the extent of the effect of a pollutant.

## 13·6   Cumulative concentration

When a pollutant is discharged into a semiconfined body of water such as a narrow estuary, or a deep bay or fiord with a shallow sill, the concentration of the effluent gradually increases to an asymptotic value (Galtsoff, Chipman, Engle, and Calderwood 1947). The observed values and symbols used in determining this final concentration are:

$p$ = the proportion of effluent in basin
$a$ = the rate of discharge of effluent in acre-feet per day
$b$ = the rate of influx of water into basin in acre-feet per day
$v$ = total volume of the basin in acre-feet
$t$ = time in days since the pollution started
$p_\infty$ = the limit that the proportion of effluent in basin approaches after a long time

The rate of influx $b$ includes both river discharge and the net tidal effect.

Assuming that the influx of the effluent and the water, and the efflux of the mixed concentration occurs once a day, then

$$p = a/(a + b)\{1 - [1 - (a + b)/v]^t\} = p_\infty[1 - (1 - k)^t] \quad (1)$$

If on the other hand it is assumed that the influx of the effluent and the water, and the efflux of the mixed concentration are continuous, then

$$d(pv)/dt = a - p(a + b)$$

giving the linear differential equation for $p$ as

$$dp/dt + [(a + b)/v]p = a/v$$

The solution of this differential equation under the condition

$$p_{t=0} = 0$$

is found to be

$$p = p_\infty(1 - \epsilon^{-kt}) \quad (2)$$

where

$$p_\infty = a/(a + b), \quad \text{and} \quad k = (a + b)/v$$

These two equations are very similar as can be shown by computing $p_\infty$ from both for the same set of data in which $a = 5$ acre-feet, $b = 9000$ acre-feet, and $v = 200{,}000$ acre-feet. In both cases $k = (a + b)/v$ $= (5 + 9000)/200{,}000 = 0.045025$. $1 - k = 0.954975$. $\epsilon^{-k} = 1/\epsilon^k$ which is quickly computed as follows: $\log_{10} \epsilon = 0.43429$. $0.43429$ times $k = \log_{10} \epsilon k = 0.01748$, the antilog, or $\epsilon^k = 1.0411$.

$$1/\epsilon^k = 1/1.0411 = 0.960523$$

The maximum difference between the two formulas occurs approximately when

$$t = (1/k)(1 - 1/4k + \cdots)$$

which is approximately 21.96 days.

Formula 1 is the simplest to calculate. Using formula 1 for $t = 100$, $p_\infty = [1 - (0.954975)^{100}]$ or $1 - 0.009977 = 0.000023$, or 99 per cent of the final concentration is reached within 100 days.

Using formula 2 for $t = 100$, $p_\infty = 1 - \epsilon^{-kt}$ or $1 - 2.71828^{-4.5025}$ $= 1 - 1/2.71828^{4.5025} = 1 - 1/90.238$ or $1 - 0.011082 = 0.988918$, or 98.9 per cent of the final concentration is reached within 100 days.

For both formulas the final concentration

$$p_\infty = a/(a + b) = 5/9005 = 0.000555$$

Obviously, if one were dealing with a pollutant in which the toxic effect did not lessen with time there would be no limit, except the necessary time itself, to the volume of water that would eventually reach the maximum concentration and therefore the maximum toxicity. Actually, this can never be the case so that, as the volume of the bay increases, or the length of the estuary taken under consideration is increased, there is a reduction in toxicity at any particular point that is some function of the time involved in reaching the maximum concentration (considering the volume of water between the particular point and the point of discharge of the pollutant).

In the report of Galtsoff et al. (1947) cited above these authors suggest two different assumptions as to the rate of removal or destruction of the poisonous constituents of a pollutant. $\pi$ being used to represent the fraction of the poisonous constituent which has not yet been removed or destroyed at any station, the poisonous effect is represented by $\pi p_\infty$. Quoting from their report:

1. The time rate of decrease of the concentration of the poisonous effect at any station

$$(d\pi p_\infty)/dt = -c'$$

is a negative constant (a constant rate, $c'$, of supply of the removing or destroying agent).

2. The time rate of decrease of the concentration of poisonous character at any station

$$(d\pi p_\infty)/dt = c''\pi p_\infty$$

is proportional to its concentration (a monomolecular reaction). The first assumption leads to the equation

$$d\pi/dv = -cc'$$

where $c'$ is some other constant.

This gives

$$\pi = 1 - cc'v$$

so that below a certain station given by

$$v = 1/cc'$$

the water will be wholly innocuous.

The second assumption leads to the equation

$$d\pi/dv = -cc''\pi$$

which gives

$$\pi = \epsilon^{-cc''v}$$

where $c''$ is still another constant.

According to this the poisonous effect will diminish exponentially with volume of water between the station and the mill but will be present to some extent throughout the whole basin and out into the bay beyond.

No conclusion was reached as to which assumption was valid, and it was suggested as a topic for further research.

## 13·7   Laboratory bioassays of test animals

The orthodox method for determining the toxicity of any material to aquatic organisms is to confine test animals in a laboratory and subject them for varying lengths of time to varying dilutions of the material dissolved in water. This would appear to be a simple straight-forward method, but in practice there are complications. Thus in choosing species to use for test animals there is wide variation among fishes in their susceptibility to different substances. Many investigators have used goldfish (*Carassius auratus*) because of their ability to survive well under the adverse biological conditions usually encountered in the laboratory. The concentration of a substance lethal to less rugged species is apt to be less than that lethal to goldfish. The types of fish fauna naturally·present in the waters to which the tests are to apply should be considered certainly. Thus goldfish in a laboratory would be of little avail in deciding on the probable mean lethal dose for trout in a cold well-aerated stream.

Perhaps the most practical method for selecting a species for a test animal is to employ only species that are habitually present in fair numbers in the same waters or similar waters to those to which the tests are to apply. Hart, Doudoroff, and Greenbank (1945) list a number of genera and species of fish, ranging in sensitivity from hardy to very sensitive, that they suggest be employed in toxicity studies. They further suggest the use of members of the genera *Lepomis, Micropterus, Salmo,* and *Salvelinus* as reference test animals. The first two are warm-water genera, the last two cold-water genera, and they should be tested under different conditions.

Perhaps the chief drawback of laboratory experiments is the practical difficulty of simulating natural conditions, rendering it difficult to determine the minimum dose that is lethal over a long period of time. When employing hatchery-reared fish for test animals, it is wise to proceed with caution as they vary greatly in condition according to the feeding and care to which they have been subjected. Thus, in testing young salmon for effects of tagging, the senior author has found that practically all of those handled may succumb in one group leaving only the controls, while in another group of supposedly similar fish no ill effects of handling are detected. In such cases subjecting the controls to equally rough handling may help to remove the inherent error, but this method cannot be applied to a chemical dilution.

It is important that the test specimens be of rather uniform size. Hart et al. (loc. cit.) suggest that *reference* test animals should be between 4 and 10 cm in over-all length with a maximum range of not over 50 per cent from the shortest to the longest. They also suggest that they be not over two-fifths the length of any test container, if a cylindrical jar, or one-fourth the sum of the length and width of a rectangular aquarium.

In laboratory experiments extreme care is required to keep each lot of fish under similar conditions. In fact, it is almost impossible to obtain complete uniformity between pools or between aquaria. The elimination of this experimental error can however be largely achieved by replications, arranged preferably in a Latin square or other systematic random design (see Cochran and Cox 1950 and Fisher 1949). The orthodox method employed in most laboratory experiments has been to keep rigid control of all variables except the concentration of the substance to be tested.

The natural waters in different sections vary considerably but it is best to use the local waters in making tests, merely being sure that they contain no appreciable amounts of free chlorine or chloramine, toxic metallic ions, or any other toxic substances that may occur in polluted waters. One should use caution in employing well water as it may differ considerably from the ordinary natural water in the area.

## 13·8   Methods of reporting bioassays

The methods of reporting bioassays differ considerably. In pharmacological studies the toxicity of drugs is normally indicated as the mean lethal dose $LD_{50}$, which is the concentration at which 50 per cent of the test subjects succumb. Most published results of tests of toxic substances on fish are not so stated. Sometimes the minimum and maximum survival time is shown for each dosage given. Sometimes the mean survival time is also shown for each dose. Sometimes the number of specimens tested is not shown.

It is desirable to know the correct dose at which 100 per cent of the fish survive. It can be demonstrated that employing the lowest dose given in any particular experiment with 100 per cent survival, as the correct dose at which all survive, puts undue weight on only a few specimens. The remainder of the data is, as it were, discarded. It is somewhat analogous to trying to extrapolate beyond the range of a regression curve in which one discards all but the final pair of co-ordinates.

The maximum amount of information, per individual tested, concerning the strength of the toxicity of a substance is derived at the point where the probability of death $p$ and the probability of survival $q$ each equal 0.50. The standard method now employed in such tests is to first discover, if no previous information is available, the approximate range of concentration of the toxic substance between $q = 0$ and $q = .100$. Dosages are then given between these limits. The concentrations should be spaced at equal logarithmic intervals.

In analysis of the data (Fisher 1949, Mather 1946) use is made of the fact that if the proportion dying from 0 to 0.50 and the proportion surviving from 0.50 to 0 are used as the ordinates $z$ in a normal curve with unit standard deviation $x$, then the deviate $x$ in most cases increases or decreases proportionately with the logarithm of the concentration of the dose. The quantity $5 + x$ called a "probit value" is used as a measure of mortality (Bliss 1935).

As pointed out by Fisher the greatest amount of information supplied by each test animal with respect to $x$ occurs at the dosage where the death rate is 50 per cent, and the least at 0 or 100 per cent. Tables to weight the probits by the amount of information supplied and also by the number of test animals are given by Fisher and Yates (1948) and by Bliss (1935).

The details of making a probit analysis will not be given here as they are fully explained in standard texts (Mather 1946). The advantage of the method lies in the fact that full use is made of all the information contained in the data, and that the toxicity of a substance is determined within narrow limits. The 100 per cent survival point is determined by this method from a regression curve that utilizes all the data; position on the dosage scale is therefore much more accurately determined.

As fish may be subjected on their migrations to polluted conditions that cannot be tolerated over a long period, but that can be borne for a short period, it is occasionally of some importance to know the mortality times at each concentration of the effluent. In running such an experiment one should avoid the contretemps made by one investigator. In testing the minimum lethal oxygen concentration he started each five fish (5 in each glass flask) at a high oxygen concentration and then reduced the oxygen at a rate of 1 ppm per hour until all died, sampling the oxygen concentration at the time each fish succumbed. Analysis of these data will show, of course, that the lower the oxygen content the longer the fish will survive! This is mentioned to emphasize the need for planning the method to be used in analyzing data before collecting it.

## 13·9    Biological indicators

Because of the day-by-day, even hour-by-hour, changes in the concentration and composition of the pollutants at any one point it is often impossible to collect and analyze sufficient water samples to determine the degree of pollution at a large number of stations. Therefore, many investigators have made use of biological indicators to estimate the degree of pollution at any site.

The use of biological indicators is predicated on two biological bases. First, plants and animals have a wide range in their susceptibility to pollution. Second, wherever biological or physical conditions for survival are severe, there is always a great tendency toward the survival of a smaller number of species, usually accompanied by an increased abundance of those that remain.

As the determination of the abundance of the various organisms would be exceedingly difficult except in a general way, it has been found better to make careful qualitative collections at a site and then to base the classification of the degree of pollution on the number of species present and their type.

The extensive use of this method requires the services of a number of taxonomic specialists in various groups. For the average survey party it is scarcely advisable to attempt many species identifications. Failing this one can make a rather general classification of the degree of pollution based wholly on the presence or absence of a few key types.

Thus Turner (1927) gives the following list of types and description:

1. Resistant forms:

Common sucker (*Catostomus commersoni*).

Sludge worms (*Tubifex*). Usually found in large numbers in muck or soft mud along the edges of septic pools.

Rat-tail maggot (*Eristalis tanax*). Usually found buried in the mud in septic pools with the "rat-tail" or breathing tube extended to the surface of the water. Because of its ability to breathe air it can exist in water devoid of oxygen.

Sewage-fly (*Psychoda alternata*).

Sewage fungi or water mold (*Sphaerotilus natans*).

Bloodworm (larvae of *Chironomus decorus*). The larvae, blood red in color, can be found in sludge deposits where recovery from the effects of pollution begins.

2. Tolerant forms.

Snails (*a*) *Physa heterostropha,* an air-breathing form which may be found even in septic regions as it crawls in an inverted position on the water surface.

(*b*) *Panorbis panus,* also an air breather and found in stagnant water.

Pondweed (*Potamogeton americanus*). Commonly found in fairly swift water and a muddy bottom.

Isopod or sow bug (*Asellus communis*). A scavenger found in muddy places.

Water boatman (*Corixa*). It carries the air it breathes behind in the form of a bubble so it can enter areas of low oxygen content.

Golden shiner (*Notemigonus crysoleucas*).

Bullhead or horned pout (*Ameiurus nebulosus*).

3. Sensitive forms.

Water net (*Hydrodictyon reticulatum*). A green alga, resembling a fine meshed veil, found in quiet stretches of a clean stream.

Caddisworm (*Hydropsyche*). The larvae of the caddisfly, usually in swift water.

Dragonfly nymph (*Anax*). Found in thick clusters of green aquatic plants in still water.

Stonefly nymph (*Perla*).

Water moss (*Hypnum riparium*). A green aquatic plant clinging to stones or gravel in swift streams.

Snail (*Campeloma decisum*).
Smallmouth bass (*Micropterus dolomieu*).
Largemouth bass (*Micropterus salmoides*).

A much more elaborate method of classifying the relative pollution of particular locations on a stream has been presented by Patrick (1949). In a survey of the Streams of the Conestoga Basin, Lancaster County, Pennsylvania, chemical determinations were made at all stations as follows:

| | |
|---|---|
| Total hardness | Silica |
| Alkalinity | Chloride |
| pH | Sulfate |
| Calcium | Carbon dioxide (dissolved) |
| Magnesium | Oxygen (dissolved) |
| Nitrogen (N as $NH_4^+$) | Suspended solids |
| Nitrogen (N as $NO_2$) | Turbidity |
| Nitrogen (N as $NO_3$) | Temperature |
| Phosphorus (P as $PO_4$) | Total conductivity |
| Iron | |

It was discovered that the chemical analyses failed to indicate the state of pollution. This was due partially to the fact that at some stations the industrial effluents were not being discharged during the period of sampling. Another reason for their failure to portray accurately the biological conditions lies in the lack of adequate knowledge concerning the limits of the concentrations of various chemicals tolerated by organisms which are part of the normal life in a stream. Altogether the evidence from the chemical analyses was found to be unsatisfactory. In most of the polluted streams the chemical analyses gave little or no indication of pollution.

In most pollution studies, categories of stream conditions have been based largely on the effect of sanitary wastes. Thus there is a septic zone of high pollution in which the dissolved oxygen is extremely low due to decomposition of wastes, and the biological oxygen demand (BOD) is very high. However, the classification of pollution chiefly on the oxygen levels is not sound—often the toxic effects of the effluents are much more damaging. Thus Patrick (op. cit.) did not find the dissolved oxygen sufficiently low at any station to be definitely limiting; yet at some stations the plant and animal life were completely wiped out.

The method that was developed depends on the use of living forms as indicators of pollution. It differs from the conventional use of biological indicators which is based on the presence or absence of a few key species. Because of similar responses to a given environment the organisms used were divided into seven groups, as follows:

1. The blue-green algae, and the following genera of green algae, *Stigeoclonium*, *Spirogyra*, and *Tribonema*; the bdelloid rotifers plus *Cephalodella megalocephala* and *Proales decipiens*.

Fig. 13·1 Titrating a water sample for chemical analysis under field conditions. (Credit: A. H. Fisher, U. S. Fish and Wildlife Service)

2. Oligochaetes, leeches, and pulmonate snails.
3. Protozoa.
4. Diatoms, red algae, and most of the green algae.
5. All rotifers not included in group one, plus clams, prosobranch snails and tricladid worms.
6. All insects and crustacea.
7. All fish.

The total number of species found in each group was expressed for each station as a per cent of the number found in an average normal stream. These percentages were then shown as a histogram for each station. Stations were classed as healthy, semihealthy, polluted, and very polluted on the basis of the relative numbers of the different groups (plotted as columns one to seven in her station histograms). The general basis of the classification outlined by Patrick is given in Table 13·1.

## TABLE 13·1

SHOWING THE CLASSIFICATION OF POLLUTION ACCORDING TO THE PERCENTAGE OF THE NORMAL NUMBER OF SPECIES IN EACH GROUP FOR EUTROPHIC STREAMS
(Adapted from Patrick 1949)

| Group | Healthy | Semihealthy | | | | Polluted | | Very polluted | |
|---|---|---|---|---|---|---|---|---|---|
| | 1 | 2 | 3 | 4 | 5 | 6 | 7 | 8 | 9 |
| 1 | | −100 | | +100 | +100 | +50 | +100 | −50 ‖ | |
| 2 | | | −100 | +100 | +100 | +50 | +100 | −50 ‖ | |
| 3 | Numerous | | | | | | | | |
| 4 | +50 | | | +100 | ‡ | | | −50 | |
| 5 | | | | | | | | | |
| 6 | +50 | −50 * | −50 * | −50 † | | 0 § | −50 | 0 | + ¶ |
| 7 | +50 | −50 * | −50 * | −50 † | | 0 § | −50 | 0 | + ¶ |

* Either 6 or 7 or both below 50%.
† Either 6 or 7 below 50%.
‡ Those species that are present very numerous.
§ Either or both absent.
‖ Either 1 or 2 below 50%.
¶ Either 6 or 7 present.

Patrick says of her method:

It should be emphasized that though the main basis of the biological measure of stream conditions as set forth in this paper is based on number of species found, one must take into consideration ecological conditions and qualitative indicators. Indeed the safety of this method lies in the multiplicity of its approaches.

. . . under healthy conditions a great many species representing the various taxonomic groups should be present, but no species should be represented by a great number of individuals . . . healthy conditions should offer habitats suitable to many different species. Competition would be severe and minor differences in ecological conditions would serve as barriers in determining varying ecological niches, and permit survival.

A pollutant would eliminate many species, thus the few which did survive would have less competition, and more chance for multiplication. The result would be the first effect of toxicity or a pollutant, a reduction in species number and a great abundance of those remaining. Some groups would be more severely affected than others. More severe toxic effects would result in the complete elimination of some groups, and a reduction in species number in other groups. Very severe toxic conditions would kill all organisms. Thus the general effect of pollution seems to be a reduction in species number with the most tolerant forms surviving.

This measure, which uses largely the organisms that are attached to the bottom or edges of the stream, will reflect the water conditions that have flowed by a given point for a considerable time before sampling, whereas a chemical analysis can only tell us the condition at the exact time it was taken. The bases of this measure are the healthy stations of the stream system being measured and not an arbitrary standard.

Although Patrick's method has real merit it is far beyond the resources of most survey parties because of the necessity for a number of taxonomic specialists to identify the species correctly.

A similar but somewhat simpler approach to the evaluation of the effects of stream pollution on fish life, geared to the facilities available to most survey parties, is that of Henderson (1949). He states:

For a great many streams there is a wealth of information as to the coliform bacteria count, the biochemical oxygen demand, total solids, color, odor, and other factors; but there is very little information as to what fish or fish-food organisms may be present.

Aquatic life in streams may be depleted generally in four ways: (1) lack of dissolved oxygen, (2) too high or too low hydrogen-ion concentration, (3) smothering effect of silt or other fine material, (4) the presence of definitely toxic substances. In general, most pollution surveys would demonstrate the first two of these conditions.

Henderson used a square-foot bottom sampler for gravel and rubble bottom and an Ekman or Peterson dredge in mud or silt. He collected the various aquatic insect larvae and other aquatic animals above and below sources of pollution. Without sufficient quantities of these organisms fish soon disappear for lack of food whether they can survive in the water or not.

The weight and number of organisms per square foot of riffle area gave a good gross index of pollution. The type of organism most numerous in each area also gave some indication as to whether the waters were normal or tended toward marginal conditions.

**References**

American Public Health Association
   1938. *Standard methods for the examination of water and sewage.* 8 ed., 3d printing. Amer. Pub. Health Assoc.: 309 pp., New York.
Bliss, Chester I.
   1935. The calculation of the dosage mortality curve. *Ann. Appl. Biology 22:* 134–167.

Chipman, Walter A., and Paul S. Galtsoff
  1949. Effects of oil mixed with carbonized sand on aquatic animals. *U. S. Fish and Wildl. Serv., Spec. Sci. Rept. Fisheries 1:* 52 pp.
Cochran, William G., and Gertrude M. Cox
  1950. *Experimental designs.* John Wiley & Sons: 454 pp., New York.
Ellis, Max M.
  1937. Detection and measurement of stream pollution. *Bull. U. S. Bur. Fish. 48* (22):365–437.
Ellis, Max M., B. A. Westfall, and Marion D. Ellis
  1946. Determination of water quality. *U. S. Fish and Wildl. Serv., Res. Rept. 9:* 122 pp.
Fisher, Ronald A.
  1949. *The design of experiments.* 5 ed. Oliver and Boyd: 242 pp., Edinburgh.
Fisher, Ronald A., and Frank Yates
  1948. *Statistical tables.* 3 ed. Oliver and Boyd, Edinburgh.
Galtsoff, Paul S., Walter A. Chipman, Jr., James B. Engle, and H. N. Calderwood
  1947. Ecological and physiological studies of the effect of sulfate pulp mill wastes on oysters in the York River, Virginia. *U. S. Fish and Wildl. Serv., Fish. Bull. 51* (43):59–186.
Hart, W. Brégy, Peter Doudoroff, and John Greenbank
  1945. *The evaluation of industrial wastes, chemicals and other substances to fresh-water fishes.* Waste Control Laboratory of Atlantic Refining Company, 1945: 317 pp.
Henderson, Croswell
  1949. Value of the bottom sampler in demonstrating the effects of pollution on fish-food organisms and fish in the Shenandoah River. *Prog. Fish-Cult. 11* (4):217–230.
Mather, K.
  1946. *Statistical analysis in biology.* Interscience Publ.: 267 pp., New York.
National Resources Committee
  1939. Water pollution in the United States. Third report of the Special Advisory Committee on water pollution. 76 Cong. 1st Sess., *House Doc. 155:* 165 pp., Washington.
Patrick, Ruth
  1949. A proposed biological measure of stream conditions, based on a survey of the Conestoga Basin, Lancaster County, Pennsylvania. *Proc. Acad. Nat. Sci. of Philadelphia 101,* 1949: 277–347.
Shaw, Paul A., and John A. Maga
  1943. The effect of mining silt on yield of fry from salmon spawning beds. *Calif. Fish and Game 29* (1):29–41.
Turner, C. L.
  1927. Biological survey of Fox, Wisconsin and Flambeau Rivers, Wisconsin, with special reference to pollution. In *Stream Pollution in Wisconsin,* Spec. Rept., Wisconsin State Bd. of Health: 242–276.

# 14 · HABITAT IMPROVEMENT

## 14·1  Introduction

Habitat improvement is a fishery management tool with the sole purpose of providing better environmental conditions for desired species of fish. The ultimate result, as with any management practice, is the production of better fishing.

In the 1930's progressive workers in fisheries began to realize, as more and more evidence accumulated from their research, that the artificial propagation and stocking of fish was not the "miracle cure" for declining fisheries. Stocking of hatchery trout or the imposition of strict regulations does not grow fish. Faced with the almost hopeless picture of wholesale destruction of many miles of good fishing waters on the one side and the constantly increasing number of anglers on the other, they turned to a more realistic program of attempting to help nature, particularly in repairing damage already committed by man. And so more and more emphasis was placed on the environment with the intention of improving it.

Government agencies, some state departments, and enthusiastic sportsmen's groups armed with unquestionable motives and little actual knowledge plunged into programs of habitat improvement. Various types of untested improvement devices were placed promiscuously in streams by unqualified individuals without thought to the biology of either the fish or other aquatic organisms. During the early days of the programs habitat improvement might better have been described as "habitat alteration" since great doubt could be expressed that the habitat had always been improved. We who have followed are fortunate in being able to profit by the mistakes of these pioneers. Provision for maintenance of the improvement structures was one of the defects of the earlier programs. A reserve fund should be provided for the periodic checking and repair of improvement devices as a little money spent in maintenance will go a long way in continuing the effectiveness of the program.

229

Biologists are in general accord that a program of habitat improvement planned and carried out by competent personnel can improve fishing. It may be applied to any area of water whether it be a stream or lake. To date, however, the greater amount of work has been done with streams.

## 14·2   Conditions to be determined before a stream improvement program is recommended

As our knowledge continues to grow, the danger of applying the same principles to all bodies of water becomes more obvious. Natural conditions vary from one stream to another and desired results may

Fig. 14·1  Abandoned logging dam on Misery Stream, Maine, showing the formation of a log jam, blocking the stream to migrating fish. (Credit: Lyndon Bond, Maine Inland Fisheries and Game)

alter the type of improvement recommended. For example, many of the Maine lakes have a scarcity of spawning grounds so that stream improvement and lake improvement, in this instance, would consist almost entirely of providing adequate gravel beds for successful spawning in the tributary streams rather than pools for shelter.

Stream improvement can provide additional shelter, an improved food supply, additional spawning areas, and a steady flow of pure, cold water. In realizing any or all of the above the stream improvement program may be fighting industrial and domestic pollution, poor soil practices which increase erosion, unwise lumbering methods, or the problem of opening a river or stream to the free migration of the fishes concerned.

We know that for trout to thrive a good, steady flow of cool, pure water is necessary. Next there should be plenty of riffle areas serving as nesting sites, sources of food, and nursery grounds for the young. Although large trout may feed in the shallower riffle areas most fishermen know that they get the big fish in the pools so the idea has grown that there should be approximately as many pools as riffle areas. If the preliminary survey shows the stream under scrutiny to be lacking in some of the attributes listed above, stream improvement may be recommended.

First some effort should be made to estimate the value of the proposed section of stream after improvement to make certain that the expenditure necessary to install the improvement devices is justified. Fortunately much of the damage done to streams in the past has been manmade, and so there is hope that man, guided by the proper motives, can at least repair his own damage.

The far-reaching aspects of habitat improvement and the care that should be exercised in beginning such a program may be realized when one considers that future control of erosion and silting through proper land management may yield larger and more permanent dividends to the angler than mere installation of improvement devices in the stream itself. No program should be begun unless all of the ramifications have been carefully reviewed.

### 14·3    Measurement of the effects of habitat improvement

One of the most unfortunate and surprising features of habitat improvement, although not so surprising when one considers the relative newness of such programs, has been the almost complete lack of quantitative evidence on which to base conclusions as to the ultimate results. In short, how do we know whether the habitat has been improved or not?

The Michigan Department of Conservation has done much of the pioneering in stream improvement, and so it is not unusual that their department gives the first complete "before and after" results of a stream improvement project. Shetter, Clark, and Hazzard (1949) present the results of a study over an 8-year period divided into a 3-year study before improvement was begun and a 5-year study after the installation of the improvement devices. Much of the following is taken from the Michigan paper.

The purpose of the investigation was to determine as accurately as possible the effects of the addition of current deflectors upon the number and depth of pools, the fish-food supply, the fish population, and the yield to the angler in a section of a small Michigan brook trout stream. Twenty-three wing deflectors were installed in September 1941, and in 1943 one additional deflector was installed in the test area, making an improvement device for each 70 feet of stream. The typical structure was a rectangular log crib 30 inches by 30 inches by 25 feet and two or more logs high. The structures were securely fastened, and the interior was filled with gravel, sand, sod, and earth. The top was well sodded to prevent surface erosion and to improve the appearance. Wings were installed at an angle of 35 to 45 degrees to the center thread of the stream with the terminal end downstream from the base.

Physical changes resulting from the installations indicated that material was swept from the pool floors by the deflector-accelerated current which also tended to concentrate the coarser gravel over the pool-bed area below the structure. A total of 19 pools was added to the experimental area. In general the cutting and deposition caused by the deflectors is local. Excavation to form pools has been equalized by deposition of sediment in bars below pools or on the upstream or downstream shoreward end of the deflectors. This process may be considered as controlled resedimentation which directs the shifting bottom materials into areas where they may eventually become stabilized by the growth of marginal vegetation.

Only preliminary studies have been made concerning the effects of the deflectors on the bottom food organisms, but apparently there was a decrease in total number and volume of all organisms with an increase in the organisms most frequently found in the stomachs of the trout from that area.

Final proof of the improvement program is the effect it has on angling. Table 14·1 presents a summary of the intensive creel census before and after the installation of the improvement devices in the experimental area of Hunt Creek, Michigan.

The figures in Table 14·1 speak for themselves. When the creel census figures for the 3-year period before and the 5-year period after improvement are averaged, the increase in the angler's catch after improvement was 120 per cent in total number, 141 per cent in total pounds of legal trout, 35 per cent in number and 46 per cent in pounds per fisherman-hour. These increases took place during an increase in fishing pressure of 64 per cent. The percentage of unsuccessful anglers decreased 20.3 per cent after improvement in spite of the increase in fishing pressure.

TABLE 14·1

(Figures in parentheses show the number of legal-sized brook trout caught and returned to the stream)

| Year | Hours of Angling | Number of Legal Brook Trout Taken | Catch per Hour | Pounds of Legal Fish Removed | Pounds per Hour | Average Size Length, Inches | Weight, Ounces | Percentage of Unsuccessful Angling Days |
|---|---|---|---|---|---|---|---|---|
| 1939 | 33.50 | 15 (6) | 0.45 | 1.11 | 0.033 | 7.4 | 2.47 | 70 |
| 1940 | 86.50 | 41 | 0.47 | 6.69 | 0.077 | 8.0 | 2.84 | 62 |
| 1941 | 74.75 | 32 | 0.43 | 5.23 | 0.069 | 7.7 | 2.68 | 64 |
| Average | 64.91 | 29.3 (2) | 0.45 | 4.34 | 0.067 | 7.8 | 2.74 | 64 |
| 1942 | 126.50 | 65 | 0.51 | 11.04 | 0.087 | 7.8 | 2.85 | 54 |
| 1943 | 73.25 | 67 (1) | 0.91 | 10.96 | 0.149 | 7.6 | 2.70 | 38 |
| 1944 | 123.50 | 77 (4) | 0.62 | 11.81 | 0.096 | 7.6 | 2.57 | 43 |
| 1945 | 77.75 | 36 | 0.46 | 7.09 | 0.091 | 8.0+ | 3.00 | 54 |
| 1946 | 132.25 | 78 | 0.59 | 11.51 | 0.087 | 7.5− | 2.36 | 61 |
| Average | 106.65 | 64.6 (1) | 0.61 | 10.48 | 0.098 | 7.7 | 2.65 | 51 |
| Percentage change in average | +64.3 | +120.4 | +35.5 | +141.5 | +46.2 | −1.2 | −3.4 | −20.3 |

* After Shetter, Clark, and Hazzard (1949).

## 14·4  Cost of stream improvement

The fairest way to measure the cost of any fishery management program is in the light of the return it furnishes to the angler. Since the cost of labor and materials fluctuates in different areas of the country and in different years these figures must of necessity be taken as relative.

Shetter, Clark, and Hazzard (1949) list $512.16 as the total cost of installing and maintaining 24 deflectors in Hunt Creek, Michigan, for a 5-year period. During this period the average difference in the number of brook trout caught and kept by anglers in the period before as compared with the period after improvement was 36.3, or a total of 181.5 for the 5 years. Actual cost then was $2.82 for each additional trout entering the catch during the period after improvement. However, the above authors predict that the deflectors, properly maintained, should function for at least 20 years. Maintenance costs have decreased as a result of the structures becoming stabilized. Actual cost per trout taken will then decrease each year that the deflectors remain in the stream.

Smith and Moyle (1944) in their biological survey and fishery management plan for the streams of Lake Superior's North Shore watershed give the total cost of improving 5½ miles of stream as $5872.69. This included preproject planning, mileage, labor, and supervisory costs. The cost per mile was $1067.94. Here again it must be pointed out that just as stream conditions vary so will the cost of installing the devices to improve them. More valuable than actual costs is the number of hours required to construct certain of the improvements. Boulder deflectors proved to be the cheapest device for the improvement of the stream channels. An average of 44 man-hours was required to install a boulder deflector properly. A boulder dam required 58 man-hours. A crib deflector averaged 66 man-hours for proper installation. The most expensive improvement device was the channel dam built of logs. This dam required an average of 78 man-hours.

Cost of a stream improvement project is dependent on so many variables that each project must be treated as an individual case. Figures given above must be treated as mere indications. Small streams can certainly be improved at a lower cost proportionately than large streams. Projects calling for the installation of deflectors will be cheaper than projects demanding the building of large and complicated dams. Availability of materials will alter the final costs. Transportation depending upon whether the area to be improved is easily accessible or not will alter the expenditures. And lastly as our knowledge concerning the proper devices and locations for these devices grows final costs will be materially reduced.

## 14·5   Types of stream improvement

Too often today individuals are prone to consider deflectors, dams, and artificial cover installed in a stream as the only improvement practices. The broad definition of habitat improvement, providing better environment for desired species of fish, encompasses many different types of action. Some of these, particularly those considered more fully in other chapters, will be only briefly referred to at this time.

Removal of harmful pollution from a stream is one of the first steps that must be taken if that stream is to be expected to produce fishing. The entire subject of pollution is treated more fully in Chapter 13. Toxic pollutants must be eliminated if a stream is to be improved at all. Too often in connection with pollution only the fish are examined for the effects when perhaps the greatest harm from the pollution is actually its effect on the microscopic animals and plants, and on the aquatic insects on which the food chain depends. Removal of pollution is a primary step in any habitat improvement program.

Fencing stream banks where cattle are grazing will prevent the breaking down of the banks with increased erosion. Cattle grazing along a stream bank feed extensively, removing the vegetation which provides shade and terrestrial insects, and, what is most important, serves to bind the bank, preventing erosion.

After the stream has been cleared of pollution or of unnecessary obstructions it may be necessary in completing the project to install artificial devices designed to provide more pools and more cover, speed up the current, or perhaps to increase spawning facilities. These improvement devices can be classified as deflectors, dams, or covers. Davis (1935) and Smith and Moyle (1944) are excellent references for construction of many of the improvement aids. All illustrations of improvement devices with one exception have been taken from Smith and Moyle (op. cit.).

## 14·6 Removal of obstructions

Removal of obstructions which retard or stop the migrations of fishes is often necessary to improve the environment. Most streams during the course of years accumulate obstructions of one sort or another. Unfortunately many of these obstructions are manmade and man-protected. Obstructing the free swimming of fishes is certainly one method of reducing their numbers and the subsequent returns to the fishermen.

Many lakes depend on small inlet or outlet streams to provide the necessary spawning areas which will serve to hatch and rear the young that constantly restock the lake. If we are to maintain populations of anadromous and adfluvial fishes they must be assured of easy access to their spawning grounds. A log, formation of a sand or gravel bar, or exceptionally low water may prevent fish from entering small feeder streams.

Care should be taken in recommending the removal of natural barriers as these may be maintaining the so-called balance of nature between the drainage areas above and below the barrier. Obstructions created by man should have fishways (Chapter 11), providing the cost can be justified, or if the obstruction is no longer serving any useful purpose it should be removed.

Beaver dams are a problem where they obstruct the movement of fish, particularly spawning migrations. The dams may also change the general ecology of the flowage area by warming the water and silting the bottom, changing the normal aquatic fauna of the stream bed.  Ordinarily a beaver colony remains in an area about 3 to 5 years depending on the availability of food and water.  After the colony migrates, the dam, unattended, may wash away.  Occasionally however dams remain as stream obstructions.

Fish screens, rarely justified, have sometimes been placed in the outlets of lakes, supposedly to keep the fish from escaping downstream never to return.  In reality the fish seen congregating near the outlet may well be mature fish seeking a suitable area in which to spawn, the results of this natural reproduction serving to maintain the population of the lake.  In rare cases a fish screen may be advisable to prevent fish from entering areas of extreme pollution, but it should be regarded as a temporary expedient.

**14·7   Deflectors**

Although much more complicated devices are used in stream improvement than the simple deflector type, more and more projects are discarding the complicated, hard-to-build-and-maintain devices in favor of deflectors.  Deflectors are primarily designed to speed up the current, thus washing out silt and providing graveled riffle areas. Increasing the speed of the current gives the water less chance for long exposure to the sun and helps to maintain the usually desired low temperature.  Types of deflectors in general use are listed below.

**Single boulder deflectors.**  The single boulder deflector is intended for speeding up the current in wide, shallow pools.  The boulders may be placed in rows the proximity depending on the depth of water that it is desired to pile up in the area behind.  Care may be taken in arranging the boulders in lines, or they may be placed haphazardly in the stream bed.  In general the boulders will speed up the current and also produce eddy currents which tend to scour the bottom and provide more movement in the pools.  They are also advantageous in preventing silting.

**Boulder deflectors.**  When large boulders are handy in an area a boulder deflector, providing it is placed correctly, is one of the easiest of the improvement devices to construct and the most rewarding.  A trench is dug in the stream bottom so that the foundation layer will be secure in the bottom.  A large boulder should be used to anchor the stream end of the boulder deflector.

**Log deflector** (Figure 14·2).  If sufficient boulders are not present then a log deflector may be constructed.  The log deflector consists of a main log or logs, mud sill, and brace.  Trenches should be dug to receive the mud sill and the main log.  Protect the face and bank and stream ends with boulders.

**Cement blocks.** Two-foot square cement blocks weighing approximately 1150 pounds were cast at the site of the project in re-usable wooden forms (Clark 1948). An iron ring was cast in each block for ease in handling. Although the weight of the blocks is a distinct disadvantage they are adaptable to most situations. If the water is deep then they can be piled on top of one another. If after the device

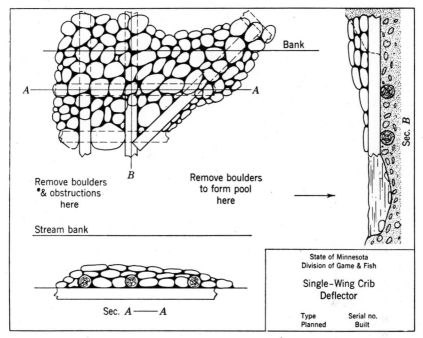

FIG. 14·2  Log deflector. (Credit Lloyd L. Smith and John Moyle)

is finished evidence suggests the advisability of alterations the blocks can be shifted easily.

Clark (1948) reports the use of an average of 64 blocks per deflector and cast a total of 512 blocks at a cost of $1312.25. Although this would bring the cost of each block to $2.50 in this particular instance it is believed that the facts discovered in this first attempt will help to lower the cost in other projects.

During the 5 years that the blocks have been in use as deflectors no maintenance has been required.

**Triangular crib deflector** (Figure 14·3). The triangular crib deflector is a solidly built device consisting of a main log slanting at the desired angle downstream and anchored well back in the stream bank. A brace running from the back (downstream side) to the bank provides additional support and also a crib which is filled with rocks or boulders. The front and back should also be lined with blocks.

**Triangular rock-filled deflector.** Where sections of the stream are too wide to be affected by bank deflectors or in sections where silt deposits have built up, the triangular rock-filled deflector may be employed to speed up the current, wash out the silt, and in general nar-

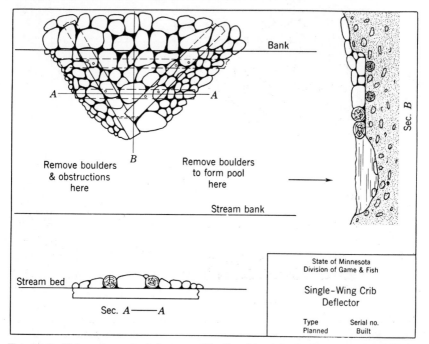

Fɪɢ. 14·3   Triangular crib deflector.  (Credit: Lloyd L. Smith and John Moyle)

row the width by dividing the current. In some cases several of these may be placed in a row in the center of the stream.

Three logs are merely joined together in a triangle and securely fastened to the bottom. The entire structure is then filled with rocks.

**Underpass deflector** (Figure 14·4). The underpass deflector is intended to "blow out" silt and a soft bottom in an effort to provide a pool. It is so constructed that the main log is held a few inches off the bottom so that the water will be forced to pass under the main log and in this manner dig the pool.

**Double-winged deflector** (Figure 14·5). This sheet piling deflector has been developed in Michigan especially for use on larger streams with low gradient.

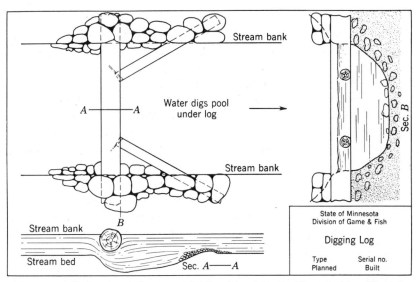

Stream bank

Water digs pool
under log

A————A

Stream bank

B

Sec. B

Stream bank

Stream bed

Sec. A————A

State of Minnesota
Division of Game & Fish

Digging Log

Type          Serial no.
Planned       Built

FIG. 14·4  Underpass deflector.  (Credit: Lloyd L. Smith and John Moyle)

FIG. 14·5  A double-winged deflector of sheet piling used by the Michigan Department of Conservation in larger streams.  The one shown is in the Big Manistee River.  (Credit: E. P. Haddon, U. S. Fish and Wildlife Service)

## 14·8  Dams

When the gradient of a stream is too steep, pools are desired, or perhaps it is necessary to impound a large volume of water to insure a steady flow of water throughout periods of low rainfall, dams can be employed with success as improvement devices.

**Rock and boulder dam** (Figure 14·6). This type of installation takes advantage of the already existing supply of rocks and boulders. The fewer that are taken from the stream bed proper the better, since it would certainly be unwise to destroy already existing habitats in an attempt to create new ones. Frequently advantage can be taken of an already existing large boulder which may be used as a keystone around which the dam can be built. Additional boulders should be placed so that they interlock with the keystone and with each other. Care should be taken to protect the banks and to insure against the water cutting around the ends of the dam.

**Single-log dam** (Figure 14·7). This type of dam is intended only for small streams and ordinarily should not be used on those over 15 to 20 feet in width. The construction makes it most adaptable to small streams with a soft bottom.

The backbone of the single-log dam is the large log extending across the stream and well into each bank resting on log mud sills, the number of mud sills depending on the width of the stream. A channel should be dug across the stream for the main log and channels upstream for each of the mud sills. Notch the mud sills to receive the main log. After the main log has been fastened securely to the mud sills heavy wire should be stapled to the main log and sills, after which the dam should be covered with a layer of heavy rocks and then topped off with earth, sand, gravel, or more boulders. The dam should have a spillway to take care of overflow in low water.

Care should be taken, as with all installations, to make certain the banks are protected so that the water will not cut around the device.

**K Dam.** This dam is designed for small streams with a hard or firm bottom. A trench several inches deep is dug across the stream bed and extended well into each bank, 4 to 6 feet, on each side. The main log should fit snugly into the trench. Braces are then attached to the downstream side and fastened to the log with drift bolts. The entire structure should be covered carefully with rocks and boulders including the spaces between the braces and banks. If the water is too deep for one log, then two logs may be securely fastened together and used as the main log.

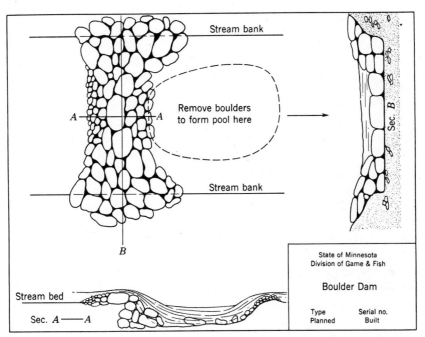

Fig. 14·6  Rock and boulder dam.  (Credit: Lloyd L. Smith and John Moyle)

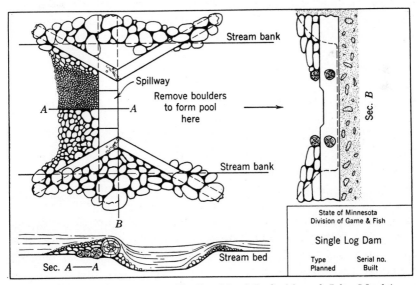

Fig. 14·7  Single-log dam.  (Credit: Lloyd L. Smith and John Moyle)

**Pyramid dam** (Figure 14·8). This type of dam derives its name from the three main logs extending across the stream. Two logs are placed in the carefully prepared trench and a third, forming the pyramid, is placed on top. All three are securely fastened together. The construction, depending on whether the stream has a soft or hard bottom, follows the general plan of the two former types.

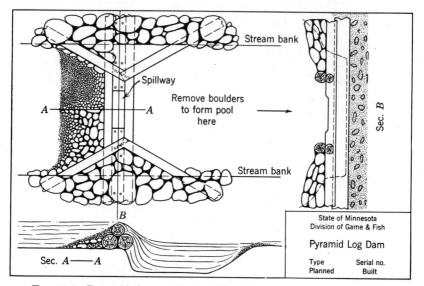

Fig. 14·8  Pyramid dam.  (Credit: Lloyd L. Smith and John Moyle)

**Log and board dam.** This dam is intended for small streams and can be adapted to almost any situation with the exception of a bedrock bottom.

A trench is first dug lengthwise of the stream which will accommodate about one third of the mud sill. Then a trench is dug into both banks and crosswise across the stream deep enough for the main log to rest firmly on the mud sill. Braces should be attached as indicated previously with earlier types of dams. The mud sill should support the main log several inches above the stream bottom thus providing shelter under the log and behind the boards.

Two-inch lumber of any width available can then be nailed directly to the main log extending upstream and with the upstream ends deep in a trench dug to receive them. As with the other dams care should be taken that the water does not cut around the ends of the dam and a spillway should be provided for periods of low water.

**Log brush dam.** Although this type of dam is intended for large streams it is adaptable to almost any size. The usual trench is dug across the stream extending well into the banks. This trench should extend upstream a distance equal to the length of the brush which will be employed in filling the dam.

The bottom of the trench should be deeper on the upstream side. Place the main log securely on the bottom in the crosswise trench. The first layer of brush is then placed in position with the butts nailed to the log and the tops extending upstream. Cover this first layer with rocks, earth, sand, or gravel, insuring that it is well covered. Place the next crosswise log slightly behind the first. Attach the boughs as before, and fill accordingly. The height of the dam may be increased by continuing the same process.

Care should be taken to protect the face of the dam and both banks with large boulders. The face of the dam should not be too steep. A pitch of 1/3 to 1/4 is recommended.

**V dam.** This dam is intended for larger streams and is not recommended for those having a width less than 20 to 25 feet. It is adaptable to a hard bottom. The name of the dam is easily understood since the backbone consists of two logs joined together in the form of a V with the apex upstream. Depth may be gained by using other logs on top. The usual trench is dug and the logs are extended into each bank. Sloping the trench toward the center will provide a spillway for low water. When passing over an obstruction water tends to take a course perpendicular to the obstruction and so is thrown to the center of the V dam.

The upstream face of the dam should be riprapped with small rocks and well shouldered at the banks.

This dam may be modified for use in soft or silty bottoms by the provision of mud sills for the main logs to rest upon.

**Truss dam.** This type of dam is a method of adapting some of the other styles to a wider stream by using two diagonal logs and one horizontal log. Angles of the cuts on the main logs will be determined by the width of the stream. Woven wire is attached, and the dam is filled with rocks and completed with sand, gravel, and rubble. Care should be taken as usual to protect the face of the dam and the sides so that there is no cutting around. A modification of the truss dam is the double truss which actually consists in a combination of two single truss dams for more strength and for use on larger streams.

**Nonsilting dam.** The nonsilting dam is designed to speed up the current and prevent silting. It is especially adaptable to an area of stream with a wide, shallow slow flow.  In general the nonsilting dam consists in narrowing the channel and providing a board overflow. Width of the board platform controls the volume of the flow.  At normal flow a small pool should be backed up from the dam.

## 14·9   Cover

In some sections of the country streams with a desirable water supply have inadequate cover which is thought to limit the size of the game fish population.  Attempts have been made to provide additional cover by several methods.

**Anchored trees.**  The stump of the tree is usually anchored securely into the bank, the branches pointing downstream.  These anchored trees are effective for a short time after which they become collectors of drift and form partial dams.  The increased pressure may pull them loose in which case they are carried downstream by the current and may become lodged in such a manner as to be harmful.

**Log and boulder cover device.**  The log and boulder cover device is designed to provide cover in streams where the natural cover is considered inadequate.  This device consists primarily of a log crib inclined upstream for several feet, leaving a large area for shelter underneath.  The boulders in the crib keep the device from floating or moving downstream with the current since it offers considerable resistance.  Log shelters may be extended from the bank to provide cover, and if covered properly with boulders and sod they are inconspicuous.  Other types of cover may be anchored in midstream, but unless they are under the water during periods of ice formation they are subject to destruction during thaws.  If they are not anchored securely they are easily lost during floods.

## 14·10   Improvement of lakes

Habitat improvement as applied to lakes has lagged behind the improvement of streams.  The difficulties encountered with lake improvement have been largely practical ones rather than theoretical.  Results are harder to measure since so many more variables are encountered.

Poisoning (considered more fully in Chapter 15) has become a widely used and publicized management tool.  Obnoxious species and unbalanced or stunted populations may be removed in this manner. It is possible to poison selectively by confining the treatment to shallow bays or to the epilimnion in which case the numbers of the warm-water species can be reduced.  The fish poisons used today are not harmful to higher animals.  In most cases results of the treatment have disappeared in a few months' time and the lake may be restocked with desirable fish. Poisoning has been particularly successful in marginal trout waters where the environmental conditions are on the borderline for both the so-called cold-water and warm-water species. Periodic poisoning reduces the number of the warm-water fishes and permits the cold-water fishes to survive in catchable numbers.

Weed control has been practiced both chemically and mechanically to remove obnoxious growths of weeds which tend to choke off portions of the water and in some instances have been the cause of an unbalanced population since the weeds offer cover for the young who thus escape capture by the older fish. Removal of dense growths of aquatic vegetation may prevent winterkill in some lakes. Chapter 9 contains a more detailed account of weed control.

Boxes of gravel or the graveling of large areas have been utilized in warm-water lakes as spawning aids for certain of the nest-building species. These spawning boxes are particularly applicable to the smallmouth bass which will not spawn successfully over a silty or mud bottom. Other spawning devices have been employed for minnows such as cut brush along the shore, spawning slabs, and even floating boards for those that lay their eggs underneath floating logs or other debris.

Stream and lake improvement may be closely correlated in situations where improvement of the inlet streams for natural reproduction will increase the existing populations of the lake.

Fertilization and shelters will be considered as separate sections.

## 14·11 Fertilization

Interest in artificial fertilization of natural lakes has been aroused by the publicity in connection with the tiny farm fish ponds which has resulted in many inquiries and much theorizing concerning the possibilities of increasing productivity of waters in this manner. Productivity of the waters is correlated directly with the productivity of the land that it drains. A stream draining rich farmlands is very probably a productive stream, and a lake situated in a rich agricultural region is likely to produce more fish per acre than a high mountain lake or a lake in a drainage area of poor land. The rich fertilizers and top dressings now applied to farmlands find their ways into streams and lakes enriching them in this manner.

Nutrients are normally lost through drainage to the ocean, absorption into the bottom, removal of fish by anglers, or, as in the case of eels, migration of the adults from the lake, taking with them nutrients absorbed during their life cycle.

Perhaps before discussing fertilization further some idea of its action in relation to the food chain should be mentioned. The addition of fertilizer to a body of water enriches it in certain inorganic nutrients of value in increasing the number of plankton organisms. Since most of the game fish in which we are interested are not plankton feeders intermediate forms must transform the plankton into a form usable by the predator game fish. Intermediate forms may be insects on which trout will feed, or perhaps a small minnow which will feed on the plankton and in turn be fed upon by the larger and more desirable game fish. Most large fish feed on larger organisms than insects, so that the forage fish in the food chain is a vital necessity to the ultimate production of large fish.

The closer the feeding habits of the fish concerned are to the base of the food chain the more the effects of fertilizer are reflected in total weight of fish produced. The effect of the fertilizer on the lower invertebrates is much more apparent than on the fish.

How can we be sure that the application of fertilizer will in fact improve the productivity? For example, if the restricted spawning area of a body of water is a limiting factor, then artificial fertilization will not change the numbers of fish produced. Unless there is some definite chemical deficiency in the water the addition of nutrients may not increase productivity. Particularly is this true if the slow growth is due to low temperature or some other variable.

As with other improvement techniques the first step toward artificial fertilization should be to collect adequate data showing whether or not fertilization will improve some basic deficiency of the habitat.

An interesting experiment on the fertilization of a trout lake was published by Smith (1948). Much of the following has been taken from this paper. It was believed that the poor production in eight lakes of Charlotte County, New Brunswick, could be attributed primarily to the small amounts of nutrient materials, such as phosphorus, in the waters. Commercial fertilizer was added to one of the lakes, Crecy, in an effort to improve trout production. One ton of ammonium phosphate (11-48-0) and 600 pounds of potassium chloride were spread over the surface of the lake, concentrating the greater portion near the shores. It was calculated that this would give, providing it was adequately mixed, a phosphorus content of 0.39 ppm which was 20 times the amount present before fertilization and 0.21 ppm of nitrogen as N.

First of all what was the concentration of these basic nutrients after fertilization, and how long did the increase last? The highest total phosphorus content of the water (0.23 ppm as P) was determined a week after fertilization. There followed a rapid decrease to values little above those found before fertilization, and by the next year the value had fallen to prefertilization levels. This drop occurred even though this particular lake had only a very slight flow of water from it. The phosphorus was evidently removed by other agencies as the plant life or the bottom materials.

After 2 months a dense growth of microscopic plants (algae) produced a "bloom" although such a bloom had not been observed before in these waters. A year later no bloom occurred, but there were clumps of filamentous algae and rooted aquatic vegetation spread over an increased area of the lake bottom taken as an indication that the bottom mud had been enriched.

The zooplankters increased for only a short period within a month after fertilization. Actually during the algal bloom there was a decrease in number as a result of the changes created by the algae. The $pH$ value during the bloom increased from 6.6 to 8.2. In this particular case the bottom fauna including immature insects, snails, and amphipods made up the principal food of the trout. A year later a greater quantity of these foods in trout stomachs indicated a possible increase in their numbers.

During the period from September 9, 1946, when planted, to May and June 1947, fingerling trout increased in average length 5.5 inches. This increase was comparable to that made by the same stock in a hatchery rearing pond. Yearlings when planted showed an increase of 3.1 inches on an average. In this case apparently fertilization coupled with stocking was necessary to improve the fishing. The survival of 3.6 per cent of the planted stock to the creel contributed 60 per cent of the angling.

Even though Crecy was a natural lake it should be realized that it was very small, 50.4 acres with a mean depth of 7.8 feet. There is no permanent inflowing stream, and the outlet almost ceases to run in later summer and early fall. The shallow depth and ability to control the outlet are of prime importance in recommending a program of fertilization as practical.

One of the chief deterrents to fertilization of natural waters is the cost. It is estimated that even a very small stream would require $1\frac{1}{2}$ tons a year to produce any effect even for a short distance below the point of application. Costs have been estimated at from $15 to $20 per acre per year in shallow water ponds with little outflow. What the cost would be for a square mile of lake of any depth and with a volume of water moving through it can hardly be imagined.

One danger of fertilization of large bodies of water is that more young fish will survive and tend toward stunted populations. Fertilization of lakes containing stunted populations will not always correct the condition. Actually it may only provide additional food for more stunted fish.

Since the addition of fertilizer to a body of water increases the number of plants the dangers of winterkill in northern areas are heightened. As long as ample sunshine penetrates the water surface and the surface of the lake is exposed to the air, plenty of oxygen will be present for the fish. In cold weather, however, when ice and then snow cover the lakes, all air and most of the light will be shut off from the water. Then the plants die and decay using up the available oxygen. During the time of oxygen deficiency the fish die.

Fertilization may sometimes cause an obnoxious growth of algae which is objectionable to fishermen, cottage owners, and swimmers. Such growths are unpredictable.

### 14·12   Shelter

The placing of shelters in lakes has received a great deal of attention. Brush shelters consisting of bushes tied together and weighted to sink are dragged out on the ice, in northern regions, and when the ice goes out the shelters fall into position. Trees may be cut along the shore when they are close enough so that their branches will extend out into the water. The disadvantage to this practice is obvious.

Some shelters as described by Rodeheffer (1945) have been more complicated. Two frames are constructed using scrub oak and maple poles. The inner frame is 9 feet square and the surrounding frame 11½ feet square. The ends of the poles for the inner frame protrude and fasten onto the outer square, making a compact unit for supporting the brush. Bundles of brush are then piled on the two frames, butt ends toward the center. When finished, these units are approximately 18 feet in diameter.

The value of brush shelters has been questioned since they tend to concentrate the fish, making them more accessible to angling. Shelters may be guilty of protecting the younger age groups from predation and thus throwing the population out of balance. Observations seem to indicate that size of shelter, depth of water in which it is placed, species for which intended, and interval between shelters are all interacting factors that should be considered before any profound conclusions are drawn concerning these devices.

## 14·13   Common mistakes in carrying out stream improvement

Although habitat improvement on a large scale is a relatively new management tool the results of earlier attempts at such improvement are providing present-day workers with valuable information on what to do and what not to do.

One early so-called improvement practice was to remove shrubs and trees from along the stream banks. Although this sort of an alteration did provide easier fishing, it did not provide better fishing, and certainly, though it did alter the habitat, it did not improve it. The roots of the trees and low shrubs along a stream bank help to retain the banks and resist erosion. The shade provided by these trees and shrubs is valuable in providing cooler water by preventing the direct rays of the sun from striking the surface. Stream bank vegetation should not be disturbed.

The building of large dams as a step in habitat improvement should be carefully considered, particularly in regard to location. Large impoundments tend to increase water temperatures. The area behind the dam often becomes a settling basin, slowly filling with silt, thus altering the bottom and destroying fish food. The reservoir may flood out long stretches of riffle area, thus limiting the area available for feeding and natural reproduction.

Often stream improvement devices are not constructed correctly. The most common mistake is in not making certain that the structure is sufficiently secure to prevent the first flood or freshet from either destroying it entirely or damaging it to such an extent that it no longer functions properly and may become an eyesore on the stream.

Not infrequently improvement devices have been used on streams that are already providing adequate environments. Enthusiastic groups have been known to overimprove an area, following the philosophy that if a little bit is good a lot more will be better. Placing structures too close together is usually more damaging than no improvement at all.

All too frequently projects are planned without regard for the ecological requirements of the other aquatic organisms present.

**References**

Clark, O. H.
  1948. Stream improvements in Michigan. *Trans. Am. Fish. Soc. 75:* 270–280.
Davis, H. S.
  1935. Methods for stream improvement. *U. S. Bur. Fish. I-Memo 133.* 27 pp.

Rodeheffer, I. A.
    1945.  Fish populations in and around brush shelters of different sizes placed at varying depths and distances apart in Douglas Lake, Michigan. *Papers Mich. Acad. Sci. Arts and Letters 30* (1944):321–345.
Shetter, D. S., O. H. Clark, and A. S. Hazzard
    1949.  The effects of deflectors in a section of a Michigan trout stream. *Trans. Am. Fish. Soc. 76:* 248–277.
Smith, Lloyd L., and S. B. Moyle
    1944.  A biological survey and fishery management plan for the streams of the Lake Superior North Shore watershed. *Minn. Fish. Res. Lab., Tech. Bull. 1:* 1–228.
Smith, M. W.
    1948.  Fertilization of a lake to improve trout angling. *Fish. Res. Bd. Canada., Atlantic Biol. Sta., Note 105:* 3–6.
Tarzwell, C. M.
    1938.  An evaluation of the methods and results of stream improvement in the southwest. *3d N. Am. Wildl. Conf.:* 339–364.

# 15 · CONTROL OF UNDESIRABLE SPECIES

## 15·1  Introduction

When a fish population becomes unbalanced or becomes "undesirable" in the ecology of an area it may be necessary in the interests of good wildlife management to control it.   Control frequently involves eliminating or reducing the abundance of the undesirable species. Fish may be classed as undesirable when:

1. They are dominant as a result of angling pressure on the more prized game fish.
2. They become stunted from an overabundance in relation to their food supply (especially true of warm-water species), and few legal-sized fish are produced.  The game-fish species then need to be sufficiently reduced in numbers to permit resumption of rapid growth with the available food.  The quantity of game fish above that desirable is superfluous, and these extra fish can be called undesirable.
3. Because of their abundance and predaceous habits they are limiting the abundance of more desirable species.
4. They are obnoxious to fishermen and consumer because of heavy infection by parasites.  This condition often precludes their commercial use, because of either prejudice or state or Federal regulation against their importation, shipment, or sale.
5. Their feeding habits are such that in shallow lakes with soft bottoms they roil the water, preventing the normal growth of aquatic vegetation.  When too abundant such species may limit the abundance of other species and so be classed as undesirable.
6. They occur in a hatchery water supply, thus providing a source of infection for the hatchery-reared fish.

Undesirable species are controlled by the use of poison, nets, weirs, biological control, regulations, and water level control.

## 15·2  Poisoning

Collections of fish were made by poisoning in the early 1900's, but the use of chemicals as a management tool to reclaim water areas began about 1930 and has since become accepted practice in many areas of the United States and Canada. Only a few states have not attempted some type of reclamation work, and it seems to be the best means for controlling fish populations in our smaller lakes and ponds.

Chemicals were first used to "wipe out" entire populations, killing all species in a lake. A short time later "selective" poisoning was introduced, in which restricted areas are treated to kill all or most of an undesirable species in the hope of restoring conditions favorable to game fish. Successful selective poisoning is only possible where the undesirable and desirable species are segregated by habitat preferences for at least a portion of the year.

Certain generalities concerning poisoning should be noted. Most of the lakes treated were under 100 acres, and few were over 30 acres. Treatment of large lakes is not economical at the present time. Complete eradication of populations has been successful only under unusual conditions, generally in small, shallow ponds. Because selective poisoning must be repeated periodically it may be uneconomical. Finally, and most important, chemical treatment will not alter the productive capacity of the waters or change a eutrophic lake into an oligotrophic lake.

Many substances are toxic to fish, including copper sulfate, cresol, calcium hypochlorite, and many insecticides and herbicides. One of the insecticides, rotenone, has been largely responsible for the progress and success of pond reclamation.

## 15·3   Rotenone

Natives in widely separated tropical and subtropical countries have long used crushed roots and extracts of plants containing rotenone to obtain fish for food. Krumholz (1948) lists many different names for the plants, and the rotenone, such as tuba, cubé, timbo, derris, and several others. A study of commercial sources of insecticides by Sievers et al. (1938) indicated that rotenone has been found in only six genera of the family Leguminosae.

The greatest single attribute of rotenone is its specificity to fish when used in recommended amounts. Other poisons effective in removing fish affect other animals adversely and even plants in some cases. Rotenone constricts the tiny capillaries in the gills, restricting the passage of the individual red blood corpuscles or erythrocytes. Consequently, unable to utilize the oxygen present in the water, the fish suffocates. Invertebrates, with the exception of the planktonic crustaceans, are less sensitive than fish to the action of the chemical (Smith 1950). Rotenone is apparently harmless to vertebrates in recommended amounts. It has been taken internally by humans;

animals drink the water without ill effects; fish-eating birds consume the poisoned fish; and fish so obtained are used for food. It is not harmful to plants in usual dosages.

Waters containing concentrations of 0.5 ppm to 1.0 ppm of derris or cubé powder (5% rotenone content) are generally accepted as lethal to most kinds of fish. The actual concentration of the rotenone is 0.025 to 0.05 ppm. At least 0.5 ppm of derris or cubé powder (5% rotenone content) is necessary for complete kill (Leonard 1939), but Brown and Ball (1943) found this ineffective below 48° F.

Rotenone is more lethal at high temperatures, although Dr. Gerald Cooper successfully poisoned Sabbath Day Lake, Maine, during the fall overturn. Opinions are that rotenone loses its toxicity more quickly in hard, alkaline waters than in soft waters. The most generally accepted period of toxicity is 4 to 6 weeks. However, this period should be viewed with caution and treated as the minimum in planning a pond reclamation project. Ponds treated as a part of the reclamation project in Maine have remained toxic up to 4 months, and reports from other workers indicate that ponds may retain a toxic level of rotenone for as long as a year.

Toxicity of the water and distribution of the poison are best determined by lowering small, wire cages containing test fish at various depths and time intervals. Such tests are necessary to check on the extent of treatment and to determine when it is safe to restock the treated waters.

Although used primarily for the eradication of fishes, rotenone may be employed in collecting fishes for studies of age, growth, populations, and taxonomy. Nets select fish within certain size ranges, but poison eliminates this factor.

## 15·4  Methods of rotenone dispersion

Various methods of dispersing rotenone have been attempted since an even distribution is far more desirable than heavy spot concentrations. Some of the methods are:

1. Pouring solutions of rotenone in the wake of an outboard motor.

2. Throwing paper bags full of the drug onto the water where they break and the rotenone disperses.

3. Setting off charges of dynamite to mix the rotenone in the deeper water.

4. Towing burlap bags full of the mixture behind boats. Much of the towing is done on the surface, but better distribution in the deep water is possible if the bags are weighted and towed at specified depths. Frequent kneading of the bag is necessary. Some of the commercial

rotenone is furnished in burlap bags for dispersion by this method. Experience of the junior author indicates that this method is too slow in providing over-all coverage. Burlap bags of rotenone are frequently weighted and permitted to sink in springs.

5. Spraying the solution with pumps. Indian pumps are very valuable in dispersing the rotenone in vegetation or over swampy areas. Power pumps mounted in boats have proved valuable in forcing the rotenone under vegetation, over swampy areas, and down into the depths.

6. Sucking the mixture down into the deeper waters by means of hoses fastened to inverted funnels.

7. Dispersing by plane. Planes have been used in several operations and appear to be economically feasible. Siegler and Pillsbury (1949) report that a plane used for 30 hours and 51 minutes at a cost of $617 reclaimed ponds with a surface area of 708 acres. The small plane was rigged with a drum in the front cockpit which drained through two pipes mounted under the wing. Two drains in each pipe were sufficient to disperse the rotenone evenly. The plane proved to be so much faster than other methods for dispersing the drug that a power mixer was employed in order to prepare the rotenone mixture quickly enough to keep the plane operating constantly.

A helicopter was employed in poisoning an area 250 acres in extent in 2½ hours (Weier and Starr 1950).

In many cases a combination of methods is necessary to give adequate dispersal.

## 15·5  Marketed rotenone preparations

Rotenone may be purchased in the powdered forms, as emulsifiable rotenone, and as the main ingredient in such commercial products as Fish Tox and Atox.

In the powdered form the difficulty and inconvenience of mixing plus the annoying and irritating dust reduce efficiency of handling. Consequently many have turned to the use of the emulsifiable rotenone furnished in tins which provides for a maximum of ease and efficiency of handling. However, the emulsifiable rotenone may cost up to 50 per cent more than the powdered forms. Stroud (1951) recommends the use of powdered derris root to which a commercial wetting agent is added. The wetting agent makes the mixing easy and removes many of the undesirable characteristics of the powdered forms. One gallon of emulsifiable rotenone will treat 6 acre-feet of water with a concentration of 0.5 ppm.

## 15·6   Recovery of treated fish

Complete kills are occasionally made, but usually some fish escape even where complete eradication of the population is the objective. Ball (1948) marked and released 456 fish (246 bluegills and 210 brook trout) prior to poisoning Ford Lake, Michigan. After the treatment 58.9 per cent of the bluegills and 44.7 per cent of the brook trout were recovered. This does not imply that the remainder were not killed, but merely that they were not recovered. Consequently one wonders about the accuracy of the figures on total poundage from poisoning reported in the literature. Small fishes and young of the year are particularly hard to recover. Moorman and Ruhr (1951) in checking population studies remark that the recoveries of marked fish were always incomplete and ranged anywhere from 22 to 65 per cent. Miller (1950) observes that the literature on reclamation is weak in data as to completeness or otherwise of the kill and the proportion of dead fish recovered when a kill was supposed to be complete.

There are many obstacles to either the complete kill or the complete recovery of fish killed in a treated area. Some of these are:

1. Roiling of water by collectors.
2. Beds of emergent vegetation holding fish which have become enmeshed during their death struggles.
3. Smaller fish eaten by larger fish in the early stages of the poisoning. Evidences of this may be seen during most poisoning operations when the larger fish, becoming affected by the drug, begin to disengorge the smaller fish eaten earlier.
4. Insects, snakes, turtles, birds, and mammals may, by eating the dead and dying fish, lower the number recovered.
5. Chemical may not reach the deeper water.
6. Swampy areas or overhangs of aquatic vegetation may prevent the thorough distribution of the drug.
7. Large springs may be present with sufficient flow to dilute the drug to harmless concentrations in their immediate vicinity.
8. Fish may escape into the outlets or inlets of a lake.
9. Small fish are difficult to find and often too numerous to gather up.

It may be concluded then that a complete kill and a complete gathering of the dead fish are rarely accomplished.

## 15·7   Eradication for improvement of waterfowl habitat

Along the shores of Sandusky Bay in Ohio large populations of carp so roiled the water during their feeding that the aquatic vegetation was destroyed (Weier and Starr 1950). In addition, the movement of the large fish was thought to be responsible for the uneasiness of the waterfowl and their subsequent flight to other areas. From a helicopter the bay was sprayed with emulsifiable rotenone at 0.5 ppm concentration. A complete kill was not obtained, and fish were observed in the area 7 months after the treatment. However, waterfowl returned to the area after the reduction of the fish population.

## 15·8  Host eradication in control of parasites

The tapeworm (*Triaenophorus crassus*) is an intestinal parasite with the terminal host the pike (*Esox lucius*). The first intermediate host is a copepod and the second intermediate host a salmonoid fish, particularly a coregonid. Reduction of the parasite in the second intermediate host (whitefish) by controlling the population of the terminal host or the pike was attempted by poisoning (Miller 1950). This is an example of selective poisoning as it was decided to poison only the spawning areas of the pike. This restricted the treatment almost entirely to the pike, and, as the spawning areas are customarily shallow, the saving on rotenone was also considerable. Atox, a commercial product with a rotenone base, was used in the first two years whereas Fish Tox was employed in the third year with apparently better results. Recoveries of fish were small. In 1947 only 21 of 436 marked fish were recovered, in 1948 only 11 out of 162, and in 1949 only 48 out of 330 marked. It became obvious that the pike were fleeing the poisoned area and Miller suggests that better results might have been obtained if nets had been set on the borders of the poisoned areas. Since the number of fish killed but not recovered is unknown and possibly large, no confidence may be placed in calculations of total populations or of total mortality based on returns of poisoned, marked fish. Other fishes were little affected. The primary object of the program was to determine the practicability of this treatment. The total infection of whitefish by worms was reduced 39 per cent, presumably the result of the pike control. The cost of the program was $5024.50 for a lake of only 2.5 square miles containing only a few thousand pike. Repopulation of the pike was a certainty so that the treatment would have to be repetitive. This method of controlling parasites is obviously impractical.

## 15·9  Netting to control undesirable species

A program of netting was introduced to remove the large population of longnose suckers (*Catostomus catostomus*) which were thought to be reducing the angling returns for rainbow trout in Pyramid Lake, Alberta, since stomach analysis indicated a competition for food (Rawson and Elsey 1950).

In seven years 27,597 longnose suckers were removed. Two thirds were taken by gill nets and the remainder in wire-mesh traps. This figure does not include the 5500 small suckers (less than 4 inches) removed by seining. Since the suckers spawned the year they became catchable there was no hope of removing the spawning population. Table 15·1 from Rawson and Elsey (op. cit.) presents the age composition of longnose suckers caught by gill nets in Pyramid Lake in 1939, 1943, 1944, and 1945.

TABLE 15·1

| Year | Percentage of Catch in Each Age Group | | | | | | | | | | |
|------|------|------|------|------|------|-----|-----|-----|-----|-----|-----|
|      | 4    | 5    | 6    | 7    | 8    | 9   | 10  | 11  | 12  | 13  | 14  |
| 1939 | 11.0 | 28.0 | 11.5 | 14.0 | 13.0 | 7.0 | 4.5 | 5.0 | 4.0 | 1.5 | 0.5 |
| 1943 | 5.0  | 33.5 | 8.5  | 21.5 | 20.0 | 7.5 | 3.0 | 1.0 |     |     |     |
| 1944 | 21.5 | 56.5 | 6.0  | 12.0 | 3.0  | 0.5 |     |     |     |     |     |
| 1945 | 7.0  | 76.5 | 10.0 | 5.5  | 1.0  |     |     |     |     |     |     |

It will be noted that the percentage of 5-year fish increased, possibly as a result of increased recruitment from increased survival, from the reduction of the older age groups. This increased survival may have nullified the results. At any rate it was concluded that the drastic reduction of the longnose sucker population had not improved the game fishery for rainbow trout.

Competition between fishes generally falls within the bounds of one or a combination of the following: predation, food, and space. The competition between the longnose sucker and rainbow trout was for food. In the following example predation is the factor.

The effect of reduction of predaceous fish on survival of young sockeye salmon at Cultus Lake was studied by Foerster and Ricker (1941). It was observed that there were heavy losses during the early life of *Oncorhynchus nerka,* the sockeye salmon. Survival from egg to seaward migration averaged 1.80 per cent in three trials. Predaceous fish in order of importance were the squawfish, char, trout, and coho salmon. A program of netting was undertaken to reduce the populations of the undesirable fishes. Gill netting was supplemented with seining, bait lines, and cage traps. From 1932 to 1938 a total of 20,047 fish were removed including 10,130 squawfish, 2300 trout, 700 char, and 720 coho salmon. Squawfish and char over 200 mm were reduced to one tenth of their original abundance. Table 15·2 (from Foerster

## TABLE 15·2

### PERCENTAGE SURVIVAL

| | Eyed-Egg Planting | | Natural Propagation | | Fry Liberated | | All Methods | |
|---|---|---|---|---|---|---|---|---|
| | Before Control | After Control | Before Control | After Control | Before Control | After Control | Before Control | After Control |
| First test | 1.64 | 8.98 | 1.13 | 7.81 | 5.83 | 13.05 | | |
| Second test | 5.58 | | 1.05 | | 3.85 | | | |
| Third test | .... | | 3.16 | | 2.81 | | | |
| Mean | 3.61 | 8.98 | 1.78 | 7.81 | 4.16 | 13.05 | 3.13 | 9.95 |
| Difference | 5.37 | | 6.03 | | 8.89 | | 6.82 | |
| Combined variance | 7.76 | | 1.43 | | 2.35 | | 4.50 | |
| | 1.57 | | 4.36 | | 5.02 | | 4.76 | |
| Degrees of freedom | 1 | | 2 | | 2 | | 9 | |
| Probability | 0.9 | | 0.05 | | 0.04 | | Less than 0.01 | |

and Ricker) shows the significance of the changes in survival rate of young sockeye before and after the beginning of predator control. This experiment presents the results of direct predator reduction. The smaller number of fry necessary to produce one migrant reduced the strain on the food supply in the lake. The authors assumed that the reduction of the predators saved 3,800,000 smolts in 3 years which would be expected to yield 380,000 adult salmon worth $95,000 to the commercial interests. Cost of the netting program was $10,000.

An experiment in removing coarse fish from a lake in Indiana was reported as providing increased angling (Ricker and Gottschalk 1941). However, subsequent attempts at seining of other lakes failed, because of either a scarcity of good seining beaches or inability to catch enough fish. The 1600-acre lake on which the seining proved successful has an average depth of 10 feet, with several good hauling beaches. Seines 800 to 1000 feet in length and 8 to 20 feet in depth were used. The following fish were removed:

| Species | Number | Average Weight, Pounds |
|---|---|---|
| Carp (*Cyprinus carpio*) | 12,281 (45 tons) | 7.35 |
| Quillback (*Carpiodes*) | 14,456 | 2.70 |
| Buffalo fish (*Ictiobus*) | 1,441 | 8.55 |
| Suckers (*Catostomus commersoni*) | 65 | 2.03 |
| Gar pike (*Lepisosteus osseus* and *L. platostomus*) | 215 | 2.21 |

Removal of the fish was followed by a clearing of the water, increased vegetation, and better angling.

## 15·10   Weirs

Much publicity has been given recently to the decline of the freshwater fisheries in some of the Great Lakes as a result of predation by the lamprey.   Present work indicates that partial control may be achieved by careful weiring of the important spawning tributaries (MacKay and MacGillivray 1949).

## 15·11   Electric shocker

Work on the Atlantic salmon streams of Maine by the authors and discussion with research biologists of the Atlantic Biological Station,

FIG. 15·1   The 220-volt d-c portable generator developed by Ph. Wolf of the Salmon and Trout Association, Malmo, Sweden, for use in collecting fishes.

St. Andrews, New Brunswick, lead to the general impression that the American eel (*Anguilla rostrata*) is a very serious predator of the young Atlantic salmon before their seaward migration.

Impressive numbers taken by electric shocking indicated that this predator may be substantially reduced by this method in areas of intensive salmon spawning.   Although some eel migration into the area can be expected, preliminary results from the Atlantic Biological Station support the supposition that they do not return immediately and in some cases not in appreciable numbers for at least 6 weeks.

If reduction of the eel population can be timed to coincide with hatching of the salmon fry, then much predation on the sac and advanced fry might be prevented.

FIG. 15·2   Showing the stream equipment used with the d-c generator for fish shocking.   The extra insulated wire is carried on a self-winding spool as a back pack.   The operator wears high rubber waders, and the insulated handle on the positive electrode has as a safety feature a pressure hand switch that breaks contact whenever the grip is relaxed.

## 15·12   Biological control

It is frequently suggested that fast-growing populations of warmwater fishes might be controlled by introducing a larger game-fish predator capable of reducing the populations.   The northern pike (*Esox lucius*) and. the yellow pike-perch (*Stizostedion vitreum*) are usually suggested.   Quantitative results on the application of the theory are not available, and this method should be approached with extreme caution.

FIG. 15·3  Loading portable generator into skiff for electric shocking.  (Credit: Missouri Conservation Commission)

FIG. 15·4  Using electric seine and prods to collect samples of fish in Salt River, northeast Missouri; the electric generator is in the skiff.  (Credit: Missouri Conservation Commission)

Fig. 15·5 Starfish mops are dragged over the oyster beds, entangling the starfish. The mop shown, loaded with these potent oyster enemies, is being immersed in a tank of hot water to kill the starfish before it is again lowered to the bottom. (Credit: V. L. Loosanoff, U. S. Fish and Wildlife Service)

## 15·13  Liberalized fishing

Of interest to fishery biologists are the programs of liberalized fishing in the huge reservoirs of the South and in other areas such as Ohio, in direct opposition to the strict regulatory measures adopted generally. By liberalized fishing is meant the opening of fishing throughout the year to the taking of any size and any number of fish. This aids in preventing the stunting of warm-water panfish and improves the fishing by providing more food and space for the raising of the larger, more prized species of game fish. Liberalized fishing might better be attempted where anglers complain of "too many small fish" than the practice followed in some localities of dumping in more fish from the hatcheries to aggravate the situation further. Although trout ponds have been observed where a stunting of the population was occurring, the principles of liberalized fishing will generally be applied to the more productive warm-water fishes.

## 15·14 Water-level control

Controlled water level is a practical method of managing fish populations. Various fishes, sunfishes, minnows, suckers, perch, pike, pickerel, and carp, spawn in shallow waters in the littoral zones of lakes. Information on spawning times and areas controls the time and amount of water-level reduction. Eggs and nests are destroyed and the population decreased.

Dams at the outlets of lakes, particularly oligotrophic lakes, raise water levels resulting in a more than proportionate increase in the warm, shallow littoral zone. This increases the habitat favorable to undesirable fishes and to the stunting of existing populations of warm-water fishes.

Wood (1951) discusses the significance of water-level fluctuations in relation to basic fertility and productivity of impounded waters, fish populations and management, and increased yields.

### References

Ball, R. C.
  1948. Recovery of marked fish following a second poisoning of the population in Ford Lake, Michigan. *Trans. Am. Fish. Soc. 75:* 36–42.
Brown, C. J. D., and R. C. Ball
  1943. An experiment in the use of derris root (rotenone) on the fish and fish-food organisms of Third Sister Lake. *Trans. Am. Fish. Soc. 72:* 267–284.
Foerster, R. Earle, and William E. Ricker
  1941. The effect of reduction of predaceous fish on survival of young sockeye at Cultus Lake. *J. Fish. Res. Bd. Canada 5* (4):315–336.
Krumholz, Louis A.
  1948. The use of rotenone in fisheries research. *J. Wildl. Management 12* (3):305–317.
Leonard, J. W.
  1939. Notes on the use of derris as a fish poison. *Trans. Am. Fish. Soc. 68:* 270–280.
MacKay, H. H., and E. MacGillivray
  1949. Recent investigation on the sea lamprey, *Petromyzon marinus* in Ontario. *Trans. Am. Fish. Soc. 76:* 148–159.
Miller, R. B.
  1950a. A critique of the need and use of poisons in fisheries research and management. *Can. Fish Cult. 8:* 30–33.
  1950b. The Square Lake experiment: An attempt to control *Triaenophorus crassus* by poisoning pike. *Can. Fish Cult. 7:* 3–18.
Moorman, R. B., and C. E. Ruhr
  1951. Suggestions for improving the collection of fish with rotenone. *Prog. Fish-Cult. 13* (3):149–152.
Rawson, D. S., and C. A. Elsey
  1950. Reduction in the longnose sucker population of Pyramid Lake, Alberta, in an attempt to improve angling. *Trans. Am. Fish. Soc. 78:* 13–31.

Ricker, William E., and John Gottschalk
   1941. An experiment in removing coarse fish from a lake. *Trans. Am. Fish. Soc. 70:* 382–390.
Siegler, H. R., and H. Pillsbury
   1949. Progress in reclamation techniques. *Prog. Fish-Cult. 11* (2) :125–137.
Sievers, A. F., et al.
   1938. Studies on the possibilities of devil's shoestring (*Tephrosia virginiana*) and other native species of *Tephrosia* as commercial sources of insecticides. *U. S. Dept. Agr., Tech. Bull. 595:* 1–40.
Smith, M. W.
   1950. The use of poisons to control undesirable fish in Canadian fresh waters. *Can. Fish Cult. 8:* 17–29.
Stroud, R. H.
   1951. Use of a wetting agent to facilitate pond reclamation. *Prog. Fish-Cult. 13* (3) :143-145.
Weier, J. L., and D. F. Starr
   1950. The use of rotenone to remove rough fish for the purpose of improving migratory waterfowl refuge areas. *J. Wildl. Management 14* (2) :203–205.
Wood, Roy
   1951. The significance of managed water levels in developing the fisheries of large impoundments. *J. Tenn. Acad. Sci. 26* (3) :214-235.

# PART VII · TAGGING OF FISH

## 16 · TYPES OF TAGS AND INFORMATION SOUGHT

### 16·1  Development of marking

Tagging of fish was started by wealthy owners of riparian rights interested in discovering facts to conserve salmon and sea trout fisheries. As these early attempts were scattered and unorganized few tagged fish were recovered. The first successful tagging took place nearly 80 years ago, in 1873, when Charles G. Atkins tagged Atlantic salmon in the Penobscot River and a fair number of tagged salmon were later recovered.

For many years tagging of fish developed very slowly, and the first 100,000 had not been tagged until 1910. By 1933 the total was only 462,000 fish. Tagging was handicapped by lack of efficient types of tags for most species of fish. Also tagging was used chiefly as a means for studying migrations, since the techniques for utilizing the returns for studies of mortality and population size were slow in developing. Within the last 15 years tagging and recovery of fish has come to be recognized as a very powerful tool for studying population dynamics.

### 16·2  Information derived from marking

The ability to account for the presence of a particular fish or group of fish in time or space furnishes an important tool to the fishery manager. Happily, the day of marking fish merely to find out what happens is almost past. Today, a biologist decides what information is needed to solve a problem. If marking of fish is indicated as a tool, it is so used. The reason for· marking is known; and the numbers marked, the sites chosen, the type of mark, season of marking, etc., are decided according to the problem. The following are questions that can often be answered through marking:

**Parent-stream theory.** The problem of the return of anadromous fishes to their natal river has been the subject of much investigation. In the majority of experiments to determine whether they return, the young fish have been marked by fin clipping (see Section 16·27). Tagging of salmon smolts has also been tried without signal success. Calderwood (Dahl and Somme 1936) tagged 6500 smolts in the River Tay in Scotland in 1905, by means of a silver wire put through the front of the dorsal fin and twisted, but only 110 were recaptured. Dahl used a similar mark in 1909 on 964 smolts in Norway; four were retaken at sea. In any experiment to determine the degree of homing, it is crucial to the test that other streams be searched as fully as the home stream; otherwise the validity of any conclusions is open to serious question.

**Racial studies.** For racial studies it is usually preferable to tag fish on the spawning grounds to insure sampling a pure population; there is evidence that some races may mingle on the feeding grounds. As tagged fish can only be returned from areas in which fishing occurs, failure to obtain recaptures from any particular region does not necessarily mean that the population does not migrate there unless one has information accompanying the tag recoveries on the quantities of fish caught in different areas and can show that the recoveries were significantly below the number expected (see Section 4·11). Thus one must always be sure that the boundaries of a population as shown by tag returns are actual boundaries of the stock and not merely the limitation set on tag recovery by the intensity of the fishery.

**Age and growth.** For many species the age and rate of growth cannot be obtained from studies of the scale structure. In such cases the recapture and remeasurement of individual fish after a known period at liberty is a valuable means of obtaining accurate data on growth. Even where the scale markings are of value in determining age, the recovery of tagged individuals from which scales are obtained before tagging and after recapture forms a valuable check on the validity of the age interpretations from the scales.

**Mortality rates.** In studying mortality rates, it is necessary to know the sizes (or ages) of the fish tagged and of those recaptured, in order to compare the rates of mortality shown by the tagging with the rates indicated by the changes in age composition and catch per unit of fishing effort of the fishery.

**Speed and migration routes.** Few tagging experiments have been designed to show either of these factors, since the usual procedure has been to tag a large number of fish at one time and place, and then to base all conclusions on the resulting recaptures. O'Malley and Rich (1919) tagged sockeye salmon throughout the summer of 1918 at five different points in Puget Sound. Thus they obtained data on the speed and route followed by the salmon that migrated at different times during the season. Davidson and Christey (1938) tagged pink salmon during 1935 and 1936 each week throughout the fishing season at Cape Chacon. Recaptures showed that the salmon migrating past Cape Chacon during different portions of the season were bound for spawning grounds in the streams of widely separated regions.

**Survival and growth of transplants.** In Europe valuable information has been obtained on the increase in growth rate of young plaice transplanted from crowded inshore areas to the offshore banks. Measurements were made of the tagged fish before release and after recapture, and of the fish remaining in the inshore waters as well. To obtain directly comparable results in such an experiment, fish of similar size should be tagged and released on the inshore banks at the time of transplanting, so that any effect on the growth or survival due to tagging may be eliminated from the comparison.

**Survival of hatchery plants.** Marking of hatchery-liberated fish has been a very valuable aid in gaining accurate information to guide stocking policies: i.e., the proper season and locality in which to stock and the ages and sizes suitable. It also is used to compare the relative efficiency of natural and artificial propagation.

## 16·3   How to compare tags

It is best to compare the efficiency of various tags in a live car or aquarium before making trials in the field. The condition of the fish tested is highly important; if they are weak the tagged ones may die whereas the controls will live. The same experiment duplicated on healthy fish may give a totally different picture.

In aquarium experiments it is practically impossible to be certain that conditions of light, water supply, disease, feeding, etc., are uniform for every tank. Each should therefore contain controls, and, when possible, the same number of fish bearing each tag to be tested should be kept in each tank. In this way one will have as many comparisons between tags as there are tanks, and if an adverse condition arises in any one tank it will affect all tags equally.

When using a live car, one may achieve segregation of each type of tag, and also of the controls by portioning the live car into 9, 16, 25, or 36 compartments and distributing the various experiments in a random manner so as to form a Latin square. For mackerel which is a very fast-swimming fish Sette (1950) found it necessary to provide a very large enclosure, as they cannot respire properly unless they have ample space to swim freely.

When you have eliminated the least efficient tags by aquarium or live car trials, the remaining types of tags should be compared by actual liberation of sufficient numbers of fish so judgment can be formed as to their effectiveness.

The correct procedure for field testing of tags is to mark every second, third, or fourth fish with a different tag, according to the number of types to be compared (Rounsefell 1942). The practice of tagging first with one type and later with another is unsound, since one then is comparing the difference between two lots of fish as well as the difference between tags, and the two effects cannot be separated. Field experiments test both the survival of the tagged fish (or retention of the tag) and the degree to which the tags are discovered by the fishermen. This latter may vary with the position at which the tag is affixed to the fish, its color, etc. In comparing results of experiments it should be remembered that a failure to obtain recoveries does not necessarily mean that the tag did not remain on the fish or that the fish succumbed; it may be due to failure of the fishermen to send in tags.

The chief reason for discovering an efficient tag before starting a large-scale tagging program lies in the difficulty of properly evaluating mortality rates if the type of tag is changed during the course of the program.

### 16·4  Materials for making tags

Many materials have been used for making tags, and the results should be of great interest to anyone contemplating a tagging experiment. Unfortunately some of the best materials, such as platinum and silver, are often too expensive to use. Aluminum is light and cheap, but its durability has been somewhat variable, depending probably on its purity. Because of its ductility and tensile strength silver is the best wire for piercing tissues. Probably its germicidal properties have contributed to its success. Monel metal and nickel are very durable in sea water but are so tough that it is sometimes difficult to obtain smooth edges on tags stamped out from dies unless the tags are well tumbled. For Petersen tags nickel is excellent material for the pins, being sufficiently stiff to pierce tissues without the use of an awl or a hollow needle. Silk thread or ribbon is apparently very irritating to tissues and should not be used where it contacts an open wound. Celluloid is one of the best materials because it is durable and because a great deal of information can be printed on the tag.

Table 16·1 lists the materials for which information is available.

### 16·5  Types of tags

Eighteen general types of tags are defined and described by Rounsefell and Kask (1945). A few of these types are either obsolete or were

## TABLE 16·1

### TAG MATERIALS AND THEIR DURABILITY

| | Use | | | |
|---|---|---|---|---|
| Material | Material External to the Tissues | Material Piercing the Tissues | Internal Tags | Remarks |
| Aluminum, pure | Good | Good | | Corrodes if not pure |
| Bone | Decays | | | |
| Brass | Fair | | | |
| Cadmium plating | | | Poisonous | |
| Celluloid | Excellent | Good | Excellent | Must be smooth |
| Copper | Corrodes | Corrodes | | |
| Ebonite | Good | | | |
| Glass | Good | | | |
| Leather | Poor | | | |
| Monel metal | Excellent | Excellent | | |
| Nickel | Excellent | Excellent | Excellent | Very heavy |
| Nickel plating | | | Excellent | |
| Platinum | Excellent | Excellent | | |
| Rubber, soft | Fair | | Fair | |
| Silk ribbon | Poor | Poor | Poor | Keeps wound open |
| Silk thread | Poor | Poor | | Keeps wound open |
| Silver | Excellent | Excellent | | Best for wire |
| Silver, oxidized | Excellent | | | |
| Silver plating | Good | | | |
| Steel | | | Excellent | |
| Tin | Fair | | | |
| Vulcanite | Good | | | |

never extensively used. The most important tag to be developed since their report is the hydrostatic tag of Einar Lea. The report of Rounsefell and Kask in Volume 73 of the *Transactions of the American Fisheries Society* has been one of the chief sources of material for this chapter. The definitions used for each type do not always apply to a single tag, but are intended to apply to all tags that can be conveniently grouped because of some specific characteristic. Of these characteristics the method of attachment has received the most weight. As an alternative to tagging, fish are often marked by mutilation, chiefly the removal of certain fins and the clipping off or notching of maxillary or opercular bones. Fish have also been marked by incisions with or without the introduction of dyes and by tattooing. These latter methods have not been very successful. The following sections describe each type of mark and its variations.

## 16·6    Archer tag

This tag consisted originally of a single plate attached by two wires, one at either end, that pierce the tissues, and are then twisted or clinched. Variations include the use of pins through holes in the plate to replace the wire, and in the use of two plates, one usually being on each side of the part pierced. The tag was devised by William E. Archer in 1888 for use on salmon in Norway. By 1896 Calderwood was using it in Scotland. The original tag was made of silver and was only 10 mm long, with two 8-mm points, and 4 mm wide. The latest modification (used on Canadian salmon) was two Celluloid plates each 31 mm by 8 mm by 0.6 mm thick. One plate is placed on each side of the dorsal fin, and the plates are held in place by two nickel pins 1¼ inch (32 mm) in length of no. 20 B. & S. gage (0.032 inch or 0.9 mm) with a head of 0.080 inch in diameter. This tag has been used principally on adult salmon attached to the dorsal or adipose fin. It has not been adequately tested, but it is not highly regarded.

## 16·7    Atkins tag

This tag is extremely simple, consisting of a bead or flat plate attached by a thread or wire that pierces the tissues, forming a loop. In its simplest form it closely resembles a luggage tag. It was used in 1873 by Charles G. Atkins on Atlantic salmon on the Penobscot River. Various sizes, shapes, and materials have been tried, as well as different points of attachment. Good results have been obtained using an oblong silver plate 24 mm by 9 mm attached with soft silver wire through the back at the front of the dorsal fin. It is highly approved by Europeans for marking salmon.

Ph. Wolf of the Salmon and Trout Association, Malmö, Sweden, has been using an Atkins tag consisting of a piece of white Celluloid printed with a serial number and mailing directions. This is sealed between two pieces of transparent Celluloid of the same size. It is attached by a very fine wire threaded on a needle in order to leave a very small wound in attaching it. One size is 25 mm by 8 mm, and a smaller size is only 14 mm by 5 mm.

## 16·8    Bachelor button tag

This tag consists of two plates or disks held together rigidly by a shaft that pierces the tissues. The first employment was in 1908 by Charles W. Greene on Pacific salmon in the Columbia River. It was given an extensive trial on sockeye salmon in Puget Sound and on Pacific halibut.  The silver type with concave edges cut off the circulation, and the tissues decayed so that the tag fell off, leaving a hole in

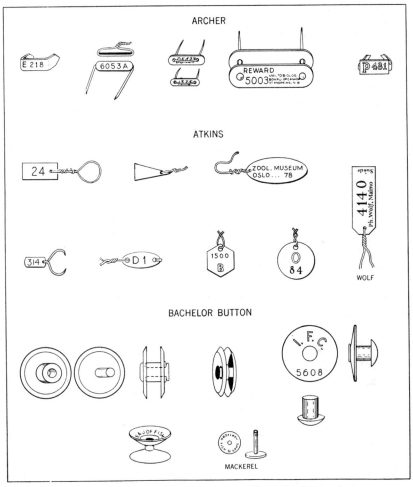

Fig. 16·1  Types of Archer, Atkins, and bachelor button tags.

the operculum.  The flat aluminum type (disks 19 mm by 1 mm, the solid shaft 4 mm by 9 mm, the hollow shaft 7 mm by 7 mm, weight 2.6 grams) used on the opercle of sockeye salmon (*Oncorhynchus nerka*) gave as good returns as the strap tag on the caudal peduncle. Neither the concave silver type nor the flat rivet type of Monel metal were efficient on halibut, as many tags came off.  The cupped bachelor button was devised in 1932 by William C. Herrington for use on had-dock. The outer cupped disk of aluminum is 15.7 mm in diameter, 0.5 mm in thickness, and is cupped 3 mm, outside measurement. It has a hollow shaft tapering from 5.0 to 4.5 mm to a shoulder. Beyond the shoulder, the shaft is 3.3 mm in diameter to fit through a hole in the Celluloid disk. This narrow portion is only 1.5 mm in length and is crimped onto the Celluloid disk. The shaft from the disk to the shoulder is 3.5 mm in length for use on larger fish and 2.3 mm for smaller fish. The second disk, of Celluloid (to use inside the opercle), is very slightly concave, 15.5 mm in diameter and 0.7 mm in thickness with a central hole 3.5 mm in diameter. Because of the cupped shape this tag did not stop the circulation of blood in the tissues. The cupping was supposed to prevent overgrowth by opercular tissue, but within one year these tags are sometimes completely hidden by oper-cular tissue. The rigid shaft may contribute to this overgrowth. This tag is as good as or better than the modern Petersen tag on haddock, but it requires special pliers that are difficult to keep in adjustment, and it cannot be attached as quickly as the Petersen.

A very small bachelor button tag with the disks only 9 mm in diam-eter has been tried experimentally on mackerel with indifferent success. The flat inside disk of aluminum has a hollow shaft that pierces a hole in the opercle and is then clinched through the other disk of red Celluloid. The shaft is about 3 mm in outside diameter, and the disks are 3 mm apart when the tag is clinched. This tag has definite possi-bilities and should be given further tests on other species.

A bachelor button has been developed by Cable (1950) for use on the cheek of shad. The description is as follows:

The rivets are machined of stainless steel USS 18-8. The round head is 0.032 inch thick and ½ inch in diameter. The outer and inner edges of the rim are smoothly rounded. The shank is ⁵⁄₁₆ inch long and 0.062 inch in diameter, leaving a 0.006-inch-thick side wall to form a flange when clinched.

The external disk . . . held in place on the cheek by the rivet described above, is of red cellulose acetate, ¹⁄₁₆ inch thick and ½ inch in diameter with a 0.07-inch hole in the centre. It is brightly coloured, to be conspicuous in appearance for ready detection for fish handlers.

## 16·9   Barb tag

This is any tag consisting of a straight shaft with or without an attached plate, that is pushed into the tissues and that depends for holding wholly on one or more barbs. It was first tried by Heldt to mark tuna and swordfish in Tunis, but it was not adequately tested. Templeman used a barb of Celluloid to mark lobsters in Newfoundland by pushing it between the segments in the abdominal side of the tail segments. The same tag has also been used to mark spiny lob-

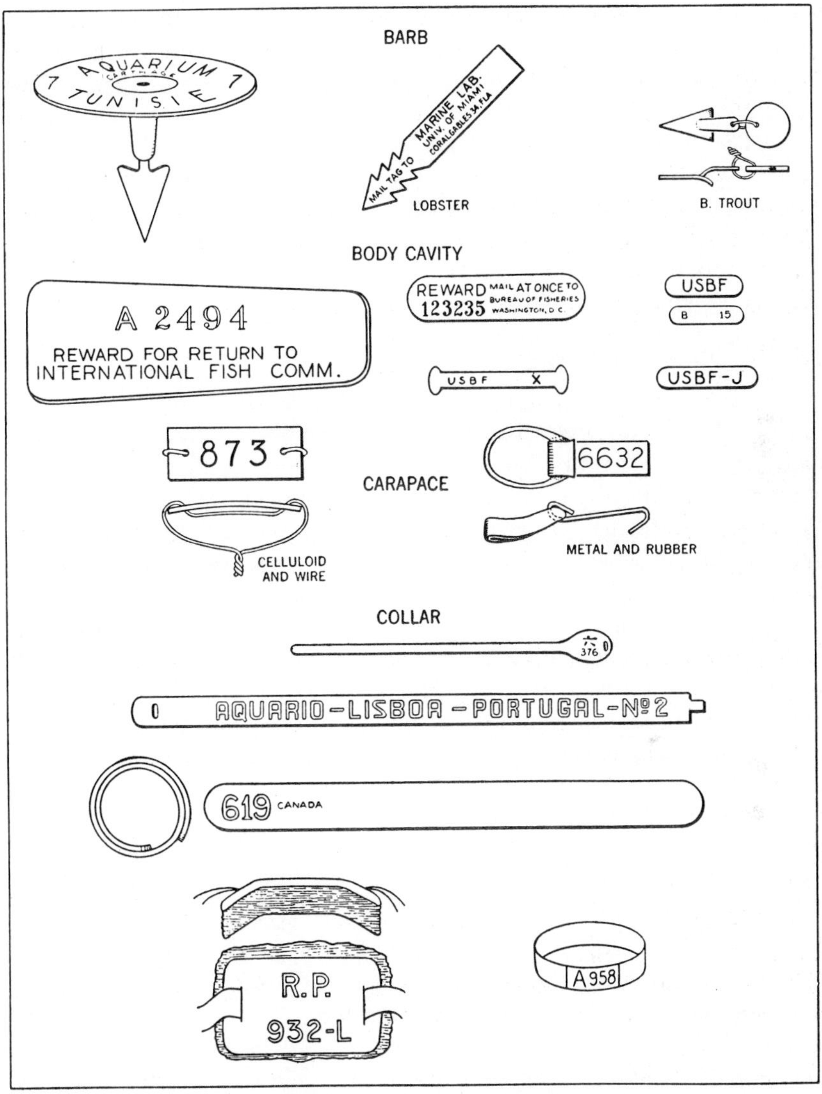

FIG. 16·2 Types of barb, body-cavity, carapace, and collar tags.

sters by the Marine Laboratory of the University of Miami. One of these tags, on hand, consists of a piece of stiff white Celluloid over ½ mm thick, measuring 40 mm by 6 mm. One end is sharpened to a point 6 mm long, with three triangular-shaped notches (or barbs) on each side. Each notch is 1 mm deep and 2½ mm long. The front edge of each notch is perpendicular to the long axis of the tag. One side of the tag is printed with the address, and the reverse gives directions, "Tell where, when, and by whom caught." The two surfaces are covered (over the printing) with a very thin layer of transparent Celluloid.

A barb tag used on brown trout by A. E. Eipper at Cornell consists of a thin piece of aluminum 15 mm long with a sharp point and two barbs bent slightly down. A red Celluloid disk 9.5 mm in diameter and ½ mm thick is attached to the shaft of the barb by a metal link. It is thrust into the skin just in front of the dorsal fin and pulled back slightly to anchor the barbs.

## 16·10   Body-cavity tag

This tag can be defined as any material inserted loose into the body cavity. It was invented by Robert A. Nesbit for marking squeteague in Chesapeake Bay in 1931. His original tag consisted of a strip of colored Celluloid about 0.7 mm thick that was usually about 1⅝ by ¼ inches. Later he changed the shape to make the tags wider. This type of tag is attached by making a small vertical incision in the body wall, usually with a scalpel, and inserting the tag.

Various sizes of Celluloid body-cavity tags have been used. The very large wedge-shaped tag was devised in 1935 by John L. Kask (1936). It is made of red Celluloid 1.5 mm in thickness, for use on halibut. Sizes as small as 12 mm by 3 mm by 1 mm have been used on various other species including trout, salmon, cod, haddock, and mackerel. It is the only tag, with the possible exception of the internal anchor, that can be applied to very small fish and remain with the fish to be returned from the adult fish after it has made a tremendous increase in size.

The magnetic body-cavity tag was devised by George A. Rounsefell and Edwin H. Dahlgren in 1932. The first tags were used on Alaska herring. They were very small (13 mm by 3 mm by 0.7 mm) and made of pure nickel. The chief advantage of the magnetic tag lay in the ability to recover tags by electromagnets from the reduction plants as the fish are processed into meal. These tags were modified by Rounsefell and Dahlgren in 1934 to a larger size (19 mm by 4 mm by 1.0 mm) and they were now made of steel as the nickel was not sufficiently magnetic to be readily recoverable by the magnets except under ideal conditions. Although most of the steel tags were nickel-plated, it was soon discovered that the bare steel did not corrode in the body cavity. However, plating renders the tags much brighter and easier to detect when one is searching the magnets.

Attempts have been made to improve the shape of these tags to prevent shedding of tags. Dahlgren (1936) tried the dumbbell-shaped tags, and Janssen and Aplin (1945) tried square ends, but in neither case was there any significant improvement, either in shedding or in the magnetic recovery. As soon as the magnetic body-cavity tags proved their value on the Alaska herring, they were widely adopted along the Pacific Coast for use on herring, pilchards (sardines) (*Sardinops caerulea*), and mackerel (*Pneumatophorus diego*). In 1937 Dahlgren varied the thickness of tags trying metal of 0.5, 1.0, and 2.0 mm in thickness and found that the 2.0-mm tags were superior.

An electronic tag detector (Dahlgren 1936) was developed in 1935 by Edwin H. Dahlgren with the aid of the electrical engineering faculty of the University of Washington. With this instrument the fish bearing the metal tags could be detected as they were unloaded from the fishing vessel instead of after being processed into meal. It was now possible for the first time to gain very accurate data on locality of recapture of small schooling fish.

## 16·11   Collar tag

This is a ring of any material attached wholly by encirclement without piercing any tissues. It may bear an attached plate. Early attempts by Atkins in 1872 using rubber bands and by Sella in 1911 using copper chains yielded no returns. Rubber bands on yellowtail (*Seriola quinqueradiata*) in Japan gave a few returns, and later they were tried on mackerel in the Black Sea with only slightly better results.

The first successful collar tag was a thin flat strip of silver on the caudal peduncle of Japanese yellowtail (9.0 per cent recovery) and Japanese mackerel (0.7 per cent recovery).

Commencing in 1925 several thousand mackerel were tagged on the Atlantic Coast of the United States and Canada with Celluloid poultry leg bands around the caudal peduncle. Recaptures were usually less than 2 per cent. A few remained at liberty as long as 3 years, but usually the fish were very emaciated, and the caudal peduncle showed severe chafing.

Sette (1950) experimented with several types of collar tags on mackerel confined in a large outdoor pool. The Celluloid band used in these experiments was a strip 0.635 mm thick, 8 mm wide, and 50 mm long, molded to form a circle 11.1 mm in inside diameter and overlapping about one third of the circumference. A Celluloid ring was also tried made of rods of Celluloid 2.5 mm in diameter and 38 mm in length cut obliquely at the ends to fit together when molded to a circle of 9.5 mm inside diameter. A third collar tag tested was a rubber band made of drainage tubing 9.5 mm in diameter with walls 0.33 mm thick cut into sections 9.5 mm wide.

None of the three tags was fully successful, but the Celluloid rings gave the best results, the rubber bands the poorest. These experiments did show that if a collar tag is at all loose on the caudal peduncle it may slip off over the tail. This limits the use of these tags since sufficient allowance for future growth cannot be made in tagging young mackerel.

## 16·12   Heincke ring tag

This was a special tag devised by Fr. Heincke that pierced the tissues and depended entirely on the spring of the metal and friction to hold it. It was used from 1902 to 1904 for marking 1766 European plaice (*Pleuronectes platessa*). The tag was an aluminum strip 20 mm by 6 mm by 0.75 mm thick and weighed 0.56 to 0.86 gram. Attachment was through the muscles near the posterior end of the dorsal fin. As recoveries were only 8.8 per cent, the least for any plaice-marking experiment, the tag was abandoned.

## 16·13   Heincke stud tag

This tag, also sometimes called the "collar button tag," consists of a disk to which is rigidly fastened a shaft with a pointed knob on the end. A second disk of rubber is slipped over the pointed knob. The tag was of ebonite, with the base 15 mm in diameter; the shaft was 4 mm in diameter and 10 mm in height. The head or knob of the shaft was 7 mm in height from its point to its base and 7 mm in diameter at the base. The ring that was slipped over the head was originally of hard black rubber. Later soft red rubber was also used and preferred by some.

From 1903 to 1911 over 27,000 European plaice were marked with this tag. Recoveries averaged 20.8 per cent which is below the average for the Petersen types of tags. It has been discontinued, but some modifications, using a smaller head and shaft to reduce the size of the wound, might give better results.

## 16·14   Hook tag

This is a shaft piercing the tissues and held by the curve of the shaft and usually by one or more barbs. This is sometimes not actually a tag but a method of marking commercial fishing hooks so that when a fish breaks the line and escapes the fisherman can report the incident, and if the fish is recaptured bearing the hook its movement can

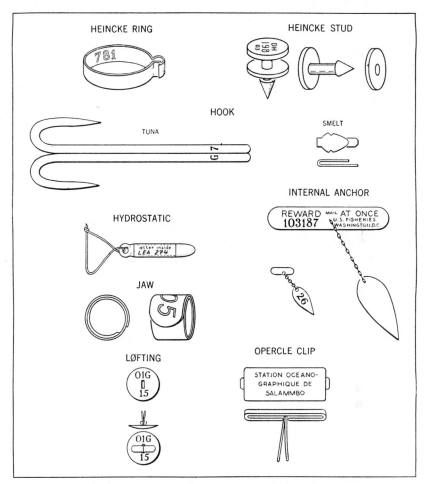

Fig. 16·3  Types of tags including Heincke ring, Heincke stud, hook, hydrostatic, internal anchor, jaw, Løfting, and opercle clip.

be computed.  Tuna hooks were marked in Portugal and France with the locality and a number for the year.  John R. Webster of the U. S. Fish and Wildlife Service refined this system by stamping serial numbers on the lily irons of the harpoons of co-operative swordfishermen sailing out of Boston and Gloucester.  He obtained a few recoveries.

A tag developed by R. A. McKenzie (1950) of the Fisheries Research Board of Canada in 1942 should probably be classified as a hook tag since it depends on the bend of the shaft for attachment. It was used on several thousand smelt (*Osmerus mordax*) in the Miramichi River, New Brunswick. The tag consists of a very thin strip of red Celluloid (less than ⅛ mm) bent back on itself. It is thrust through a small incision in the opercle. The inner portion is 15 mm long by 2.5 mm wide and pointed. The outer half is of the same width for 2 mm and then swells in width to form a tear-shaped disk 12 mm long by 8 mm wide. This disk is variously notched on the edges to indicate different marking experiments.

## 16·15   Hydrostatic tag

This tag is attached by a wire piercing the tissues; the tag itself is hollowed so that its specific gravity is very slightly less than that of water. Developed by Einar Lea of Norway it has given remarkably high recoveries compared with the Petersen tag. It is made of a piece of hollow Celluloid tube. Each end is stopped with a short Celluloid rod. The rear end is tapered. The forward end is flattened and contains a small hole for attaching the wire.

Inside of the hollow tag complete directions are printed in two languages on a roll of thin tissue paper 14.5 cm long. The sample tag on hand measures 28 mm over-all and nearly 4 mm in diameter. The tag is very conspicuous as the center transparent section is of a yellowish tinge, while the ends have been dipped in a bright blue. This may prove to be the most important tag to be developed in recent years.

## 16·16   Internal anchor tag

This tag consists of a flexible chain or thread (with or without any attached material on the outside) that pierces the body wall and is held by being attached to material inside the body cavity.

This tag was developed in 1936 by George A. Rounsefell, to meet the need for an externally visible tag in which the wound could heal quite completely and the fish could undergo a very large increase in size without losing the tag. The idea was furnished by John L. Kask, who in 1930 tried a metal tag in the body cavity, with a protruding chain, on a few flounders in a live car, and found that the wound healed completely. The small-sized internal anchor was tested in 1937 on young sockeye salmon 2 to 6 inches in length, held in tanks. The wound completely healed within a few days, but the experiment had to be terminated at the end of 9 months. Haddock were tagged in Maine with 2 large sizes of internal anchors, which yielded returns comparable to those from the Herrington bachelor button or the improved Petersen, from haddock tagged in the same experiment.

The internal anchor tag has one great advantage over the body-cavity tag. It has long been known that a significant proportion of the fish marked with body-cavity tags lose them within a short time after tagging. Thus Janssen and Aplin (1945) discovered in holding experiments with sardines that 8 to 58 per cent of the body-cavity tags were shed within 5 months. The internal anchor tag is not shed as the chain prevents it from moving either forward or backward in the body cavity, and thus it cannot escape by the insertion wound. Being held in one position against the body wall it is quickly encysted firmly by tissue. Body cavity tags move freely about at first and often move against the heart. In all of the fish examined that had been tagged with internal anchor tags, the tag was encysted against the body wall where it had been inserted.

## 16·17  Jaw tag

This is any tag that is attached by encirclement of any of the bones of the jaw. It was developed by David S. Shetter, for use on fresh-water fishes, by deforming ordinary strap tags so that they are more or less circular and can be placed around a jaw bone. Later he used a C-shaped tag and special pliers. Recently this practice has been criticized on the grounds that there is evidence that fish so tagged do not feed properly. They lose weight and become significantly thinner than unmarked fish. There is also some question whether or not they compare with unmarked fish in their catchability.

John L. Hart of the Fisheries Research Board of Canada has designed a jaw tag for use on the maxillary of the cultus or ling cod (*Ophiodon elongatus*). It is a red Celluloid strip that forms a ring, overlapping itself almost twice. The strip is 13 mm wide and about 0.7 mm thick with rounded and tapered ends. All edges are carefully smoothed, which is very important with Celluloid to prevent chafing. He reports that it has not affected growth. This appears to be an ideal tag for this particular species and may be adaptable to many others.

## 16·18  Løfting tag

The Løfting type consists of two plates or disks, in which a shaft or wire that pierces the tissues is rigidly attached to one disk, loosely attached to the other. It was devised in 1901 by Løfting, and consists of two silver disks, 10 mm and 12 mm in diameter. The smaller disk carries in the center a cylindrical shaft 3 mm high, on which are soldered two flat arms. The larger disk has an oblong hole in the center.  It is attached by punching a hole through the opercle, and placing the smaller disk underneath with the shaft protrduing out through the hole and through the hole in the larger disk.  The disks are fastened together by pressing the two arms of the shaft down on the outer disk.  The slightly convex side of the outer disk is applied toward the gill cover.  Disks of 8 and 9 mm are used on smaller fish.  This mark has one disk fastened rigidly, the other loosely, to the shaft, differing in this respect from the bachelor button with both disks fastened rigidly to the shaft, and from the Petersen tag in which the two disks are connected loosely by a pin or wire.  The Løfting tag was used on Atlantic salmon in the Gudenaa River, Denmark, from 1901 to 1912 but gave poor results.

### 16·19    Opercle clip tag

This consists of a single plate or disk rigidly attached at one point to two wires or shafts that pierce the opercle and are spread apart.  Heldt in 1932 used this tag made of silver or aluminum to mark tuna in Tunis, without, however, stating the size of the tag, or the quantity used.  It cannot be recommended.

### 16·20    Petersen tag

This popular tag consists of two plates or disks (sometimes double) attached loosely together by a wire or a pin that pierces the tissues.  Invented by Petersen in 1894 for use on the European plaice (*Pleuronectes platessa*), this is perhaps the most widely used and the most generally successful of all tags in present use.  It first consisted of two bone disks connected by a silver wire twisted at either end.  It is attached to the opercle, the caudal peduncle, the nape, or the back under the dorsal fin.  In spite of the rapid deterioration of bone in sea water, early investigators favored its use as they feared that placing metal plates in contact with the surface of the fish would cause necrosis of the underlying tissues.  The identifying numbers burned into the surface of the bone soon became illegible as the organic material rotted in sea water.  To remedy this fault one or more brass disks were attached outside of the bone disks to carry the serial numbers.  As many as 4 disks were used, two bone disks next to the tissues, and a brass disk over each bone disk.  As early as 1902 Garstang in marking plaice used a white bone disk on the underside and an oval, concave disk of brass on the upper side.  The concavity of the brass disk was supposed to prevent the tissues from growing over the tag as often happens after tags have been out for some time.

A Petersen tag of two silver disks fastened together with a silver pin, head inside, was used by Hjort for tagging large cod on the opercle in 1913.

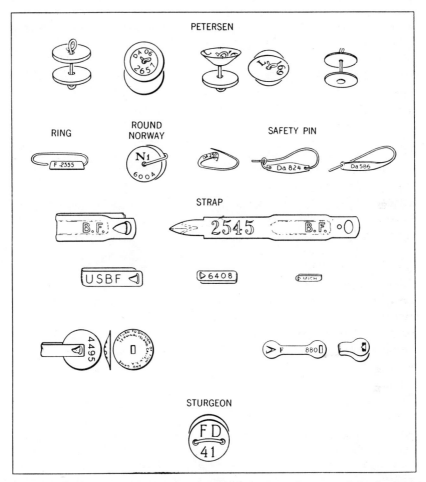

Fig. 16·4  Types of tags including Petersen, ring, round Norway, safety pin, strap, and sturgeon.

Commencing about 1905, ebonite disks often were substituted for bone. Soon it became customary to use two ebonite disks, especially for marking cod and plaice. This tag became identified by the name of the Scottish plaice label. Later Celluloid was often substituted for ebonite. Various sizes of tags were used varying from about 6.5 to 16.5 mm.

A modification of the Petersen tag was made in 1930 by Robert A. Nesbit which consisted of a pure nickel pin instead of a silver wire, and thin Celluloid disks with printed instructions on them covered by a thin coat of transparent Celluloid. His disks were usually 12.5 mm in diameter and 0.6 mm thick. They were used on striped bass, flounders, scup, shad, cod, haddock, etc. Usually one red and one white disk are used, with either the red or white disk outside according to the color of the fish.

A white disk of 13.5 mm with a red center 7.5 mm in diameter was used by Kask to mark sockeye salmon in British Columbia so that they could be easily spotted while on the spawning beds.

The disks for use on shrimp along the South Atlantic and Gulf Coasts are 10 mm in diameter for large shrimp and 8 mm for small shrimp. Disks of 10 mm were used by Scattergood for tagging lobsters.

## 16·21   Ring tag

This consists of a rigid ring that pierces the tissues. The ends are free but the tag holds because of its shape. A silver ring through the adipose fin was tried by Archer in 1884 on 10 Atlantic salmon in the Sands River, Norway; none were recaptured. Løfting in 1898 clamped a horseshoe-shaped ring on the first dorsal fin ray of Atlantic salmon. He abandoned the mark, and so it was doubtless a failure. The ring illustrated is after Russell (1932).

## 16·22   Round Norway tag

Two disks are connected by a wire through a hole in each disk. The wire pierces the tissues twice making a complete circle with the ends fastened together. This tag, used on cod in Norway, has no desirable features.

## 16·23   Safety-pin tag

This tag is essentially a safety pin. It consists of a bent wire or pin (it may carry a plate or have a flattened portion) that pierces the tissues and is held by the point on one end springing against a groove or resting in a loop of the other end. A safety-pin tag of aluminum bearing an aluminum plate was used by Farran in 1905 and 1906 on 197 plaice in Ireland. The point of the tag pierced about 1.5 cm of skin on the back of the plaice, was sprung into a groove on the other end, and pinched together with pliers. Only 44 tags were recovered.

Young sea trout were marked by Johansen and Løfting with a safety pin through the back in front of the dorsal fin. Results are not known.

The safety-pin tag has been a failure.

### 16·24   Strap tag

This is a flat metal strip (which occasionally carries an attached plate or disk), in which one pointed end pierces the tissues and is clinched through a hole in the other end.

The original strap tag was adapted from the cattle ear tag by Charles H. Gilbert for tagging salmon in Alaska. It was made of pure aluminum, 69 mm when stretched out, 9.5 mm at the widest point, and about

Fig. 16·5   A smallmouth black bass taken in an electric seine and marked with a strap tag on the opercle. (Credit: Missouri Conservation Commission)

1.4 mm in thickness. The strap clinched with special pliers onto the upper lobe of the caudal fin, is still widely used for tagging salmon on the Pacific Coast. Out of over 83,000 Pacific salmon tagged with the strap tags from 1922 to 1936, recoveries averaged 26.9 per cent.

Strap tags were used by William C. Schroeder from 1923 until 1933 to tag cod, haddock, and pollock off New England. His strap tag measured 57.5 mm in length, 6.4 mm in width, and 0.7 mm in thickness. He tried tags made of silver, aluminum, copper, silver-plated copper, and Monel metal, but found no obvious differences in recoveries between the different metals, and so after 1923 all of his tags were of Monel metal. From 1923 until 1933 nearly 52,000 cod, over 18,000 haddock, and nearly 5000 pollock were tagged by the United

States and Canada in the Atlantic with strap tags on the upper lobe of the caudal fin. Schroeder states that some were tagged on the jaw in 1927, but although it seemed impossible for the tag to become dislodged the recoveries from the jaw-tagged fish were not sufficiently better to justify the discontinuance of the tail-marking method. Since the numbers so tagged are not even given, it is impossible to verify the soundness of this conclusion. Schroeder mentions the capture by the tagging vessels of 42 cod that had been at liberty for at least one year, and at the same time the vessels captured 63 cod with scars on their tails where tags had fallen off. The use of a strap tag on the tail is excusable only for short-term experiments.

Commencing in 1925 the International Fisheries Commission used strap tags very successfully on the opercle of halibut. High percentages of recoveries have been made and fish have been retaken after over a decade at sea. As the opercle grows, the tag maintains about the same position relative to the edge of the opercle, leaving behind the small wound a long healed-over scar to show where the tag had been in past years when the opercle was smaller. Their large strap tag was 69 mm by 8 mm by 1.0 mm and weighed 4 grams. This large strap was changed in 1927 to 69 mm by 9 mm by 0.65 mm and weighed 2.6 grams. The strap used for smaller halibut was 58 mm by 6.5 mm by 0.6 mm and weighed 1.6 grams. The tags always are attached to the upper side of the halibut.

A smaller strap tag, 35 mm by 3.5 mm by 0.6 mm, has been used unsuccessfully on the opercle of mullet, herring, steelhead trout, and Pacific mackerel.

A very small strap tag, or "fingerling" tag was introduced by Carl L. Hubbs in 1930 for young trout and other small freshwater species. It measures 21 mm (9.4 mm clinched), by 2 mm by 0.3 mm and weighs only 0.0675 gram. It has been used with considerable success on freshwater species, attached to fins, opercle, and the upper or lower jaw. These tags of pure nickel were tried on Alaska herring, but recoveries were only 0.5 per cent against 4.0 per cent for the nickel body-cavity tag, and so it was discontinued.

Four thousand tuna were marked from 1934 to 1938 in California by H. C. Godsil with a sterling silver strap tag bearing a red Celluloid disk. None were recaptured. The tuna were tagged on the preopercle.

Strap tags, because of the uniformity and speed with which they can be applied, have been very popular. In spite of their great popularity they have proved successful only on halibut, except for very short-term use on salmon.

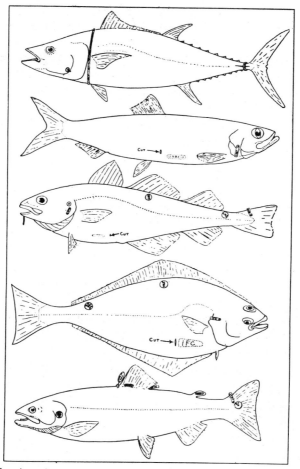

Fig. 16·6  Showing placement of tags on different types of fishes.  Top, mackerel-like fishes; next, herring-like fishes; next, gadoid fishes; next, flatfishes; and bottom, Salmonidae.

## 16·25  Sturgeon tag

It consists of two disks, each with two holes.  A wire pierces the tissues in two places making a complete circle and attaches the disks together on each side of the fish.  It closely resembles the Archer tag and is attached through the skin at the base of the front of the dorsal fin.  The illustration is after Russell (1932).

## 16·26  Carapace tag

These tags (Figures 16·2 and 16·6) are used on crustacea.  There are various modifications, but the two illustrated are typical.  The metal and rubber tag is used only on lobsters, the rubber over the rostrum and the metal hook over the posterior end of the telson.

FIG. 16·7   Lobster marked with a Celluloid and wire carapace tag.   (Credit: Leslie W. Scattergood)

### 16·27   Mutilation.   Fin clipping

The marking of young salmon has been chiefly by clipping of fins of the downstream migrants, because of the necessity for a mark that would remain on the fish throughout a long period of very rapid growth. Where several experiments are going on simultaneously, the mark is too limited, as there are only ten combinations of two-fin marks (excluding the pectorals) available. Because of the occasional regeneration of fins that are not clipped off closely at the base, and the occasional natural occurrence of fish with one fin missing, it is not safe to mark only one fin. The half-dorsal and half-anal marks that have sometimes been used are difficult to distinguish between a fully clipped fin that has slightly regenerated. Such half-fin marks are not realistic. The anal fin is very difficult to clip on small fish. The sizes marked vary from about 1½ inches to 6 inches or more.

The estimates of time required to mark fish vary widely. After marking several hundred thousand we find that many estimates are extremely optimistic. When one does nothing else but mark (someone else does the weighing, catching, removal of fish, etc.), a rate of 300 fish per hour is a very respectable rate if the fish are of a convenient size, about 3 to 5 inches. Women may attain and maintain up to 400 fish per hour, but many men never exceed 300.

For some species such as the smallmouth black bass, the end of the maxillary bone may be clipped off for a mark. It is not a conspicuous mark and may easily be overlooked by a sportsman.

**References**

Atkins, Charles G.
1885. The biennial spawning of salmon. (The Bucksport Experiments.) *Trans. Am. Fish. Soc.* 1885, pp. 89–94.

Cable, Louella E.
1950. A cheek tag for marking fish, with semi-automatic pliers for application of tag. *J. du Conseil 16* (2):185–191. (Tag illustrated.)

Dahl, Knut
1914. Merkning av utvandrende laksyngel. *Norsk Fiskeritidende* 1914, p. 251.

Dahl, Knut, and Sven Somme
1936. Experiments in salmon marking in Norway, 1935. Skrifter utgitt av Det Norske Videnskaps-Akademi i Oslo. I. *Matematisk-Naturviden-skapelig Klasse,* 1935, part 2, no. 12.

Dahlgren, Edwin H.
1936. Further developments in the tagging of the Pacific herring, *Clupea pallasii. J. du Conseil 11* (2):229–247 (Electronic tag detector).

Davidson, Frederick A., and Leroy S. Christey
1938. The migrations of pink salmon (Oncorhynchus gorbuscha) in the Clarence and Sumner Straits regions of southeastern Alaska. *Bull. U. S. Bur. Fish. 48* (25):643–666.

Janssen, John F., and J. Alfred Aplin
1945. The effect of internal tags upon sardines. *Calif. Div. Fish and Game, Bur. Mar. Fish., Bull. 61:* 43–62.

Kask, John L.
1936. The experimental marking of halibut. *Science, N.S. 83:* 435–436.

McKenzie, R. A.
  1950. A new celluloid opercular tag. *Trans. Am. Fish. Soc. 78:* 114–116. (Tag illustrated.)
Nesbit, Robert A.
  1933. A new method of marking fish by means of internal tags. *Trans. Am. Fish. Soc. 63:* 306–307.
O'Malley, Henry, and Willis H. Rich
  1919. Migration of adult sockeye salmon in Puget Sound and Fraser River. *U. S. Comm. Fish. Rept.* 1918, App. 8: 1–38.
Rounsefell, George A.
  1942. Field experiments in selecting the most efficient tag for use in haddock studies. *Trans. Am. Fish. Soc. 71:* 228–235.
Rounsefell, George A., and Edwin H. Dahlgren
  1933. Tagging experiments on the Pacific herring, *Clupea pallasii. J. du Conseil 8* (3):371–384.
Rounsefell, George A., and Edwin H. Dahlgren
  1935. Races of herring, *Clupea pallasii,* in southeastern Alaska. *Bull. U. S. Bur. Fish. 48* (17):119–141.
Rounsefell, George A., and John L. Kask
  1945. How to mark fish. *Trans. Am. Fish. Soc. 73:* 320–363. (Extensive bibliography.)
Russell, E. S.
  1932. Guide to the fish marks used by the members of the International Council for the Exploration of the Sea and by some non-participant countries. *J. du Conseil 7* (1):133–165.
Schroeder, William C.
  1930. Migrations and other phases in the life history of the cod off southern New England. *Bull. U. S. Bur. Fish. 46:* 1–136.
Sette, Oscar Elton
  1950. Biology of the Atlantic mackerel (*Scomber scombrus*) of North America. Part II. Migrations and habits. *U. S. Fish and Wildl. Serv., Fish. Bull. 51* (49):251–358.

# 17 · TECHNIQUES OF TAGGING AND RECOVERY

## 17·1   What tag should be used?

The best tag for any experiment depends upon several factors, such as:

**The length of the time that the tag should remain on the fish.** The tagging of adult Pacific salmon in which the whole experiment can occupy only a few months can be accomplished with a strap tag, but the same tag is poor for immature salmon that will remain longer at sea. Body-cavity tags have probably the best record for staying on fish, but because of the difficulty of recovery they are often excluded from consideration. It is better when in doubt to test the types of tag that may be suitable rather than to select one empirically.

**Personnel available for tagging.** Doubt will be cast on the interpretation of the results of experiments if there is any lack of uniformity in technique. Unless the work is competently supervised there is always danger of rough handling and improper technique. Tags such as the Archer, body cavity, and internal anchors should only be applied by a skilled tagger.

**Species.** Tags that remain well on one type of fish may be of little value on another. The indiscriminate use of the same tag on various types of fish is not likely to furnish quantitative results. Thus, the strap tag, although excellent when attached to the opercle of the halibut, has proved very poor on cod, haddock, and pollock. The body-cavity tag will work on nearly any species, but its lack of external visibility often precludes its use.

No adequate external tag has been used on the mackerel-like fishes. The collar tags caused considerable chafing. The Petersen failed on the opercle. The strap on the opercle yielded very low recoveries. The body-cavity tag works well where magnets can be installed to recover tags from processed fish. In other areas the internal anchor may be the answer.

On herring and pilchards the magnetic body-cavity tag is the most successful one in use.

For soft-bodied fishes the Celluloid body-cavity tag has been successful on the squeteague and scup. For external use on such types both the hydrostatic and the internal anchor should be considered.

**Methods of capture and handling.** The usual methods by which fish are captured and handled are important in the selection of a tag and its proper application. For species that are handled individually and cleaned at the time of catching there is a large choice of tags. A fair-sized brightly colored Celluloid body-cavity tag is usually found when cleaning. The fact that it will remain with the fish for a long period often outweighs the consideration of the possibility of it being overlooked in cleaning. Kask (1936) discovered that, when halibut tagged with both a strap tag on the opercle and the large halibut body-cavity tag were caught, the fishermen were as likely to overlook the strap tag as the other. It is of great importance in using external tags always to attach them to the side of the fish that is customarily held uppermost in cleaning.

Although the body-cavity tag works successfully with Atlantic Coast mackerel, it is not used because the fish are shipped to the markets without cleaning, and tags returned from the markets do not give the desired information.

For small fish that are captured by the million the magnetic tag is the only answer thus far.

## 17·2   How are tags recovered?

Every proposal for tagging fish should be accompanied with a plan for recovering tags. Throughout the literature one finds failure to obtain recoveries because of neglect of this feature of a tagging experiment. When Archer (1893) commenced marking Norwegian salmon, he also started payment of rewards for the return of the tags with information as to recapture. He fitted out a boat and personally canvassed outlying districts.

Robert A. Nesbit (1933) commenced the custom of printing full directions on Celluloid Petersen and body-cavity tags. This included the address, notice of a reward, and full directions on the reverse side of the body-cavity tags as follows:

State when and where caught or when and from whom purchased. Measure fish by tracing its outline carefully on paper. Send about 20 scales from each side of the fish.

The Celluloid disks and plates are made of laminated Celluloid, and the final printing on the outside of the red or white disks is covered with a thin transparent Celluloid layer. Such attention to detail makes a great difference in the number of tag returns as fishermen obtaining a tag without an address often will not bother to inquire about it. Often too a fisherman finding a tag and ignorant of the fact that a reward is offered for its return will keep the tag as a talisman.

Every halibut vessel on the Pacific Coast is furnished a log book free of charge by the International Fisheries Commission. The fly leaf describes the tagging experiments, and a place in the book is furnished to record tags with the pertinent information as the fish are caught. Agents in the principal halibut ports pay double rewards if they view the fish and take otoliths and measurements.

Fish buyers sometimes collect tags from the fishermen and pay the rewards. This method is very useful in getting full coverage of small scattered ports.

Pacific salmon are often tagged at the mouths of rivers to learn which tributaries are being utilized by runs entering the river at particular times. This necessitates sending parties into the field to observe the salmon on the spawning beds. Here a conspicuous tag such as the target-centered Petersen is very useful.

The problem of recovering tags from very small fish taken in large quantities has been solved by the use of the electromagnetic method of tag recovery by Rounsefell and Dahlgren (1933). This method was quickly adopted for sardines (pilchards) and mackerel on the Pacific Coast. The electronic tag detector developed by Dahlgren (1936) which permits the recovery of tags from any fish that in the course of handling can be passed through a coil offers wonderful possibilities, that have so far not been fully exploited.

It is important that any reward be sufficiently large to act as an inducement. Rewards have varied from 25 cents to $1.00, depending largely on the species of fish, the amount of information required, and the number of fish tagged. If funds for rewards are strictly limited, it is advisable to release fewer fish rather than to cut the reward. It is also poor policy to vary the amount of the reward in different years, or for different species; such a procedure causes ill will on the part of the fishermen. In the North Atlantic area the Fish and Wildlife Service facilitates the receipt of tags by giving out to sportsmen, dealers, and fishermen a double cardboard postal card containing inside a coin envelope for the tag and scale samples, and complete directions for recording measurements and information.

All advertising and publicity concerning tagging should cover a much wider area than that from which the investigator expects recoveries. Otherwise a noncompensatory error is introduced which cannot be estimated.

## 17·3   Tagging technique

Tagging methods are largely determined by the physical circumstances; tagging at sea in rough weather is quite different from tagging on a scow anchored in a harbor, from a live car in a stream, or from a hatchery trough. Strap tags come from the manufacturers on wooden or metal sticks, fifty tags, in serial order, on each stick. Petersen tags usually are in envelopes containing 100 consecutively numbered disks mixed together. As the serial number is only on one disk (usually the white Celluloid disk), the unnumbered disks can be kept in a shallow tray, or, better, the unnumbered disks can be threaded on pins in the laboratory, with the printing all facing the same way. This makes it easy to pick off one disk at a time with wet hands. The numbered disks should be threaded onto soft wire (silver wire is excellent) in batches of 100 in serial order. If a piece of parchment paper or perhaps a red disk is threaded on whenever a number is missing, attention will be drawn to it when recording. Some place the disks in shallow slots cut along a board which is handy for picking them up, but is not so handy when the sea is rough and the tags become mixed as the ship lurches. With the wire system not only can all of the tags be sorted on shore, but at sea one simply winds one end of the soft wire around a nail or staple in the side of the tagging box and picks the tags one at a time as needed off the other end. A slight kink in the wire will prevent any tags from sliding off.

Body-cavity tags and internal anchor tags can be kept in serial order by placing the tags consecutively between coils of a small spring. Each spring full of tags is kept in a coin envelope until ready for use.

For vessel tagging when it is cold or the spray is flying it is best to arrange a small canvas shelter in which the recorder can sit and jot down all measurements, weights, etc., as they are called out. If scale samples are being taken, use serially numbered coin envelopes with the number on each envelope corresponding to that on the tag. In good weather measurements are sometimes written on the coin envelopes *before* the scales are put in the envelopes, but usually it is best to use them merely as scale receptacles and to have a serially numbered data sheet ready. When no recorder is available, use sheets of opaque white Celluloid with a roughened surface, and you can write on it with wet hands. Afterwards you can file the sheets or scrub them off to use again.

For cod, salmon, and other fish with slimy scales a special handy notebook was developed by C. H. Gilbert and W. H. Rich. The book measures 3¾ inches by 6¾ inches. Each of the 24 pages of high-quality water-resistant paper is ruled horizontally on one side into five spaces. The scales are scraped off the knife onto the edge of the page (5 samples per page), which is then folded over for 1¾ inches so that the scales are sealed between two thicknesses of paper to which they firmly adhere. The remaining 1¼ inches on the left margin of the page is available to jot down weights and measurements on each sample. The book has a heavy glazed cardboard cover.

For tagging large active fish like salmon it is best to use a cradle or box. For salmon, when using strap tags on the caudal one man slides the fish into a small padded box while another clamps the tag on the tail which protrudes from the short box. The first man then tosses the salmon clear of the nets. Under favorable conditions 150 to 200 pink salmon can be tagged per hour. Since pinks are all two-year-old fish, no scales or measurements are required.

Clark (1934) wrote concerning the tagging of striped bass:

When a bass is caught on the line, it is brought aboard the boat or on shore. The back of the fish is grasped with the left hand, using a wet gunny sack to protect the hand from spines and to prevent rubbing off of more slime than necessary. Next, the hook is removed as carefully as possible, the gunny sack thrown over the snout of the fish, and the fish placed on its belly on a flat surface. Then with a small awl (⅟₁₆ inch in diameter), a hole is punched through the back of the fish at right angles to the length of the fish, ¼ inch below the ridge of the back. The pin, with the white disc against its head, lettering exposed, is put through the awl hole; the red disc is put on the pin; and the pin is then curled over with a small pair of pointed-nosed pliers. The length of the fish from snout to end of tail is measured and recorded, and the fish is returned alive to the water. The whole operation of tagging takes about one minute, and in no case has it seemed to weaken the fish to any extent.

Tagging fish caught by otter trawls (except for flatfish) has not been very successful, as many are drowned or crushed in capture. Haddock have been successfully tagged when caught by hook-and-line gear in water up to 30 fathoms in depth, and perhaps otter trawl gear may be so fished as to bring fish to the surface in sufficiently good condition for marking. Fish with large swim bladders must be brought to the surface very gradually, or the bladder is forced out through the mouth as the tremendous pressure is released.

The tagging of Pacific halibut is well described by Thompson and Herrington (1930) who state:

The capture of halibut for marking purposes has in all cases been accomplished by the commercial hook and line method. . . . The gear was allowed to "soak" (remain on the bottom) from two to four hours only, instead of the more protracted period which is the accepted practice now among the commercial vessels. ˙. . . When brought to the surface on the gear, each halibut was lifted inboard as carefully as possible by the fisherman at the roller. If the fish was hooked in such a manner that the injury was obviously mortal, it was thrown into the checkers. . . . If the injury did not appear to be certainly mortal, the ganging (short line from the hook to the ground line) was immediately cut and the fish passed over to one of the scientific assistants for tagging . . . the hook was carefully and quickly removed by means of pliers, cutters, and a specially designed wooden instrument somewhat similar to the fisherman's "gob stock." The degree of injury to the fish was then ascertained. If an important artery had been cut, the gills injured, or the visceral cavity punctured or opened, the fish was discarded for tagging purposes. In all of the marking work on the banks south of Cape Spencer 36.9 per cent of the halibut caught have been tagged, and on the banks north and west of Cape Spencer 29.8 per cent.

The halibut . . . was measured . . . on a board, or tagging "cradle." This was a heavy wooden trough, with a head piece across one end so designed as to fit the convex under surface of the fish. Thus the fish was held in a natural position, and, when the longitudinal axis of the cradle was placed parallel to that of the ship, the concavity prevented the sliding of the fish from side to side with the roll of the vessel. . . . Measurement and the attachment of the tag were quickly done. The greatest number tagged in one day was 361, although the average was much below this. It was found that the fish could be handled as fast as brought in on the gear, so that, practically, the limiting factor for the number marked was the rate of capture.

For tagging herring in Alaska the fish are first confined in a live car made in sections and held together by half-inch bolts so that it can be quickly dismantled for transport from place to place. Buoyed up by pontoons, it is usually about 10 feet wide by 20 feet long and 3 feet deep. It is made of 2-inch plank with wire hardware cloth on a portion of the bottom. After capture with a beach seine or purse seine the fish are allowed to swim into part of the livecar. A canvas shelter is erected over the anchored end of the live box to protect against the wind. The herring are dipped into a large tub or half barrel. One man holds each fish in both hands firmly while a second man makes an incision in the body wall just anterior to the ventral fin and inserts the steel tag into the body cavity. From 300 to 400 fish per hour can be tagged by this method. The tagged fish are dropped into a section of the car, and once or twice a day they are released as a small school. This reduces the loss from predation which occurs when they are released singly.

Pilchards are often tagged from live bait tanks on the decks of vessels, which are provided with a circulating pump to keep the water fresh. Each tagged pilchard has usually been released as tagged, sometimes with the vessel underway.

In attaching bachelor button and Petersen tags to the opercle the usual procedure is first to make a hole with a leather punch. In tagging haddock with the improved Petersen tag this is unnecessary as the

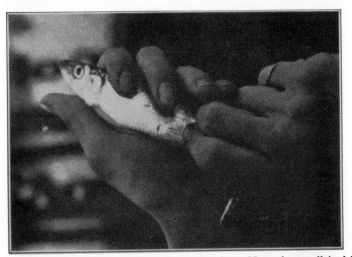

FIG. 17·1 Inserting a body-cavity tag into a herring. Note the small incision in the body wall. (Credit: J. C. Stevenson, Fisheries Research Board, Canada)

nickel pins are stiff enough to pierce the opercle at the point of attachment. This smaller hole is desirable. Petersen tags should not be put on too tightly as they will cut off the circulation in the tissues. The tissues will die, and a hole will result through which the inside disk will fall out and the tag will be lost.

Great caution should always be observed never to use tags with rough edges. Metal body-cavity tags are usually tumbled to remove all sharp edges, and the same should be done to Celluloid tags as the smallest sliver of Celluloid may penetrate a vital organ, and Celluloid when stamped out presents tiny toothlike projections.

**References**

Archer, William E.
  1893. Natural history notes on salmon in Norway. *Scotland Fish. Bd. Ann. Rept. 11* (2):55–71.
Clark, G. H.
  1934. Tagging of striped bass. *Calif. Fish and Game 20* (1):14–19.

Dahlgren, Edwin H.
 1936. Further developments in the tagging of the Pacific herring, *Clupea pallasii. J. du Conseil 11* (2) :229–247.
Kask, John L.
 1936. The experimental marking of halibut. *Science, N.S. 83:* 435–436.
Nesbit, Robert A.
 1933. A new method of marking fish by means of internal tags. *Trans. Am. Fish. Soc. 63:* 306–307.
Rounsefell, George A., and John L. Kask
 1945. How to mark fish. *Trans. Am. Fish. Soc. 73:* 320–363. (Extensive bibliography.)
Thompson, W. F., and William C. Herrington
 1930. Life history of the Pacific halibut: (1) Marking experiments. *Rept. Int. Fish Comm. 2:* 137 pp.

# 18 · HOW TO DETERMINE AGE

## 18·1 Introduction

The age composition of a population should be known for proper management. A biologist working on a management program for the striped bass should know that these fish can be expected to live up to 31 years of age while the biologist interested in the control of the longnose gar needs to know that these fish can be expected to live about 11 years. Knowledge of the correct age of fish is essential in solving such life-history problems as longevity, rates of growth, and age at maturity or spawning time.

Age and growth are closely related, but since the actual processes of determining them are different we shall deal with them in separate chapters.

Three general methods of determining the age of fishes are available, namely: comparison of length–frequency distributions, recovery of marked fish, and interpretation of the layers that are laid down in the hard parts of the fish.

## 18·2 Length–frequency

The length–frequency distribution has been used to estimate the age of fish since the last part of the 19th century. This method is based on the fact that the lengths of fish of one age tend to form a normal distribution. Ages are determined then merely by counting the peaks (see Figure 18·1). The length–frequency method has often been adequate for the first 2 to 4 years of life, but has failed to separate reliably the older age groups, because of increasing overlap in length distribution (Figure 18·1). The overlap is due to the increased dispersion, which is measured by a larger standard deviation; furthermore, the increased overlap is due also to the lessened distance between modes. Other major disadvantages of the length–frequency method are: (1) Fishes of a size tend to school together; (2) hatching may occur at irregular times yielding size groupings not indicative of year

classes; (3) parts of a given year class may develop under variable
conditions resulting in groupings of different size but of the same age;
(4) one or more of the year classes may be poorly represented or lacking in the sample. To employ this method large random samples of the
population are necessary. Where the fish are scaleless or the scales
and hard structures too difficult to interpret, length–frequencies may
have to be resorted to. Frequently this method is used as a check on
the scale method of age determination, at least for the younger age
groups.

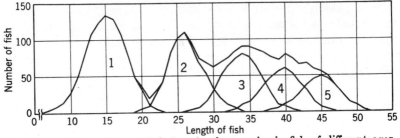

Fig. 18·1 Showing the overlapping size frequencies in fish of different ages.

## 18·3   Marking

The most direct and positive way of determining the age of fish is
by the liberation and recovery of marked or tagged fish of known age.
When these fish are subsequently recaptured, there can be no doubt,
providing accurate records have been kept, as to the age of each
specimen. The chief value of this method lies in checking the scale
method, as marking or tagging fish often becomes a costly and time-
consuming operation considering the low percentage of returns.

## 18·4   Interpretation of layers laid down in the hard parts of fish

Interpreting the annual layers deposited in the hard parts of fish is
the most generally accepted method for determining age. By far the
most important structure so employed is the scale, with the otolith or
ear stone, spine, and bony structures, such as the vertebra, the dentary
bone, and cross sections of other bony structures, following in that
order. This whole method depends on changes in the rate of growth
or metabolism during certain periods of the year as evidenced in these
hard parts. Accuracy in determining the age is dependent on the
ability to interpret these layers correctly. Clarity of the layers varies
with species and structure.

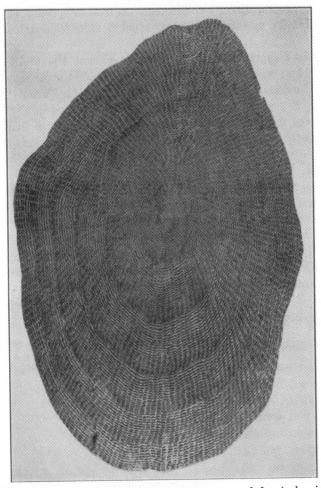

FIG. 18·2 The scale of a haddock (*Melanogrammus aeglefinus*) showing six annual rings. (Credit: Howard Schuck, U. S. Fish and Wildlife Service)

## 18·5 Otoliths

Otoliths are used frequently in determining the age of fish which are either scaleless or in which the scale sculpturing cannot be interpreted consistently and also for age determinations in species which have readable scales as a check on the scale determinations. Although each teleost has 6 otoliths, 3 on each side, the one ordinarily used in age determinations is the sagitta or sacculolith formed in the sacculus of the inner ear. A calcareous concretion, the otolith is laid down in concentric layers, a process which is probably going on at all times.

Unknown factors, possibly connected with food or seasons, cause slight color or density variations which produce definite laminations in some species.

There is disagreement as to whether or not the otoliths should be ground and polished. Martin (1941) sectioned the otoliths for reading, but Clemens (1951) found this unnecessary for burbot (*Lota lota maculosa*) 6 years of age and under. Otoliths, placed in a watch glass and covered with water, were oriented until a uniform field of light struck the convex surface at right angles. Otoliths were examined fresh and after they had been kept in a 3 per cent solution of trisodium phosphate.

With an increase in age, and this also holds true for the scale and such bones as vertebrae, opercles, and other face bones, an exact age determination becomes increasingly difficult to make as with the slowing down of growth the rings become too crowded to distinguish clearly. Frequently a species has an otolith too small or too irregular in shape to use. Use of the otolith necessitates killing of the fish, occasionally a disadvantage where a small population is concerned.

Adams' (1940) discussion of the otoliths of American Ostariophysi is a fine general reference.

## 18·6  Spines and rays

There are instances where spines and rays have been found serviceable, as the growth is regular with an annular addition of material so differentiated that it can be accurately read. Use of the spines and rays does not necessitate killing the fish.

Age determinations were made for the lake sturgeon, using cross sections of the marginal ray of the pectoral fin (Cuerrier and Roussow 1951). Rays were obtained by pincers or by cutting off near the fin base with a knife. Transverse sections, approximately 0.3 to 0.5 mm in thickness, were cut with a fine jeweler's saw. The slices were then placed in glycerin on a thin glass slide and examined under the binocular microscope.

Boyko (1946, as reprinted 1950) concludes that in the majority of fishes listed in his paper the annual rings are more distinctly expressed on their fin rays than on the scales. Further he records the percentage of indistinct annuli as 1 to 2 per cent of the fin rays, as compared to 15 to 20 per cent for scales. It was found that work with fin rays, including all procedures, required no more time than the usual routines with otoliths and scales. Others are cautioned to observe the following conditions:

1. Sections must be carefully dried, or, in some cases, heated before reading (Salmonidae, Clupeidae, and some other fishes) to make the annual rings visible.

2. Care must be taken to cut the fin rays exactly transversely.

The left pectoral spines (modified soft rays) of the channel catfish (*Ictalurus punctatus*) were used in determining the age of this species (Sneed 1951). The spines were loosened by pulling outward and rotating clockwise with a pair of pliers. No special treatment of the spines was necessary, and the author cautions against placing in formalin because this checks and cracks the bone, obscuring the year marks. It was necessary, if all annual rings were to be included, to cut the cross sections near the base, or articulating portion, of the spine.

## 18·7   Vertebrae

When scales and otoliths have not been available it has been possible to use the vertebrae. Aikawa (1937) working on the chub mackerel (*Pneumatophorus japonicus*) found that the scale sculpturing was too vague to interpret. However, when the centrum of the vertebrae was used, especially of the first five prehaemals, the layers of rings were fairly conspicuous and always measurable at the defined part of the vertebrae. Appelget and Smith (1951) selected the fifth vertebra for study of the age and rate of growth of the channel catfish (*Ictalurus punctatus*). Various methods of sectioning were tried but proved impractical. It was determined that direct observation of growth rings from the face of the centrum was practical. Tissue adhering to the centra was removed by a digesting solution made up of 0.7% pepsin in 0.2% hydrochloric acid. The vertebra was placed in 10 milliliters of the digestive solution and incubated for 24 hours at a temperature of 100° F. Annuli were determined with the aid of a low-power (7×) dissecting microscope.

## 18·8   Formation of the teleost scale

Although much investigation on other structures has been made, the scale still remains the most trustworthy and dependable means of estimating the age and calculating the growth of fishes. An understanding of the process of the formation of the teleost scale will serve as an aid in interpreting the structure. Neave (1943) has done much to supplement our histological knowledge of scale formation. The laying down of bone is associated with the presence of certain cells known as osteoblasts. In the teleost scale these osteoblasts are concentrated in primary papillae which first appear along the lateral line in the posterior region of the body. These primary papillae send out oblique outgrowths above and below the lateral line from which, at regular intervals, arise secondary papillae. Scales first appear in the primary papillae and then in the secondary papillae as the papillae are formed.

The usual teleost scale consists of an outer bony layer and an inner fibrillary plate consisting of closely applied fibrous lamellae. The scale first appears as osteoid tissue within a close investment of osteoblasts. The osteoid tissue is collagenous (containing collagen, an organic material) and does not become definitive bony tissue until the process of calcification is complete. The bony layer is formed only at the margin of the scale, through the activity of the osteoblasts lying at the periphery of the scale pocket. As long as the scale continues to grow, osteoid tissue is present at the outer margins. The term hyalodentine, long applied to the bony layer, has been used because of the erroneous belief that the bony layer was laid down by a single layer of osteoblasts on one side only, making it comparable with tooth formation. Actual sections show, however, that the bony tissue is laid down as a flat plate surrounded by the osteoblasts. The fibrillary plate appears as a very thin layer in immediate contact with the bony layer. It increases in thickness through the addition of broad, thin sheets from the connective tissue from the floor of the scale pocket. The fibrillary plate, like the bony layer, is collagenous at first, becoming infiltrated later with ichthylepidin, an organic substance recognized in teleost scales. The fibrillary plate is laid down behind the bony layer.

The ridges or circuli provide the sculpturing that is used in determining the age of fish; they are continuous and homogeneous with the general bony layer and are the result of elevations of the osteoid marginal area. The circuli increase in height during the process of calcification. Their formation probably depends on the presence of more bone-forming materials in the intercellular fluid than can be utilized at the growing margins.

Radii represent the lines of flexibility in the scale. The flexible condition is attained by the absence of the bony layer and through a special condition whereby the underlying fibrillary plate does not become impregnated with ichthylepidin beneath the radii or grooves.

### 18·9    Distinction between ctenoid and cycloid scales

Ctenoid and cycloid scales are the types most commonly used in age determinations and growth calculations. The most obvious distinction between these two types is the presence of the ctenii, small spines, on the posterior of the ctenoid scale. In general, fishes with soft-rayed fins have cycloid scales whereas the spiny fishes possess the ctenoid type. There are interesting combinations of the two. Some sea perches have ctenoid scales above the lateral line and cycloid below. Many of the flatfishes have ctenoid scales on the upper side and cycloid on the underside. Scales may be weakly ctenoid with small ctenii or strongly ctenoid with long, coarse spines. All scales begin as cycloid scales, and even in spiny fishes some may never develop ctenii. Such scales are found most commonly on the head, cheek, and opercle. In the rock bass (*Ambloplites rupestris*) the scales though typically ctenoid are sometimes without ctenii after the sixth year. One of the arguments for the continual growth of the scale is the presence of long, sharp ctenii on the posterior margin of the scales of even the oldest fish.

## 18·10 Scale characteristics

There are certain structures common to both types of scales. The *focus* near the center of the scale is a small, clear area which presumably represents the original scale platelet of the young fish. *Ridges* or *circuli* are the numerous more or less concentric striations around the focus. The circuli are continuous and homogeneous with the general bony surface resulting from elevations of the osteoid marginal area. The ridges or circuli provide the sculpturing that is interpreted in determining the age. *Radii* represent the lines of flexibility in the scale. Examination of the scales tends to show more radii present where greater body movement is necessary. In the absence of the ctenii, as in the cycloid scale of the white sucker, radii may be found in the posterior field.

Several attempts have been made to develop taxonomic keys to fishes on the basis of scale characteristics and shape. The future shape of a scale depends on the amount of space available between it and the scales around it. In the mirror carp, a mutant form of *Cyprinus carpio*, the scales, few and isolated, grow to an immense size and have rounded margins. The scales of the burbot and the brook trout retain their juvenile, embedded condition as regular, circular cycloid scales. In this type of scale the focus remains in the approximate center surrounded by equal growth. Ctenoid scales with overlapping or imbrication have an unequal growth of the anterior and/or the posterior fields which shifts the relative position of the focus and serves to change the general outline of the scale.

## 18·11　Irregularities

In examining a series of scales irregularities are frequently observed. The most common irregularity is *regenerated* (latinucleate) *scales* in which the clear, well-defined focus is replaced by an expanded central area, devoid of circuli, rough or granular in appearance and irregular in outline. The relative size of this regenerated center depends on the size of the scale at time regeneration began. Although growth beyond the regenerated portion is normal these scales are for the most part of no value in estimating age. Small scars or patches commonly found on scales are presumably the repaired injuries which have occurred on the former margins of the scale. An interesting irregularity occurs when a young scale becomes dislocated and turns slightly in the scale pocket. This results in the appearance of a smaller scale off center in a larger scale. In some instances two papillae may grow together so that one scale may develop with two foci.

## 18·12　The scale method of back-calculating body lengths

The scale method is based on the assumption that it is possible to interpret scale pattern correctly to determine the age of fish and to calculate body lengths of a fish at previous ages. Leeuwenhoek, the pioneer microscopist, is generally given credit for making the first generalization that the rings, or annuli, on fish scales had something to do with the age of the fish. Hoffbauer (1898), working with carp of known age, correctly interpreted the age of the fish from the scales as shown by sketches included in his paper. Following Hoffbauer's pioneer work investigators began to shift from examination of the scale structure to the study of the sculpturing of the scale as an additional aid in life history studies.

## 18·13　Primary conditions on which the scale method is founded

The accuracy of the scale method hinges on three primary conditions (Van Oosten 1929):

1. The scales must remain constant in number and identity throughout the life of the fish. That they retain their identity is proved when one examines the nuclear area or focus of the scales from young fish and finds them structurally identical with the scales of the older fish. All regenerated scales (Section 18·11) have a characteristic central portion. Scales increase in size with growth of the body of the fish. That the number of scales remains reasonably constant in all but a few species is shown by the use of the lateral line scales and other

scale counts to distinguish between closely related species and sub-species of fish.

2. Growth of the scale must be proportional to the growth of the fish, but scale growth rarely bears an exact linear relation to body growth. However, agreement has been found among the growth histories of different age groups of the same year class and among different year classes as to the relative amount of growth in certain calendar years. Supposing a sample is taken annually to follow the survival of fish of a certain species hatched in 1940 in one area. Environmental conditions during 1943 made it a very poor growing year. This poor growth will be recorded on all fish of the 1940 year class surviving during and subsequent to that time whether they be taken in the 4-year age group or in the 8-year age group. On the other hand, fish hatched in 1938 or 1942, though belonging to other year classes, should still reflect the poor growing season of 1943 on their scales, providing of course they survived through that year.

3. The annulus must be formed yearly and at the same approximate time each year. The majority of experiments designed to test this have shown that the annulus may be used in determining the age of fish. There is a definite correlation between age and growth, the number of annuli increasing as the fish grows. Modes in length-frequency distributions of younger fish coincide with modal lengths of age groups based on scale interpretation. The persistent abundance or scarcity of certain year classes further prove this contention.

## 18·14   Definition and recognition of the annulus

Although characters are frequently given for recognizing the annulus there is no substitute for experience in actually reading scales. Scales of different species have peculiarities that can be learned only by observation. One of the best and surest characters, especially with ctenoid scales, is the so-called "cutting over" or "crossing over." This is brought about in the fall or with the cessation of scale development when the outer ridges or circuli tend to flare outward so that several of them may end on the side of the scale. The greater the eccentricity of the focus, the greater the discontinuity of the circuli. The first circulus laid down in the spring follows regularly around the entire scale margin and thus must "cut across" or "cross over" the incomplete ridges which did not grow completely around the scale at the cessation of scale development the previous fall. Another recognition character is the presence of discontinuous circuli, commonly observed in the sculpturing of cycloid scales. Individual circuli arising at different loci around the scale never grow completely together as a result of cessation of scale growth. Crowding of the circuli prior to the resumption of growth and, in some species, the erosion of the scale during the spawning period may be clues to the exact location of the annulus.

## 18·15   Causes of annulus formation

These irregularities in the sculpturing of the scale are undoubtedly reflections of some environmental change acting on the physiological processes of the fish. Temperature is thought to be the most effective single factor. The most apparent effect caused by a drop in temperature is the reduction of the metabolic rate resulting in the cessation of active feeding. An unusually high temperature may produce the same effect. In general then the time of annulus formation can be readily correlated with water temperature.

One must be alert to detect accessory year marks or false annuli, which are usually less distinct or less continuous than the true annulus. These accessory marks or false annuli may occur as the result of changes in the rate of growth during the spawning period, seasonal variation in amount of food, extremes of climatic conditions, periods of floods, or times of drought. In many cases the close proximity of the false annulus to a true annulus will aid in its detection. An interesting annulus formation is that of a "natal annulus" formed at birth in some members of the family Embiotocidae presumably because the embryonic food supply is cut off and a temporary reduction in the food supply occurs until the young fish •becomes adapted to capturing food in its new environment (Hubbs 1921).

Just as one must be on the alert for accessory annuli so must one be watching for the omission of annuli, apparently, however, a rarity in this hemisphere. This omission might occur in species occupying an environment with uniform temperature conditions.

## 18·16   Collection of scales and preparation for examination

It is a common practice to take ctenoid scales in the region of the tip of the pectoral fin, whereas cycloid scales are generally removed from an area between the dorsal fin and the lateral line. Choosing the area from which to take the scale samples is discussed more fully in Chapter 19 in connection with the use of the scales in determining the growth of younger age groups. The scales are usually removed with a knife or a pair of stout forceps. The scales are then either placed in small envelopes or pressed between cut pieces of paper or folded pages of a notebook held together by the mucous on the scales. In either case data are recorded as to species, place, weight, length, collector, and, many times, sex, maturity, method by which the specimen was taken, and time. The manner in which the scales are to be prepared and examined is determined by the type of scale and the information desired of the investigation.

Temporary mounts of both ctenoid and cycloid scales can be made by simply cleaning the scales and examining them in water. Dry temporary mounts can be made by placing the scales between glass slides for examination, and some workers prefer this method for certain species.

Permanent mounts can be prepared by fixing the scales on slides with cover slips. The mounting medium may be of several types such as euparol, glycerin–gelatin, and gum arabic, although care must be taken to employ a mounting medium of different refractive index from that of the scale. For example, scales mounted in balsam are almost impossible to find, much less use. Euparol, a common mounting medium, works very well with scales.

Another excellent and permanent method (developed by Harlan B. Holmes for mounting salmon scales) is to fix the scales between slides in dehydrated water glass. Potassium silicate is better than sodium silicate. Boil the water glass in a flask over a gas burner until it is very thick, then pour the thick, sticky material into tooth paste tubes, and seal the ends. Clean the scales in a long tray of paraffin with depressions for each sample of scales. Fill each depression with a very dilute solution of sodium hydroxide to remove the mucus. Dip each scale into an *unboiled* solution of water glass, and place it sculptured side down on the slide. Leave each slide until the scales are well stuck to it. Now open the cap on a tube of the *boiled* water glass and squeeze a good-sized "worm" of the thick material the length of the slide. Place a clean slide on top, and press down gently to remove all bubbles. Clamp the two slides together with a clothes pin or, better, a spring-type paper clamp, and hang up to dry. When the slide is dry, scrape off the excess material around the edges, and dip the edges of the slide into a shallow dish of Duco to exclude air. Hang up again to dry. After 15 years these mounts remain perfect.

When only age is desired, one scale can be mounted from each fish, about 30 mounts being allowed on each slide. In this case it pays to place each scale momentarily under a dissecting microscope while it is held in the forceps before being dipped in the dilute water glass. Scales with regenerated centers are easily noted and rejected. We recommend mounting more than one scale from each fish if measurements are desired, as some scales have more clearly defined annuli.

For keeping a permanent record of scales the Celluloid impression method originally described by Nesbit (1934) is very popular at present. This does not give such good results with thin cycloid scales as it does with ctenoid scales. The Celluloid impression records only the sculpturing of the scale, making it very valuable for the examination of thick scales through which the transmission of light is very difficult.

Originally Celluloid was used in preparing the impressions, but recent plastics (lumarith cellulose acetate) work equally well and have the advantage of not being inflammable. Generally the impression method consists of softening the surface of the plastic slide and then pressing the scale, sculptured side down, firmly into the softened area. The scale is then removed and the impression is ready for study.

Softening the surface may be done with acetone or by heat. Original presses were designed from discarded notary's seals, but these were soon replaced by a design invented by Lyle M. Thorpe, Fisheries Board of Connecticut. Thorpe's press works on the principle of the screw and can be turned down more easily and firmly. The construction is simple and durable. Either of the above presses is satisfactory for small numbers of scales, but for larger numbers more refined modifications of the scale presses have been developed. These soften the slide with thermostatically controlled heat; then the slide travels between two rollers easily adjusted for the correct pressure. With these presses tremendous numbers of impressions may be made in assembly-line fashion.

The plastic slides may be cut on paper cutters or with modified saws of several types. For less extensive work the slides are usually cut to fit into standard slide boxes. For the making of great numbers of impressions mount the scales on slides cut to fit into the standard $3 \times 5$-inch file drawers to save space.

## 18·17   Age determinations

The binocular microscope serves very nicely in examinations when only the age is to be determined. A discussion of the various scale projectors has been reserved for the following chapter on growth studies where it becomes necessary to measure areas of the scales.

Determination of age should ordinarily be made without reference to the size of the fish in question. Information on the size has the effect consciously or otherwise of introducing bias into the age determinations. Exception to the above may occur in working out methods and criteria for recognizing annuli in a given species when it may be very helpful to start with scales from fish of known age or of early ages determined by size frequencies. Scales should be read at least twice and at different times. When the two age determinations differ, they should be read a third time, and, if consistent interpretation is impossible, these specimens should be discarded.

Errors in age determinations from scales increase with the increasing age of the fish. As growth slows down, the circuli (and annuli) become very much crowded together and the age becomes increasingly hard to determine. Furthermore circuli formed in later years tend to flare outward less than in earlier years, resulting in a lessening of the characteristic curving over. Errors are often made in determining the location of the first annulus; this may be caused by late spawning whereby the young fish may not show enough differentiation between the first summer and the first winter's growth.

The age is particularly hard to determine if the fish have been taken during a period when the annulus is being laid down. In that case some fish will have the annulus on the margin of the scale, and others may not have formed it at all.

Some authors have followed the custom of reporting annuli in Roman numerals and growing seasons in Arabic numerals. In either case it is important to establish the criterion. For example: Determining the age of a smallmouth black bass in October would mean that the age if decided merely on the basis of the number of annuli present would be one less than the growing seasons the fish has been exposed to, since the last annulus on the scale in this case would have been laid down in late spring or early summer. After October or November little growth would take place. This point is important where comparisons of growth are made, and sometimes necessitates an annulus being postulated at the edge of each scale.

If one uses the terminology in which fish up to one year of age are called the 0-age group, the age averages 6 months low. A better method perhaps is to use only Arabic numerals and call a fish in the first year (group 1) when it is 0 to 1 year old and 2 when it is 1 to 2 years old, and so forth. For anadromous fish it is customary to designate both the freshwater and sea life in stating the age. Thus a salmon aged $5_3$ migrated to the sea in its third year (always reckoned from the time the eggs are spawned), and is returning to spawn in its fifth year. Since such a fish is almost exactly 5 years of age at spawning time the use of the 5 for the fifth year is a very convenient and meaningful designation. The terminology occasionally employed, especially in freshwater studies, of using only the annulus would result in this fish being called a 4-year-old, even though it belongs in a 5-year cycle.

## References

Adams, L. A.
1940. Some characteristic otoliths of American Ostariophysi. *J. Morph. 66* (3):497–527.

Aikawa, H.
1937. Age determinations of chub-mackerel, *Scomber japonicus* (Houttyn) *Bull. Jap. Soc. Sci. Fish. Tokyo 6:* 9–12.

Appelget, J., and L. L. Smith, Jr.
1951. The determination of age and rate of growth from vertebrae of the channel catfish, *Ictalurus lacustris punctatus. Trans. Am. Fish. Soc. 80:* 119–139.

Boyko, E. G.
1950. Age determination in fishes, based on examination of finray sections. *Prog. Fish-Cult. 12* (1):47–48. As reprinted from *Comptes Rendus,* Academy of Science, Moskow, *New Ser. 53* (5):483–484.

Clemens, H. P.
1951. The growth of the burbot *Lota lota maculosa* (LeSueur). *Trans. Am. Fish. Soc. 80:* 163–173.

Cuerrier, J. P., and G. Roussow.
1951. Age and growth of lake sturgeon from Lake St. Francis, St. Lawrence River. Report on material collected in 1947. *Can. Fish Cult. 10:* 17–29.

Hoffbauer, C.
1898. Die Alterbestimmung des Karpfen an seiner Schuppe. *Allg. Fisch. Zeit., Jg. 23:* 341–343.

Hubbs, C. L.
1921. The ecology and life-history of *Amphigonopterus aurora* and of other viviparous perches of California. *Biol. Bull. 40* (4):181–209.

Martin, W. R.
1941. Rate of growth of the ling, *Lota lota maculosa* (LeSueur). *Trans. Am. Fish. Soc. 70:* 77–79.

Neave, Ferris
1936. The development of the scales of *Salmo. Trans. Royal Soc. Canada 30,* Sec. V: 55–76.
1943. Scale pattern and scale counting methods in relation to certain trout and other salmonids. *Trans. Royal Soc. Canada 37,* Sec. V: 79–91.

Nesbit, R. A.
1934. A convenient method for preparing celluloid impressions of fish scales. *J. du Conseil 9* (3):373–376.

Sneed, K. E.
1951. A method for calculating the growth of channel catfish, *Ictalurus lacustris punctatus. Trans. Am. Fish. Soc. 80:* 174–183.

Van Oosten, John
1929. Life history of the lake herring (*Leucichthys artedi* Le Sueur) of Lake Huron as revealed by its scales with a critique on the scale method. *Bull. U. S. Bur. Fish. 44:* 265–448.

# 19 · GROWTH

## 19·1  Definition of growth

Growth may be defined quite simply as an increase in size. Actually, however, growth is a general term for a very complex change depending on many factors from the simple imbibition of water to the complicated results of nutrition chemistry. Growth is the direct result of the chemical, osmotic, and other forces by which material is introduced into an organism and transferred throughout the many parts.

## 19·2  The growth curve

Increases in size are usually measured during successive intervals of time. The growth curve is actually made up of points defining dimensions at specified times measuring time along the $x$-axis and the dimension (length, weight) along the $y$-axis. Thus length plotted in relation to time produces a vector diagram which is known as a growth curve. In the particular example of length plotted against time we are really examining the velocity of the change in length or the "rate of growth."

The curves which are used the most are time diagrams. Each has a beginning and an end. Thus the same type of curve may illustrate the life of a man, the economic history of a country, the increase in mileage of the American railroads or the increase in horsepower of airplane engines through the years since the first flight was made. Typically the curve that fits the above variables is the S-shaped population curve or sigmoid curve. This curve may illustrate the rate of cooling, a loss of electric charge, or the chemical action of a ferment. What is important to this discussion is that the S-shaped curve illustrates growth of either an individual organism or a population of many individuals.

## 19·3  The growth rate of fish

The growth rate of fish varies far more than does that of a warm-blooded animal. The general character of the curve remains the same, except that because fish continue to grow even in extreme old age, it draws toward its ultimate or limiting growth with exceeding slowness. This has been called indeterminate growth. Absolute growth in mammals begins slowly, attains a maximum velocity somewhat early in the life history, and then slows down, approaching a point where growth may cease altogether. Such growth is commonly referred to as determinate. In cold-blooded animals, however, the deceleration is greatly protracted, and the size only approaches asymptotically the maximum limit. Exception to the above generalities are the seemingly indeterminate growth of whales and other marine mammals and the determinate growth of the males of the Poeciliidae.

The rate of growth is directly affected by temperature, and by other physical conditions. This influence of temperature is particularly obvious in the case of the cold-blooded or poikilothermal animals such as fish.

The several parts and organs of the body of a fish have their own rates of growth. Form is a direct function of these differential growth rates of bodily parts. These rates may differ in degree or form "gradients," from one point of an organism to another. The rates in different parts and in different directions tend to maintain more or less constant ratios to one another in each organism. That the form of a fish is in general regular and constant is dependent on the regularity and constancy of these relative rates of growth. The changes of form which accompany development are due to the fact that these ratios are not absolutely constant but tend to be altered in the course of time in an orderly manner. Much of the theory of recapitulation is dependent on the close relation between growth and form.

### 19·4  Autocatalytic concepts of growth

Some chemical reactions, including many in plants and animals, are activated, and their rates determined, by catalyzing agents. This catalytic action occurs when some substance, often in minute quantity, by its presence produces or accelerates a reaction without itself being diminished or used up. This catalyst diminishes the resistance to the reaction. The curve of the reaction is not altered in form as the amount of energy in the system is not affected by the presence of the catalyst and the rate of action gradually slows down.

Sometimes the catalyzing agent is formed as a by-product of the main reaction. In this case the reaction continues with increasing velocity until some limiting condition such as a failure of some necessary ingredient, or the production of some toxic substance destroys the original reaction. This sort of action is known as autocatalysis. Enzymes are powerful catalyzers, and so protoplasm itself expresses the autocatalytic action. Growth is a composite of many reactions, many of which are autocatalytic.

The S-shaped curve of growth resembles in general characteristics the curve of chemical autocatalysis. Likewise the curve of growth of a population resembles it. This analogous similarity is mathematical rather than biological. A chemical reaction draws to a close when chemical equilibrium is reached whereas the growth of an organism comes to an end with gradual differentiation into parts followed by a slackening or complete stoppage of growth.

The analogy between organic growth and chemical autocatalysis is sufficiently close, however, so that the same mathematics may be applied in expressing the curves by certain formulas.

## 19·5  Absolute growth

Absolute growth is the average total size at each age. It is usually plotted as the regression of length on age, or average length for each

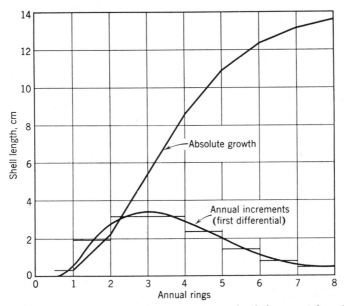

Fig. 19·1  Curve of absolute growth. Showing growth of the razor clam (*Siliqua patula*) at Hallo Bay, Alaska. (From Weymouth and McMillin 1931)

age group. In general the absolute growth curve rises slowly at first with an increasing slope followed by a decreasing slope during the remainder of the curve (Figure 19·1). The point at which the growth rate changes from an increasing to a decreasing rate has become known as the point of inflection and will be considered in Section 19·7.

A useful reference on the general subject of growth is the publication of Weymouth and McMillin (1931) on the razor clam. To show the rate of absolute growth in the razor clam in a slightly different manner, the annual increments, or differences between successive total lengths, are plotted against the age (Figure 19·1). This type of curve is known as the first differential of the absolute growth curve. The curve shows an increase of growth rate which reaches a maximum at the point of inflection of the total length curve. After the maximum, the rate declines throughout life and for a time closely approximates a descending geometric series which is another way of saying that each yearly growth is a certain percentage of the preceding. This relation breaks down in extreme old age when growth is actually greater than predicted.

## 19·6  Relative growth

Relative growth may be defined as percentage growth in which the increase in growth in each time interval is expressed as a percentage of the growth at the beginning of the time interval. This type of growth may be shown (Figure 19·2) by either of two curves by plotting the logarithms of the total size against time (line A) or by plotting percentage yearly increases against time (line B). When the logarithm of the total dimension is used, the curve rises steeply at first, but the slope continually declines throughout life. When the percentage yearly gains are plotted against time the continually decreasing increment is obvious.

## 19·7  Comparison of absolute and relative growth curves

The greatest difference in the absolute and relative treatment of growth comes in early life since the slow growth of old age differs little whether regarded from the absolute or the relative viewpoint. The absolute growth of young organisms is slow, but it increases constantly up to the maximum at the point of inflection, after which it declines regularly. Relative growth on the other hand is most rapid at the youngest ages and declines constantly. The most significant difference between the two viewpoints relates to the rate of growth. An example to demonstrate this can be taken from Weymouth and McMillin (1931) on the growth of clams. Absolute growth in the first growing season was 0.38 cm and in the twelfth growing season was 0.36 cm. As far as absolute growth is concerned these two are practically the same, but from the viewpoint of relative growth rate there is a tremendous difference. In the first case the growth in the first growing season is from the egg with a diameter of 0.01 cm to 0.38 cm whereas the twelfth growing season began with a clam already 12.25 cm in length. This makes the relative growths approximately 3700 and 3 per cent, and the relative growth during the first summer is 1233 times as fast as the relative growth during the twelfth growing season.

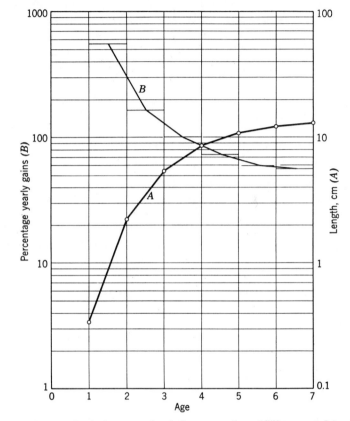

Fig. 19·2  Curve of relative growth of the razor clam (*Siliqua patula*) at Hallo Bay, Alaska. (From Weymouth and McMillin 1931)

The definition of rate is important not only in early growth but also at the time of inflection on the absolute growth curve. Authors have at one time or another claimed certain points of significance for the inflection. Some of these are maximum velocity of growth, age of puberty, lowest specific mortality, and equivalence in age of different animals. Actually, however, the plain meaning of the inflection point is not known. An animal growing at a constantly decreasing relative rate will, providing the starting rate is initially high, show for a time an increasing absolute rate with each increment being larger than the preceding. The falling relative rate will after a time offset the increasing body size; and the total gains will slacken (point of inflection of the growth curve) and become progressively less. The point of inflection in this case is a mathematical consequence in the course of growth and has no significant biological implication. Absolute growth curves then indicate a slow growth in the early ages when each unit is putting forth a maximum of energy to increase in size. When the absolute growth curve is examined, the point of inflection would seem to be the most rapid period of growth, whereas actually the inflection is at the point where the increasing body size and decreasing growth rate makes a maximum contribution of new tissue. Growth rate is constantly decreasing.

### 19·8　The Gompertz curve as an interpretation of normal growth

An examination of Figure 19·2, relative growth expressed by plotting percentage yearly increases against time, indicates that the decline of relative growth is a regular and orderly process. As shown by Weymouth and McMillin (1931), this decline approximates an exponential series, so that the log of the relative growth rates plotted on age gives a straight line. Therefore, to quote directly from the above paper:

$$P_L = \frac{d \log L}{dt} = \text{relative growth rate}$$

$$\log P_L = a - kt$$

where $a$ = initial relative growth
　　　　$k$ = rate of decline
　　　　$t$ = time

$$\frac{d \log L}{dt} = \epsilon^{a-k}$$

$$= A\epsilon^{-kt} \quad \text{where} \quad A = \epsilon^a$$

$$\log L = \frac{A}{-k} \epsilon^{-kt} + b$$

$$= b - c\epsilon^{-kt} \quad \text{where} \quad c = A/k$$

$$L = \epsilon^{b - c\epsilon^{-kt}}$$

$$= B\epsilon^{-c\epsilon^{-kt}} \quad \text{where} \quad B = \epsilon^b$$

This formula will be applicable where the percental growth rate declines at a constant percentage rate.

## 19·9   Walford's growth transformation

Growth curves such as have been discussed up to this point are difficult to compare and classify. Their formulas and the mathematical methods of fitting the curves are tedious and often very impractical from a management standpoint.

Since the portion of the growth below the inflection point on the S-shaped growth curve is usually completed early in the life of the

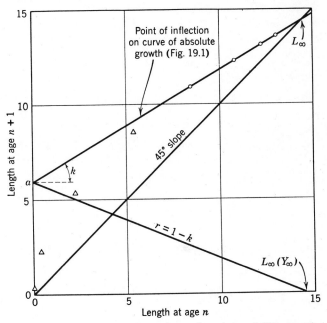

Fig. 19·3   Walford's growth transformation using data of Weymouth and Mc-Millin (1931) for razor clams at Hallo Bay, Alaska. Straight line fits after clams pass the inflection on the curve of absolute growth.

organism from a management viewpoint it is often not pertinent. The period of growth above the inflection point is usually of greatest importance. Using the part of the growth curve above the inflection point, Walford (1946) represents the data by a straight line easily treated statistically.

By means of Walford's method body lengths at ages 1, 2, 3, 4, 5, $\cdots$, $n$ are plotted along the x-axis against lengths at ages 2, 3, 4, 5, 6, $\cdots$, $n + 1$ along the y-axis. For the several species of fish investigated by Walford the points fell along a straight line. Walford regards this line as a transformation of the growth curve (Figure 19·3).

Figure $19 \cdot 3$ reveals several interesting features of this transformed growth curve. The ultimate length $l_\infty$ can be located graphically at the point where the length at age $n$ equals the length at age $n + 1$. The ultimate length can also be determined as the point where the curve intersects a line drawn at 45 degrees through the zero point.

When the transformation results in a straight line as shown in Figure $19 \cdot 3$ the increments between years of age for equal time intervals have several interrelations, where $l_n$ refers to the length at any given age and at the end of any given time interval.

$$\frac{l_3 - l_2}{l_2 - l_1} = \frac{l_4 - l_3}{l_3 - l_2} = \frac{l_5 - l_4}{l_4 - l_3} \cdots = \frac{l_n - l_{n-1}}{l_{n-1} - l_{n-2}} = k$$

or      $l_n - l_{n-1} = k(l_{n-1} - l_{n-2})$            (1)

The constant $k$ is a positive number and less than one which indicates that the yearly growth increments decrease. This relationship depends on the growth capacity being approached from the inflection point at a constant percentage rate. To continue Walford's series of equations:

When            $l_0 = 0$

$$l_2 - l_1 = k(l_1 - l_0) = kl_1$$

$$l_3 - l_2 = k(l_2 - l_1) = k \cdot kl_1 \quad \text{or} \quad k^2 l_1$$

$$l_4 - l_3 = k(l_3 - l_2) = k \cdot k^2 l_1 \quad \text{or} \quad k^3 l_1$$

$$l_5 - l_4 = k(l_4 - l_3) = k \cdot k^3 l_1 \quad \text{or} \quad k^4 l_1$$

$$\cdot \quad \cdot \quad \cdot \quad \cdot \quad \cdot \quad \cdot \quad \cdot \quad \cdot \quad \cdot \quad \cdot \quad \cdot \quad \cdot \quad \cdot \quad \cdot \quad \cdot \quad \cdot \quad \cdot$$

$$l_n - l_{n-1} = k(l_{n-1} - l_{n-2}) = kk^{n-2}l_1 = k^{n-1}l_1 \qquad (2)$$

The ultimate length or limiting length $l_\infty$ can be calculated according to the following formulas:

The length $l_n$ is attained by adding to $l_1$ the successive increments,

$$l_n = l_1 + (l_2 - l_1) + (l_3 - l_2) + (l_4 - l_3) + \cdots + (l_n - l_{n-1})$$

These increments have already been expressed thus:

$$l_2 - l_1 = kl_1, \qquad l_3 - l_2 = k^2 l_1 \cdots l_n - l_{n-1} = k^{n-1}l_n \qquad (3)$$

Therefore,

$$l_n = l_1 + kl_1 + k^2 l_1 + k^3 l_1 + \cdots + k^{n-1}l_1 = l_1 \frac{1 - k^n}{1 - k} \qquad (4)\cdot$$

by the well-known formula for the geometric series. When $n$ approaches $\infty$, $l_n$ tends to $l_\infty$ and $k^n$ to 0, and so

$$l_\infty = \frac{l_1}{1 - k} \tag{5}$$

The ultimate length or limiting length $l_\infty$ may be computed from the $y$ intercept and the slope of the fitted straight line, $k$. The slope $k$ may be calculated easily from any of the ratios preceding equation 1. The slope of the transformed growth curve $k$ may be given by the ratio $\dfrac{l_n - l_{n-1}}{l_{n-1} - l_{n-2}} = k$ and also by the ratio $\dfrac{l_\infty - l_{n+1}}{l_\infty - l_n} = k$. The higher the value of $k$, the more slowly is the ultimate length approached.

Walford's transformation provides two growth characteristics, $k$ the slope of the line, and $l_\infty$ the ultimate length, from which the upper segment of the length-on-time growth curve can be reproduced. Since these constants are easily and simply derived they are practical to use for large numbers of individuals. These constants provide an easy means of studying growth rates within and between populations, particularly in distinguishing between races of animals if their growth patterns are different. This growth transformation is recommended for the study of growth rates of fishes whose scales lend themselves easily to age determinations from which the growth history can be estimated.

## 19·10   Similarity of Walford's ultimate attainable size and ultimate yield

In Figure 19·3 the ultimate attainable size $l_\infty$ is in reality the same statistic defined in Section 7·13 as $Y_\infty$, or as $P_0$ when no natural mortality is postulated.

Thus DeLury's second formula

$$C/U(t) = kP_0 - kC(t)$$

is equivalent to the straight-line formula

$$y = a - bx$$

If this is applied to Figure 19·3 (bottom), it is apparent that

$$l \text{ or } Y = a - rl \quad \text{and} \quad r \text{ is } 1 - k$$

In Figure 19·3 if the empirically fitted line is projected to $x = 0$, then the intercept $a$ is approximately 6. By formula 5 in Section 19·9,

$$l_\infty = \frac{a}{1-k} = \frac{a}{r}.$$ As $k$ is by inspection about 0.60, $r$ is about 0.40 and

$l_\infty = 6/0.40 = 15$.   But, if we merely substitute terms and call the intercept $a$, $C_0$ and $l_\infty$, $Y_\infty$, we see at once that the formula in Section 7·15

$$\lim_{t \to \infty} Y = C_0/r \quad \text{is identical with}$$

$$l_\infty = a/1 - k = a/r$$

This follows because the calculation of both $l_\infty$ and $Y_\infty$ is based on negative compound interest.  By determining the rate of interest and the initial payment it is easy to determine the initial sum.

## 19·11   Length–weight relationship

Length and weight of fishes may be determined with accuracy. Weight of fishes may be considered a function of the length.  This relationship of the length and weight follows approximately the cube law relationship expressed by the formula, $K = W/L^3$, in which $W$ is the symbol for weight and $L$ the symbol for length.

If form and specific gravity were constant throughout life the relationship could be used to describe the general length–weight relationship in populations of fishes and thus serve as the basis for the calculation of unknown weights of fish of known length or to determine the lengths of fish of known weight.  Unfortunately a fish, or any animal, is continually prone to change its bodily proportions during life so that the simple cube law expression does not hold throughout the life history and growth of the fish.  Since the instances where the cube law does apply throughout the growth of a fish are the exceptions, a more satisfactory formula for the expression of the relationship is

$$W = cL^n$$

in which $W$ = weight
$\qquad L$ = length
$\qquad c$ and $n$ = constants

or expressed logarithmically

$$\log W = \log c + n \log L$$

The values of the constants $c$ and $n$ may be determined by fitting a straight line to the logarithms of $L$ and $W$ or by computing them from the following normal equations:

$$\log c = \frac{\Sigma \log W \cdot \Sigma (\log L)^2 - \Sigma \log L \cdot (\Sigma \log L \cdot \log W)}{N \cdot \Sigma (\log L)^2 - (\Sigma \log L)^2}$$

and

$$n = \frac{\Sigma \log W - N \log c}{\Sigma \log L}$$

Beckman (1948) presents a thorough description of the length–weight relationship together with some of the constants for Michigan fishes. Figure 19·4 shows a typical length–weight relationship using data from the striped bass (Merriman 1941).

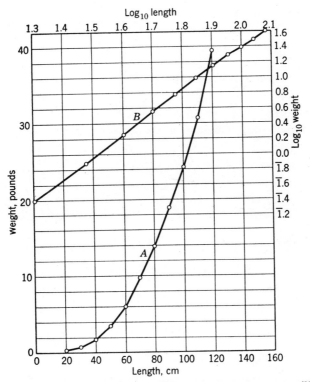

FIG. 19·4   Length–weight relations in the striped bass (*Roccus saxatilis*). (After Merriman 1941)   Curve *A* shows the absolute values; curve *B* shows the log–log transformation.

Some workers have made use of this relationship by merely plotting the log of the weight against the log of the length.   This gives a straight-line regression which may be easily compared with other curves of a similar nature.

Another use of the cube law relationship although an entirely different expression from the length–weight relationship is the so-called condition factor or the coefficient of condition.   Values of the condition

factor or the coefficient of condition are interpreted as expressing the
relative well-being of the fishes. By general usage the coefficient of
condition $K$ is determined by the following formula:

$$K = \frac{100,000W}{L^3}$$

$W$ = weight in grams
$L$ = standard length in millimeters

Interest in the English system of weights and measures made advisable
a method of converting the metric coefficient $K$ into the English coefficient $C$. The English coefficient is based on total length in inches
and weight in pounds. The equation for the conversion is

$$C = 36.1 \, r^3 K_m$$

$r$ = ratio of standard to total length
$K_m$ = coefficient of condition in the metric system

The above equation was originally proposed by Ralph Hile and included in the length–weight relationship paper by Beckman (op. cit.).

The coefficient of condition is used to indicate suitability of an environment or to compare fish from one lake or area with a general
average for an entire region. As fish grow older they tend to gain
proportionately more in weight than in length so that the value of $K$
(or $C$) will increase with age. Often sexual dimorphism or the time
of year the sample is taken must be accounted for. Maturing fish cannot be compared with fish that have just spawned.

Proper sampling will tend to minimize many of the above difficulties,
but comparison can be considered valid only if fish of the same length,
age, and sex, taken as nearly as practical on the same date, are used.

## 19·12   The scale as an indication of growth of the fish

In Chapter 18 the use of the scales of fishes for determining the age
was discussed. A second important source of information gained from
the fish scale has been the use of certain scale measurements in back-
calculating body lengths. Back calculation of body lengths is the
procedure by which past body lengths may be determined, if certain
growth relationships are assumed between the scales of fishes and
body length. Many formulas have been proposed and employed to
accurately determine the growth of fishes prior to their capture.

## 19·13   Direct-proportion formula

Early workers using the method of calculating body lengths at
younger ages from the scales of a fish assumed that a direct proportion

existed between the scale and body growth throughout the entire life of the fish. The basis for this assumption came from the general knowledge that although fish may vary in size they possess approximately the same body contour, that the scale counts of small and large fish are similar, and that the outlines of the scales in both small and large fish are approximately the same. The direct-proportion formula assumes then that isogonic growth is demonstrated by the scale and body length or that their growth is at the same proportional rate.

A second assumption of the direct proportion formula is that the body and scale growth demonstrate a straight-line relationship with the origin of the line passing through zero (line *A*, Figure 19·5). Subsequent workers attempting to use the direct proportion formula in calculations have found in almost all studies that the calculated body lengths are much lower than the empirical lengths and have explained this relationship as due to the fact that the fish has attained some body length before the scales are laid down so that the intercept will be negative (line *B*, Figure

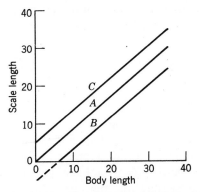

FIG. 19·5  Showing the relation of body length and scale length.

19·5). A positive intercept on the *y* axis, of the regression line (line *C*, Figure 19·5) would indicate that the calculated body lengths would be higher than the empirical lengths.

The formula for the back calculation of body lengths if a direct proportion between the scale and body growth is assumed is

$$\frac{\text{Length of scale radius to annulus } x \ (S')}{\text{Length of total scale radius } (S)}$$

$$= \frac{\text{Length of fish when annulus } x \text{ was formed } (L')}{\text{Length of fish at time scale sample was obtained } (L)}$$

or
$$\frac{S'}{S} = \frac{L'}{L} \qquad L' = \frac{S'}{S} L$$

**19·14   Introduction of the correction factor to correct for either positive or negative intercept of the straight-line relationship**

Since the introduction of the direct-proportion formula, biologists have attempted to improve it by introducing various correction factors.

Working on the growth of the king salmon (*Oncorhynchus tshawy-tscha*), Fraser was the first to use the body length at time of scale formation as a correction factor in the formula. The correction factor in this case should be subtracted as this body length was attained before any scale growth. Smallmouth black bass are approximately 2 cm, the eastern brook trout about 3.6 cm, the king salmon about 5 cm, and the cod 3 to 4 cm in body length before the scales begin to appear. If the symbol $C$ is used as the correction factor representing the body length at scale formation, the formula for the back calculation of body lengths becomes

$$L' - C = \frac{S'}{S}(L - C)$$

or
$$L' = C + \frac{S'}{S}(L - C)$$

To be absolutely certain of obtaining the correct body length at scale formation it must be determined by actual observation. However the correction factor is usually determined by extrapolating the regression line represented by plotting the scale measurement against the body length. The value on the $x$ axis where it is cut by the regression line is the correction factor. It may be either plus or minus.

Fortunately it is not often necessary to know the length of a fish before the first annulus has been formed so that the intercept as calculated above is valid in calculating past lengths.

## 19·15   Curvilinear relationship

Up to this point only a linear relationship between body length and scale length has been considered. There are however small differences in the body proportions between small and large individuals which make heterogonic rather than isogonic growth the more correct assumption describing the growth relationship of the scale and fish. Usually the relationship between scale and body length when plotted graphically is found to be curvilinear (Creaser 1926). In some cases the relationship may be represented even by a sigmoid curve.

Usually the greatest curvilinearity is in the youngest ages back-calculated from scales of older fish, assuming a straight- or nearly straight-line relationship. The problem of curvilinearity can then be solved by omitting the earliest years and back-calculating only those ages that do not deviate appreciably from a straight line. The formula for a straight-line relationship with the intercept as the correction factor may be used to calculate past lengths.

If the *entire* range of the curve between scale and body length deviates significantly from a straight line then it may be necessary to transform the data. A logarithmic transformation may straighten out the regression. The formula for the back calculation of lengths with the logarithmic transformation is

$$L' = cS'^n$$

or changed to logarithms becomes

$$\log L' = \log c + n(\log S')$$

$L'$ = length to be calculated
$S'$ = measurement of scale
$c$ and $n$ = constants derived from the data

Where a sigmoid curve best fits the body length-scale length relation it may be necessary to derive two formulas: one to fit the data below the inflection point and the other to fit the data above the inflection. Possibly only the data above the inflection are pertinent in which case the formula as suggested above for the curvilinear relationship would be employed.

## 19·16   Choosing the scales

Care should be taken to determine a location or area on the fish where the scales occur in regular order, with little variation in size and with a minimum of regenerated scales. It is common practice to take cycloid scales from the region between the dorsal fin and lateral line and ctenoid scales from the area immediately behind the pectoral fin.

Some biologists have followed the practice of taking key scales. By actual count the same scale, or perhaps the same three scales, are taken from the same location on all fish. This practice is time-consuming, and Everhart (1950) has shown that the practice cannot be justified by increased accuracy in calculating past lengths. Several scales taken from either of the two general areas suggested appear to give the best results.

## 19·17   Measuring the scales

Extensive investigations usually require some means of projecting the scales to a size and location convenient for measurement. It would be entirely possible, however, although tedious and time-consuming, to measure scales, using an ocular micrometer. A good scale projector has been designed and presented by Van Oosten, Deason, and Jobes

(1934). A magnification of 40 diameters makes a convenient enlargement with which to work.

In some projectors, as with the type mentioned above, the scales are measured with an attached folding ruler. Others as Schuck (1949) project the scale and make all measurements, recording only the lengths of the fish at each annulus. Schuck recommends a "fish-size calculator" developed by William C. Herrington. Fry (1943) has also developed a calculator which, given the scale measurements, can calculate the desired body length. These calculators are so constructed that a correction factor may be introduced.

Some investigators project the scale image and record the distances to the annuli on strips of paper or on cards so that the measurements are recorded permanently. Following this the cards or strips are placed in the calculator and body lengths determined from them.

## 19·18 Relationship of body length to length of spines and vertebrae

The relationship of body length to length of the cross section of the spines was assumed to be a straight line in a growth study of the channel catfish employing the left pectoral spine (Sneed 1951). The straight line fitted to the measurements of fish length and spine radius for 187 fish had an intercept of −3.25 mm of fish length. Treating this intercept value as zero, lengths were calculated using the direct-proportion formula. A correlation coefficient of 0.969 was obtained between total fish length and spine radius. This compares very favorably with correlations between body length and scale radius.

A second-degree parabola ($L = a + bx + cx^2$) described the relationship between body length and vertebral radius in a determination of age and rate of growth for the channel catfish (Appelget and Smith 1951). The following formula describes this relationship:

$$L = 0.639793 + 0.262434r - 0.000537r^2$$

where $L$ equals total length in inches and $r$ equals the ventral radius of the vertebra in millimeters times 18 (magnification by scale projector). A satisfactory comparison was obtained between the calculated curve and empirical data.

### References

Appelget, J., and L. L. Smith, Jr.
  1951. The determination of age and rate of growth from vertebrae of the channel catfish, *Ictalurus lacustris punctatus*. *Trans. Am. Fish. Soc. 80:* 119–139.

Beckman, W. C.
   1948. The length–weight relationship, factors for conversions between standard and total lengths, and coefficients of condition for seven Michigan fishes. *Trans. Am. Fish. Soc. 75:* 237–256.
Creaser, C. W.
   1926. The structure and growth of the scales of fishes in relation to the interpretation of their life-history, with special reference to the sunfish, *Eupomotis gibbosus. Misc. Publ. Univ. Mich. Mus. Zool. 17:* 82 pp.
Everhart, W. Harry
   1950. A critical study of the relation between body length and several scale measurements on the smallmouth bass, *Micropterus dolomieu* Lacépède. *J. Wildl. Management 14* (3):266–276.
Fry, F. E. J.
   1943. A method for calculating the growth of fishes from scale measurements. *Univ. Toronto Stud. Biol. 51, Pub. Ontario Fish. Res. Lab. 61.*
Merriman, Daniel
   1941. Studies on the striped bass (*Roccus saxatilis*) of the Atlantic Coast. *Fish. Bull. U. S. Fish Wildl. Serv. 50* (35):1–77.
Schuck, Howard A.
   1949. Problems in calculating size of fish at various ages from proportional measurements of fish and scale sizes. *J. Wildl. Management 13* (3):298–303.
Sneed, K. E.
   1951. A method for calculating the growth of channel catfish, *Ictalurus lacustris punctatus. Trans. Am. Fish. Soc. 80:* 174–183.
Thompson, D'Arcy W.
   1948. *On growth and form.* Macmillan: 2d ed. 1–1116, New York.
Van Oosten, John, H. J. Deason, and F. W. Jobes
   1934. A microprojection machine designed for the study of fish scales. *J. du Conseil 9* (2):241–248.
Walford, Lionel A.
   1946. A new graphic method of describing the growth of animals. *Biol. Bull. 90* (2):141–147.
Weymouth, Frank W., and Harvey C. McMillin
   1931. Relative growth and mortality of the Pacific razor clam (*Siliqua patula* Dixon) and their bearing on the commercial fishery. *Bull. U. S. Bur. Fish. 46:* 543–567.

# 20 · FISHERY STATISTICS

## 20·1 Uses of fishery statistics

The ultimate use of the statistics collected determines the type of information sought as well as the manner of obtaining it. The chief purposes are:

1. For gathering taxes.
2. For estimating economic importance and trends.
3. For estimating variations in the fish populations.

Statistics gathered for one purpose may be inadequate or misleading if used for another. If they are compiled for tax purposes the stress is on the volume of the raw or processed product with little information about either the localities where catches were made, the gear, or the effort expended. There is apt to be evasion, of course, and in addition such listings necessarily neglect nontaxable items. Trade statistics are often more specific on localities and on gear, but they tend to vary widely both in accuracy and coverage.

For estimating trends in the fish populations statistical systems should be designed to supply specific information needed. No statistical system maintains a uniform standard of accuracy or coverage unless the data are used currently so that all errors in data or changes in trade practice are immediately detected.

## 20·2 Information needed

A wide hiatus usually exists between the information that could be useful to the biostatistician and the amount of information that it is practical to collect. The size of this hiatus depends chiefly on the economics and practices of each fishery. For fisheries employing only a few large units of gear, e.g., salmon traps, tuna vessels, or menhaden seiners, the problem is simplified.

When many small units of gear are fished the collection may still be relatively simple if the bulk of the catch is handled by a few dealers.

This applies sometimes to salmon gill netting where scores of boats land at a few canneries.

Fisheries in which many small units of gear land catches in widely separated localities are the most difficult to cover, especially if the catch is not always sold through the same dealers. This applies to the shad, lobster, and crab fisheries, in which some of the catch is often sold by the fishermen directly to restaurants, peddlers, or even con-

FIG. 20·1 Biologists taking scales and length measurements of fish aboard an otter trawler to determine the age and size composition of the catches. (Credit: E. L. Arnold, Jr., U. S. Fish and Wildlife Service)

sumers. Obviously it is not always practical to obtain very detailed information about a large number of small catches landed by many fishing units. Fortunately, this is not always necessary since the smaller vessels do not usually travel far from their port of landing, so that their fishing radius is restricted.

The information essential to the biologist is:

1. The total catch (by numbers or weight) in each area. The "area" depends on the species. To have biological significance the area must apply to individual populations. Thus catches of alewives must be related to a particular stream, whereas catches of cod may be related to a large bank.

2. The catch by amounts of fishing effort (see Sections 6·9 and 6·10). Where total coverage is impractical, adequate samples can be made to

suffice. Indeed it is often unnecessary, as well as too expensive, to try to collect catch per unit of fishing effort for an entire fishery.

3. The total effort expended. This usually cannot be obtained in precise detail, but a good estimate is important, for, as stressed in Section 6·5, the catch per unit of fishing effort is influenced by the number of units in operation.

4. In a mixed fishery, the amounts of each species taken, with data when practicable, on the area or depth where each species was taken.

5. When quantities are measured by weight, the trade category or other designation of size is necessary for some species. Such trade categories give valuable evidence of shifts in sizes, especially if the statistical data are supplemented by occasional sampling of these categories so that the biologist knows what they mean in actual sizes of fish. Resampling is very important as the sizes of fish included in each trade category often shift back and forth from year to year and from season to season in accordance with demand for certain sizes, shifts in the amounts of each size landed, changes in the size composition of the population, and gradual changes in the uses of the raw product.

## 20·3  Types of collection systems

Several types of collection systems are in use. As no one system fits all localities or fisheries, a combination of systems may be necessary to fit different fisheries even in the same area. The best system for each fishery is usually one that can be fitted into, and become an integral part of, the bookkeeping system of the trade. This insures accuracy, lessens expense, and avoids opposition and occasional neglect by dealers who naturally resent having to recopy their records. The chief types of collection systems are:

**The annual canvass.** This is usually a compilation, made once a year, from whatever records are obtainable. The annual canvasses made by the Fish and Wildlife Service and its predecessors were not made every year in most areas. The accuracy of the statistics from each area varied from one canvass to another, depending on the experience and energy of the statistical agent, and on the time allotted for their collection. The statistics of catches were compiled by fishing vessels, so that theoretically the agent interviewed each vessel captain. In practice this is impossible, and reliance was necessarily placed on the sales records of fish dealers and shipments by transportation companies, supplemented by some interviews. The smaller vessels could never be fully covered by this system. One very serious defect is the fact that the canvass is made months after the fish are caught so that fishermen's records are often lost or missing. Many fishermen keep a record only of the cash received for their fish and have only the haziest notion of the quantities they landed.

A second serious defect of this annual collection by vessels is the fact that the areas of catch were not, and in practice could not, be ascertained. This defect was heightened by the practice of crediting each vessel's catch to its port of registry, regardless of the area in which it fished. For instance, the Massachusetts annual canvass would show large catches of scup and summer flounder, made by Gloucester vessels on their annual winter visit to the fishing grounds off the Virginia capes.

The annual canvass is recommended only as a supplementary tool to cover minor fisheries or areas, or to collect facts concerning fishing gear that are not fully covered by a more effective system. It does not furnish the statistics necessary for an analysis of population abundance, except in a very crude fashion.

**The sales slip.** A system with considerable merit employs a copy of the sales slip. This system is often called the pink ticket system because of the color of the sales slips used in California where the system has been used successfully in extensive and varied fisheries for over 30 years. It has been successful because it is used by all fish handlers and dealers as an integral part of their bookkeeping system serving as a record of a business transaction. The serially numbered sales slips are printed in books in triplicate. One slip is given to the fisherman as a receipt for the fish received, the duplicate slip is mailed to the Division of Fish and Game for a statistical record, and the third slip is retained by the buyer for his own records. All sales of fish in the State must be recorded on these slips, and there are penalties for noncompliance.

Each slip gives the date; the name of the purchaser, whether an individual or a company; the name of the vessel captain (or individual fisherman); the type of fishing gear used; the name of the fishing vessel; the area where the fish were captured; the weights (or numbers) of fish with the unit and total prices, and the manner in which the raw fish are to be processed or resold (canning, reduction, frozen, etc.).

This system, over a period of years, has yielded a vast amount of information of value in the management of the fisheries, and is best calculated to give uniform and consistent coverage for varied fisheries. It has had to be supplemented for some of the more important fisheries with information on the amount of effort expended, and on the exact grounds fished. Some of this additional information is obtained by consistent interviews of vessel captains at ports of landing and some by log books placed aboard vessels for keeping a detailed record of fishing operations.

**Vessel landings.** In the extensive vessel fisheries of New England the landings of individual vessels were collected for Boston and Gloucester as early as 1891. For many years the banks listed as having been fished were those "hailed" by the captain when the fish were auctioned. This system has since been extended to cover all the major New England ports (Rounsefell 1948).

From the weighout slips of the New England Fish Exchange in Boston, and of the fish buyers and fish exchanges in other ports, is obtained a detailed record of the catch of each vessel for each trip. This information is then supplemented in two ways. First, for all ports vessels are interviewed with sufficient frequency to determine where their catches were made according to biostatistical subareas (Figure 20·2). (Rounsefell 1948.) Second, detailed interviews are made of each vessel landing at Boston, Gloucester, or New Bedford to obtain information on fishing effort for each trip by depth and by subarea, and to ascertain in what depth and in which subarea the different species in the catch were taken. This information is needed for accurate studies of fluctuations in abundance and distribution of the various species.

The interviews are made by showing the first mate or captain a Celluloid-enclosed miniature chart of the fishing banks and inquiring as to the exact localities fished, the depths fished, the approximate quantity of fish taken and time fished at each location, the amount of fishing time lost from bad weather, torn gear, or other mishap, and the hour and date of sailing and landing. A sample interview chart is shown in Figure 20·3.

**Log books.** Some types of vessel fisheries are peculiarly adapted to the use of log books. Where they can be used, the detailed on-the-spot records of fishing activity, fishing depths and locations, effort expended, and quantities captured are superior to the information obtainable from interviews made at the time of landing. If log books are to be carefully and consistently kept, they must become the property of the vessel. The International Fisheries Commission (United States and Canada), studying halibut, solved this problem by furnishing to the vessels without charge convenient-sized log books with spaces for all desired information as well as the usual log book entries. The information sought was then copied from these log books from time to time, but log books were always returned promptly to the vessel.

Vessels can also be supplied with charts on which the fishing areas are marked off and designated by some convenient system of numbers or letters so that they can be easily and quickly entered in the log. The manner in which the fishing effort is recorded varies with the

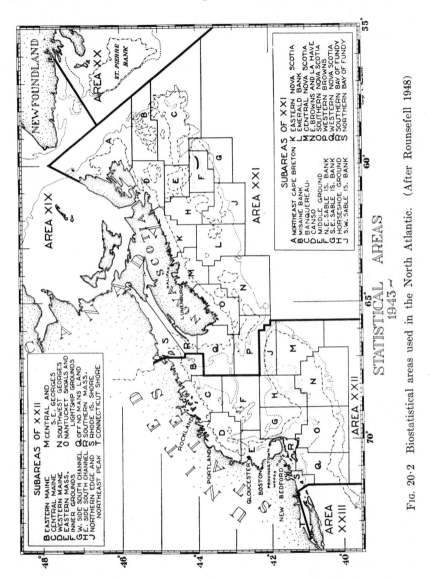

Fig. 20·2 Biostatistical areas used in the North Atlantic. (After Rounsefell 1948)

type of gear. Thus with halibut gear the number of "skates" fished in each locality is recorded together with the catch (a skate of gear is one unit of ground line with its baited hooks on short gangings). For otter trawl vessels the number of tows is the best measure. For purse seine vessels the usual measure is the length of time spent in searching for schools of fish.

**Daily delivery sheets.** For some fisheries none of the foregoing systems are suitable. Thus there are fisheries in which many small units of gear make daily deliveries to a common point, such as a cannery, cold-storage plant, or buying vessel. Such operators seldom keep log books or records, except of quantities of fish sold—sometimes only of the price. Examples are the salmon gill net fisheries, the Puget Sound purse seine fisheries, and clam diggers selling to canneries.

For such fisheries the best records can be obtained usually from the buyer. It is a practical impossibility to collect more than a fraction of the data from individual fishermen or small vessels, but it is quite feasible to furnish the buyer with daily delivery sheets on which each purchase is recorded with the name of the fisherman or vessel, when necessary the fishing locality, and any other pertinent information. These sheets should provide the proper columns needed by the buyer and be in duplicate or triplicate so that the buyer can use them in his own bookkeeping system, obviating the necessity of recopying.

**Fixed gear records.** For records of the catches of fixed gear, such as salmon traps, weirs, and pound nets, a chronological record of each unit is of great importance for several reasons. The catching ability of each unit depends to a large extent on the site so that no two traps have exactly the same catching potentiality (Rounsefell and Kelez 1938). The records for each unit must be kept separate for proper analysis. The unit of fishing effort for fixed gear is usually some unit of time, so that a chronological record shows the elapsed time between each lift of the trap. Usually the operator of fixed gear also desires to keep the records separate so that he can appraise the net value of each site.

The best method for collecting usable data on fixed gear is to furnish the operators with sheets on which the date and catch are recorded for each lift. The sheets should also have a place to show the date the gear was placed in fishable operation, the date on which fishing was terminated, and any period during which it was not fishing.

**Sport fish records.** The amounts of fish taken by sport fishermen are generally much larger than commonly realized. It has been estimated for instance that marine sport fishermen annually take about 400 million pounds of fish in about 30 million man-days of fishing. There must be several times as many man-days of fishing in fresh waters, as there were over 16 million licensed anglers in the United States in 1951. Although the catch per day is less, the total freshwater catch is obviously large. It is very difficult to obtain accurate sport

Fig. 20-5 Chart used in interviewing vessel captains to obtain

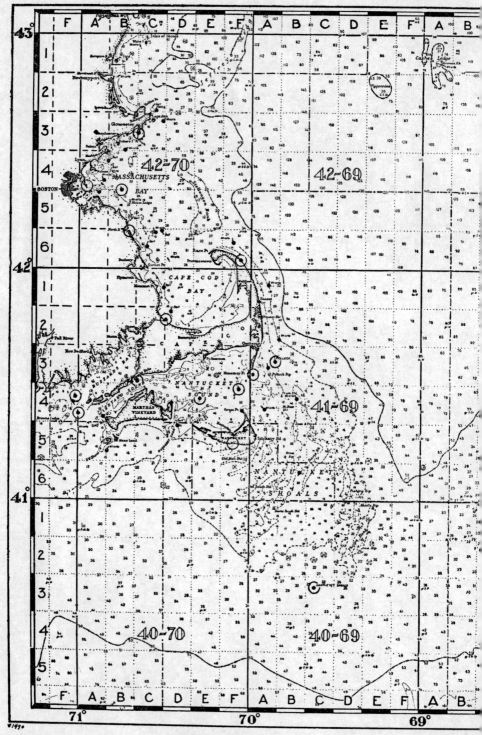

Fig. 20·3   Chart used in interviewing vessel captains to obtain

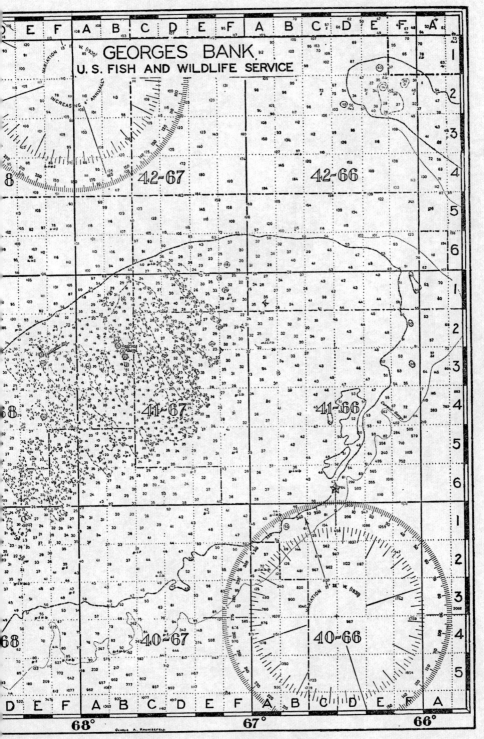

GEORGES BANK
U. S. FISH AND WILDLIFE SERVICE

tics on fishing locations and catches. (After Rounsefell 1948)

fishing records of either catch or fishing effort for any body of water as there are seldom any business records kept. Often the only method available is to make a creel census as described in Section 6·12.

In some of the coastal states a large share of the fish caught by the party sport fishing boats is sold and the records are not always collected.

Where an adequate sample of the catches and fishing effort will suffice these can sometimes be obtained for individual lakes through the co-operation of the operators of boat liveries. In some of the National Forests each fisherman is required to list his day's catch at checkout points, furnishing information of great value for management.

**References**

Rounsefell, George A.
    1948. Development of fishery statistics in the North Atlantic. *U. S. Fish and Wildl. Serv., Spec. Sci. Rept. 47:* 18 pp.
Rounsefell, George A., and George B. Kelez
    1938. The salmon and salmon fisheries of Swiftsure Bank, Puget Sound, and the Fraser River. *Bull. U. S. Bur. Fish. 49* (27):693–823.
Thompson, W. F.
    1919. The scientific investigation of marine fisheries as related to the work of the Fish and Game Commission in southern California. *Calif. Div. Fish and Game, Bur. Comm. Fish., Bull. 2:* 27 pp.

# 21 · STREAM AND LAKE SURVEYS

## 21·1  Introduction

*What* and *where* must be determined before the scientific management of the fisheries of an area can be undertaken.  An inventory of the fishery resources of a state is just as important to the successful management of its fisheries as the inventory of the stock in a large department store is necessary for the successful business future of the store.  State conservation departments should have information available on species, distribution, types of lakes and streams, pollution, fishing pressure, location of obstructions and fishways, and water level fluctuation, to make an intelligent approach toward solving fishery problems.  Without a survey, serious problems may continue unrecognized.  It should be emphasized that surveys do not answer questions or solve problems but merely uncover them and provide preliminary information of value in determining the relative importance of the problems and their possible solution.

The greatest use made of surveys in the past has been in the formulation of stocking programs for the products of artificial propagation.  Proper evaluation of the habitat may save thousands of dollars by preventing the wasteful stocking of hatchery-reared fish in unsuitable environments.

The idea of survey work is rather recent.  At one time town clerks were frequently asked to give certain information which was used in formulating regulations and management plans.  The Illinois Natural History Survey, begun in 1900, took into consideration all the flora and fauna in the area, devoting considerable time to a study of the fishes.

The New York Survey begun in 1926 was the forerunner of surveys as conducted today.  This survey laid down the general techniques and trained a large groups of biologists who went out to other states and directed surveys of their own.  At times the New York Survey had as many as 40 or 50 workers, a large percentage of whom were experts in their specific fields.

## 21·2    Planning the survey

The importance of planning the survey carefully before going into the field cannot be overemphasized. Such planning reduces over-lapping of work, cuts down on mileage and other expenditures, and in general increases the efficiency of the whole program by insuring a co-ordination of all activities.

Tentative schedules should be prepared weeks before the field crews are scheduled to begin their work. During the field work weekly schedules should be prepared and daily work schedules planned each evening for the next day's work.

Many times complicated channels for ordering material through state departments will oblige the director of the survey to plan as much as a year ahead if he is to obtain the proper equipment at the time it is needed.

Much field time can be saved if all crews are provided with maps prepared in advance. Otherwise valuable field time will be spent preparing maps that should be prepared in the office.

An important phase in the planning of the survey is the decision concerning the best geographical division of the work. The most popular approach in the past has been the practice of considering drainage areas as units. The survey is planned to permit the field crews to complete a drainage in a certain period, and an entire state is surveyed by chief drainage areas. Another method is to plan the survey to investigate a specific problem. Perhaps the lakes in a certain area are presenting a problem, and the leader of the survey may decide to work only on those lakes. Whichever the course, preplanning will lead to more conclusive results.

Anyone familiar with the lakes and streams of an area realizes that certain names are very popular, and so we have any number of Round Ponds, Mud Ponds, Crystal and Clear Lakes. Frequently the smaller bodies of water may have no name at all.

In order to avoid confusion the New York surveys (E. Moore et al. 1927–1940) used a system whereby the tributaries are numbered in order from the mouth of the largest waters up. Tributaries of tributaries are similarly numbered. Lakes are designated in order as they are encountered in numbering the streams. The tributary streams or inlets of lakes are numbered in clockwise fashion starting from the outlet and omitting the inlet if it bears the same name as the outlet. Cooper (1939–1946) used a similar system of numbering for the Maine surveys. All streams emptying into the Atlantic Ocean were desig-nated as Atlantic tributaries. Inasmuch as the bulk of the population is concentrated in the southern part of the state with a resulting in-

crease in fishery problems the surveys were begun in that area numbering the Piscataqua River on the state boundary between New
Hampshire and Maine as Atlantic tributary number 1. As tributaries
of this river were encountered they were numbered in turn. Cooper's
plan was to continue northward along the coast of Maine until the
entire state had been surveyed. The senior author, as co-ordinator of
the Atlantic Salmon Investigation in Maine, employed a numbering
system for the salmon rivers. In this instance, however, the numbering system begins at the extreme northern tip of the Maine coast and
extends southward with the far-reaching expectation that as the restoration of the salmon is successful in Maine it may continue into
other Atlantic Coast states to the south. The New Hampshire biological surveys (Hoover 1936–1938 and Warfel 1939) also used the
numbering system of designating the waters.

## 21·3   Personnel

The absolute minimum crew for a fishery survey would consist of
a fishery biologist and one assistant. A four-man crew operates very
efficiently in the field. One man acts as the leader and directs the work.
Smith and Moyle (1944) recommend a five-man crew. With the
larger crew it is particularly desirable when working on streams to
start men at various points along the stream to eliminate the retracing
of steps. Experience of the junior author in lake survey work indicates
that two-man parties are the most efficient, particularly when much of
the work is done from rowboats of average length. The over-all budget
will decide how many four-man or two-man crews can operate during
the period of field work.

## 21·4   Fishery biologist

In most cases the director of the survey will be a fishery biologist.
As director his responsibilities will be many, but specifically he will
be concerned with the species of fish and their distribution. He should
obtain all possible information on their habitats and abundance. Data
on reproduction, available spawning grounds, and general character
of the shoreline should be recorded. Age and growth data are usually
needed so that weights, lengths, and scale samples are taken from the
fish. Such information is valuable in comparing average age and
growth for different types of waters.

## 21·5   Limnologist

One of the survey crew can serve as limnologist and be responsible
for taking the soundings of lakes and for tabulating the data on their

physical and chemical stratification. Chemical analysis of the water may be conducted to obtain data on the oxygen and carbon dioxide content, $pH$, and productivity. Further study of the productivity may be carried on by an examination of the plankton content of the water. Secchi disk readings may be taken to determine the relative turbidity.

Temperatures should be taken and water analyses made during the latter part of the summer in temperate regions subject to annual or semiannual turnover, since it is the goal of the survey to determine the suitability of the habitat, and by the end of August the conditions in the hypolimnion have become as unsuitable for fish as they are apt to get during the year.

Bottom fauna may be sampled in an effort to determine available food, even though manipulative errors and sampling inadequacies often make such data questionable for quantitative interpretation. The bottom fauna in lakes is ordinarily sampled with an Ekman square-foot bottom sampler, whereas in streams where a good flow of water can be obtained a Surber square-foot bottom sampler is used.

## 21·6   Parasitologist

Knowledge of fish parasites and their distribution is sometimes important in establishing a stocking program and in general management. This is particularly so where salvaged fish are transferred from one lake to another. Most states at one time or another employ a parasitologist to make a thorough study of the fish parasites and to publish both technical reports and more or less popular accounts for the sportsmen. During the period that the parasitologist is working, the fishery biologists may have an opportunity to aid in the work. This training and the publication on the parasites of the fishes may enable the fishery biologists subsequently to handle the routine parasitology.

## 21·7   Other specialists

Aquatic plants may play an important part in the ecology of an area. Although most fishery biologists have some training in aquatic botany it is generally and understandably not intensive enough to permit a thorough study. Consequently many states employ a botanist temporarily to classify and report on the aquatic plants. With that aid the fishery bologist may carry on alone. Pollution studies from the standpoint of a survey should merely involve recognizing the condition (see Chapter 13). In agencies with limited budgets it may be necessary for the fishery biologist to conduct the work listed above without the aid of specialists.

## 21·8  Information needed for stream stocking

Much of the information obtained from the lake and stream survey should be used in formulating a stocking program in the area covered by the survey. There are certain fundamental considerations which should be taken into account however before any additional species is stocked in any waters. Fish should not be stocked where populations of suitable game fish are already making use of the water area. Particular care should be taken not to plant species that are competitive for the same spawning area or will occupy the same ecological niche as the already existing species. A good example of such unwise stocking is the introduction of brown trout into landlocked salmon waters.

Stream stocking was pioneered by George C. Embody (1927). Much of what follows has been derived from his paper, since he developed the fundamentals of stream stocking. The following information should be acquired before stocking a stream:

1. What species will most likely find conditions suitable for maintenance, growth, and reproduction?

2. How many should be planted in order to utilize the food resources fully and maintain the densest population consistent with normal growth?

3. What size of fish should be planted with the expectation of giving the desired results?

4. What, if anything aside from restocking, may be done to make the stream more productive?

Ideally field workers must become familiar with a stream throughout its whole extent. Small streams may require a full set of observations at the mouth, middle, and head waters, but larger streams should be sampled as intensively as time will permit.

As part of the preplanning most surveys are provided with mimeographed forms or cards on which the field worker may only have to check an item or jot a few words in recording the data. Embody recommended that the following field observations be made:

**Width of stream.** Several measurements should be taken in each section studied so that an average value is determined.

**Length of stream.** The total length of stream is important together with the total area available for the species that may be stocked in the stream. Unsuitable portions should be noted as well.

**Rate of flow.** Since only a rough approximation is necessary the following formula may be used:

$$R = \frac{WDaL}{T}$$

$R$ = rate of flow
$W$ = average width in feet
$D$ = average depth in feet
$L$ = distance float is carried
$T$ = time in seconds for float to cover distance $L$
$a$ = a constant for the correction of stream velocity. It may be taken as 0.8 if the bottom is rough (strewn with rocks and coarse gravel); and 0.9, if bottom is smooth (mud, fine sand, hardpan, or bedrock).

The section selected should be straight, without obstructions, of approximately the same width and with the same type of bottom throughout. One hundred feet of stream is a convenient length. Next a floating object is clocked to determine the time it takes to float the 100 feet. Embody recommends the use of a fisherman's float with the projecting arms removed. Most survey crews float pieces of wood, and it has been suggested that a lemon would be ideal for such a float since it rides just under the surface. The float should be timed over the distance three times and the average time recorded.

**Average depth.** The average depth is estimated by taking three depth measurements of the stream at each place where the width is taken (every 20 feet) by recording the depth at one fourth, midstream, and three fourths. Average depths are added and the sum is divided by four which takes into consideration the depth at the banks which grades out to zero.

The above values are substituted in the formula and the calculation will yield the flow in cubic feet per second (450 gallons per minute is equal to one cubic foot per second).

**Air and water temperature.** Care should be exercised to obtain air and water temperature together since it is necessary to know the correlation between the two. Maximum summer temperature and duration of this maximum must be known if a stream is to be stocked with trout or other cold-water species. Temperatures taken during or just after a shower will of course be misleading.

Embody (1929) prepared the following comparative table to show the relation of air and water temperatures in trout streams located in open country up to 1000 feet elevation.

| Maximum air temperature, °F | 80.0 | 82.0 | 84.0 | 86.0 | 88.0 | 90.0 | 92.0 | 94.0 |
|---|---|---|---|---|---|---|---|---|
| Maximum water temperature, brook trout | 65.0 | 66.5 | 68.0 | 70.0 | 71.5 | 73.0 | 74.0 | 75.0 |
| Maximum water temperature: Brown trout ⎫ Rainbow trout ⎭ | 69.0 | 70.5 | 72.0 | 73.5 | 75.0 | 76.5 | 78.0 | 79.0 |

The table is predicated on the principle that if at a given air temperature the water temperature is higher than that indicated for the species concerned it is probable that the temperature will become unfavorable at some time.

**Permanency.** During the late summer a stream may become partly or wholly dry, making critical conditions for the fish.

**Velocity.** Record as torrential, rapid, or sluggish.

**Dams and natural falls.** Record the maximum vertical drop in feet and the horizontal distance that fish must cover in passing over the barrier. If a pond results from the barrier, information about the pond should be listed.

**Pollution.** The nature of the pollutant should be determined and any information concerning the effects such as the distance in which it damages the stream or influences the fauna.

**Color of water.** Record as white, slightly brown, and deep brown.

**Enemies.** All predators observed should be noted on form.

**Improvements.** Areas that show the need of stream improvement should be recorded along with the recommended type of alteration.

**Spawning and nursery areas.** Spawning area and subsequent nursery area may be a vital factor in maintaining a population dense enough to permit good fishing. All principal spawning areas should be recorded and the extent of the nursery area noted. Scarcity of either of these areas would greatly influence the number and size of fish stocked.

**Natural food.** Food can only be estimated and the stream judged as (1) very rich, (2) average in richness, or (3) poor in food. This may be accomplished by a cursory examination or by actually obtaining square foot bottom samples over the stream and analyzing them carefully. Since the latter requires a great deal of time the observer will ordinarily count on his experience in recognizing one or more of the following sets of conditions:

*Grade 1. Richest in food.* Current moderate to sluggish; bottom of mud, silt, or detritus; extensive areas covered with watercress, moss, *Chara*, or other plants.

A rubble bottom in swift water with mayflies, stoneflies, and caddis-flies occurring in greatest abundance.

A stream margined with willows, alders, button bush, and tall weeds such as goldenrod receives a large contribution of terrestrial insects.

*Grade 2. Average in quantity of food.* Generally rapid with bottom of coarse gravel and flat rocks, or sluggish with muck or silt bottom,

Fig. 21·1   Showing riffle section of a stream that provides overhanging shade and shelter, and medium rubble of ideal size for spawning of trout and salmon.

without submerged plants and exposed with few sheltering trees or shrubs.

*Grade 3. Poor in food.* Bottom of fine gravel, sand, hardpan or clean bedrock; without vegetation; exposed; mayflies, stoneflies, cad-disflies uncommon or rare.

The relative abundance of the various groups should be indicated on field blanks by underscoring once if the animal is uncommon or rare, twice if common, and three times if abundant. At the same time a grade of 1, 2, or 3 should be recorded, indicating total richness of the whole stream in food.

**Pools.** Near each station pace off about 200 yards of stream length, and study the size, type, and frequency of the pools.

*Size*

1. Pools having an average width more than double that of the stream.

2. Pools having a width about equal to that of stream.

3. Pools much narrower than stream.

Fig. 21·2 Using a square-foot bottom sampler to collect fish food organisms from a stream riffle. (Credit: A. H. Fisher, U. S. Fish and Wildlife Service)

*Type*

1. Deep (2 feet or more), exposed pools containing a great luxuriance of aquatic plants harboring a rich fauna, or deep pools with abundant shelter (overhanging banks, logs, roots, boulders), much drift or detritus, shaded by forest cover or shrubs.

2. Pools intermediate in depth, shelter, plant abundance, etc.

3. Shallow exposed pools without shelter and without plants; scouring basins.

*Frequency*

1. More or less continuous pools.
2. Rather close succession of pools and rapids.
3. Pools infrequent with long stretches of swift water between them.

If we let $S$ refer to size, $T$ to type, and $F$ to frequency, then it is evident that a combination of $S1-T1-F1$ would receive the highest rating and $S3-T3-F3$ the lowest. Likewise various other combinations may be roughly recorded as intermediate, although they are not necessarily equal in value.

The letters $A$, $B$, and $C$ may be used to represent the final grade, the letter $A$ indicating the highest value. This grade letter, together with the combination of letters upon which the grade is based, should be recorded in the field outline blank.

## 21·9 Determining the number of fish to be planted

The backbone of the stocking program is usually a planting table. Table 21·1 indicates the number of 3-inch fingerlings to be planted

TABLE 21·1

PLANTING TABLE FOR TROUT STREAMS (EMBODY 1927)

Number of 3-Inch Fingerlings

| Width, Feet | $A$–1 | $A$–2 | $A$–3 | $B$–1 | $B$–2 | $B$–3 | $C$–1 | $C$–2 | $C$–3 |
|---|---|---|---|---|---|---|---|---|---|
| 1 | 144 | 117 | 90 | 117 | 90 | 63 | 90 | 63 | 36 |
| 2 | 288 | 234 | 180 | 234 | 180 | 126 | 180 | 126 | 72 |
| 3 | 432 | 351 | 270 | 351 | 270 | 189 | 270 | 189 | 108 |
| 4 | 576 | 468 | 360 | 468 | 360 | 252 | 360 | 252 | 142 |
| 5 | 720 | 585 | 450 | 585 | 450 | 315 | 450 | 315 | 180 |
| 6 | 864 | 702 | 540 | 702 | 540 | 378 | 540 | 378 | 216 |
| 7 | 1008 | 819 | 630 | 819 | 630 | 441 | 630 | 441 | 252 |
| 8 | 1152 | 936 | 720 | 936 | 720 | 504 | 720 | 504 | 284 |
| 9 | 1296 | 1053 | 810 | 1053 | 810 | 567 | 810 | 567 | 324 |
| 10 | 1440 | 1170 | 900 | 1170 | 900 | 630 | 900 | 630 | 360 |

| Size, inches | 1 | 2 | 3 | 4 | 6 |
|---|---|---|---|---|---|
| Factor | 12 | 1.7 | 1 | 0.75 | 0.6 |

| Size | 1 | 2 | 3 | 4 | 6 |
|---|---|---|---|---|---|
| Mortality, % | 95 | 65 | 40 | 20 | 0 |

yearly and per mile for streams of various widths and for different combinations of food and pool conditions. This table is based on experiments which were planned to show the number of pounds of trout produced in areas rich in food and in those poor in food. From the data obtained above, the average width of the stream, the number of miles suitable for stocking, and values for pool (A, B, and C) and food (1, 2, and 3) conditions must be determined.

The table refers to 3-inch fish only so that it is necessary to employ the factors listed under the table if another size of fish is used. The

TABLE 21·2

PLANTING TABLE FOR TROUT STREAMS (EMBODY 1928)

Number of 3-Inch Fingerlings

| Stream Width, Feet | Pool Grade A | | | Pool Grade B | | | Pool Grade C | | |
|---|---|---|---|---|---|---|---|---|---|
| | 1 * | 2 | 3 | 1 | 2 | 3 | 1 | 2 | 3 |
| 1 | 144 | 117 | 90 | 117 | 90 | 63 | 90 | 63 | 36 |
| 2 | 288 | 234 | 180 | 234 | 180 | 126 | 180 | 126 | 72 |
| 3 | 432 | 351 | 270 | 351 | 270 | 189 | 270 | 189 | 108 |
| 4 | 576 | 468 | 360 | 468 | 360 | 252 | 360 | 252 | 142 |
| 5 | 720 | 585 | 450 | 585 | 450 | 315 | 450 | 315 | 180 |
| 6 | 864 | 702 | 540 | 702 | 540 | 378 | 540 | 378 | 216 |
| 7 | 1008 | 819 | 630 | 819 | 630 | 441 | 630 | 441 | 252 |
| 8 | 1152 | 936 | 720 | 936 | 720 | 504 | 720 | 504 | 284 |
| 9 | 1296 | 1053 | 810 | 1053 | 810 | 567 | 810 | 567 | 324 |
| 10 | 1440 | 1170 | 900 | 1170 | 900 | 630 | 900 | 630 | 360 |
| 11 | 1584 | 1287 | 990 | 1287 | 990 | 693 | 990 | 693 | 396 |
| 12 | 1728 | 1404 | 1080 | 1404 | 1080 | 756 | 1080 | 756 | 432 |
| 13 | 1872 | 1521 | 1170 | 1521 | 1170 | 819 | 1170 | 819 | 468 |
| 14 | 2016 | 1638 | 1260 | 1638 | 1260 | 882 | 1260 | 882 | 504 |
| 15 | 2160 | 1755 | 1350 | 1755 | 1350 | 945 | 1350 | 945 | 540 |
| 16 | 2304 | 1872 | 1440 | 1872 | 1440 | 1008 | 1440 | 1008 | 576 |
| 17 | 2376 | 1930 | 1485 | 1930 | 1485 | 1039 | 1485 | 1039 | 594 |
| 18 | 2448 | 1989 | 1530 | 1989 | 1530 | 1071 | 1530 | 1071 | 612 |
| 19 | 2520 | 2047 | 1575 | 2047 | 1575 | 1102 | 1575 | 1102 | 630 |
| 20 | 2592 | 2106 | 1620 | 2106 | 1620 | 1134 | 1620 | 1134 | 648 |

For streams over 20 feet in width use formula $\frac{1}{2}N_1W + 8N_1 = X$.

$N_1$ = number fingerlings for stream 1 foot wide, $W$ = average width.

$X$ = number to be stocked per mile.

The above table refers to 3-inch fingerlings only. To find the number of other sizes multiply the number of fish given for the stream width in question by the following factors (dependent on size).

| Length, inches | 1 | 3 | 4 | 6 | 10 |
|---|---|---|---|---|---|
| | Fry | Fing. | Fing. | Legal | Adult |
| Factor | 12 | 1 | 0.75 | 0.6 | 0.3 |

* The figures 1, 2, 3 at the heads of columns indicate the food grade.

size factor is based on the expected mortality, also listed under the table.

The table covers stream widths up to 10 feet. Values for wider streams up to 16 feet may be determined by multiplying that given for a stream 1 foot wide by the width of the stream in question.

Leger (1910), after studying the biogenic capacity of certain streams in France, concluded that the nutritive richness is proportionately much greater in narrow than in wider streams. In streams above 5 meters in width, the richness in food diminished one half at a distance of 2 or 2½ meters from the banks. Although this has not been proved to hold in streams elsewhere, we shall have to assume that it is true pending future quantitative determinations. If we accept this quali-

TABLE 21·3

PLANTING TABLE FOR TROUT STREAMS (DAVIS 1938)

Number of 3-Inch Fingerlings

| Width Stream, Feet | Number of 3-Inch Fingerlings per Mile | | | | | | | | |
|---|---|---|---|---|---|---|---|---|---|
| | A–1 | A–2 | A–3 | B–1 | B–2 | B–3 | C–1 | C–2 | C–3 |
| 1 | 80 | 65 | 50 | 65 | 50 | 35 | 50 | 35 | 20 |
| 2 | 160 | 130 | 100 | 130 | 100 | 70 | 100 | 70 | 40 |
| 3 | 240 | 195 | 150 | 195 | 150 | 105 | 150 | 105 | 60 |
| 4 | 320 | 260 | 200 | 260 | 200 | 140 | 200 | 140 | 80 |
| 5 | 400 | 325 | 250 | 325 | 250 | 175 | 250 | 175 | 100 |
| 6 | 480 | 390 | 300 | 390 | 300 | 210 | 300 | 210 | 120 |
| 7 | 560 | 455 | 350 | 455 | 350 | 245 | 350 | 245 | 140 |
| 8 | 640 | 520 | 400 | 520 | 400 | 280 | 400 | 280 | 160 |
| 9 | 720 | 585 | 450 | 585 | 450 | 315 | 450 | 315 | 180 |
| 10 | 800 | 650 | 500 | 650 | 500 | 350 | 500 | 350 | 200 |
| 11 | 880 | 715 | 550 | 715 | 550 | 385 | 550 | 385 | 220 |
| 12 | 960 | 780 | 600 | 780 | 600 | 420 | 600 | 420 | 240 |
| 13 | 1040 | 845 | 650 | 845 | 650 | 455 | 650 | 455 | 260 |
| 14 | 1120 | 910 | 700 | 910 | 700 | 490 | 700 | 490 | 280 |
| 15 | 1200 | 975 | 750 | 975 | 750 | 525 | 750 | 525 | 300 |
| 16 | 1280 | 1040 | 800 | 1040 | 800 | 560 | 800 | 560 | 320 |
| 17 | 1360 | 1105 | 850 | 1105 | 850 | 595 | 850 | 595 | 340 |
| 18 | 1440 | 1170 | 900 | 1170 | 900 | 630 | 900 | 630 | 360 |
| 19 | 1520 | 1235 | 950 | 1235 | 950 | 665 | 950 | 665 | 380 |
| 20 | 1600 | 1300 | 1000 | 1300 | 1000 | 700 | 1000 | 700 | 400 |

Factors for determining the required number of fish and the approximate percentage of survival.

| Size, inches | 1 | 2 | 3 | 4 | 5 | 6 |
|---|---|---|---|---|---|---|
| Factor | 10 | 2.5 | 1 | 0.7 | 0.62 | 0.55 |
| Survival | 5 | 20 | 50 | 70 | 80 | 90 |

fication then the following formula must be used when fish are to be planted in streams over 16 feet (roughly 5 meters) in average width:

$$\tfrac{1}{2}n_1 w + 8n_1 = X$$

$n_1$ = number of fish recorded in Table 21·1, for a stream 1 foot wide
$w$ = average width of stream to be stocked
$X$ = number of fish desired

Embody (1928) revised his original table to include stream widths up to 20 feet and fish up to 10 inches in length. The revised Table 21·2 is included for reference.

Davis (1938), believing that Embody's table was based on streams with little natural reproduction and a heavy fishing pressure, revised the table as shown in Table 21·3. Table 21·3 covers streams up to 20 feet in width. For wider streams multiply the number given for a stream 1 foot wide by the width of the stream in question. As in Embody's tables (21·1 and 21·2) 3-inch fish are referred to so that one of the factors listed is used if trout of another size are to be planted. Table 21·3 does not take into consideration the relative productivity of the narrower and wider streams.

Reference to the survival figures listed in Chapter 23, and a study of the experiments designed to test survival, will indicate that both Embody and Davis were extremely optimistic about survival of the hatchery-reared trout.

Hoover (1937–1939) apparently employed Embody's original table without modification in formulating the stocking policies in the New Hampshire surveys.

## 21·10  Further modifications of stream stocking tables

Embody specified food grades of 1, 2, and 3 on the basis of good, medium, or poor and did not give strict delimitations on the amount of food per unit area. Hazzard (1935) revised these classifications and made them more specific by designating food grades, based on square-foot samples, as follows:

Grade I.  Volume greater than 2 cc (2 grams), 50 or more organisms.
Grade II.  Volume from 1 to 2 cc (1 to 2 grams), 1 to 50 organisms.
Grade III.  Volume less than 1 cc (1 gram), 1 to 50 organisms.

Davis (1938) modified the above to omit the numbers of organisms. Smith and Moyle (1944) follow Davis.

Hazzard (1935) and Davis (1938) revised Embody's classification of pools used in determining the $A$, $B$, and $C$ to make it more specific and recommended that the actual number of pools per mile be taken into consideration in evaluating the stream.

Smith and Moyle (1944) evaluated the pools as follows:

Type *A*.  Deep pools (3 times average depth of stream) with good shelter created either by submerged logs and rocks or undercut banks with a high production of food organisms on the bottom.  This pool will usually have a silt, muck, or detritus bottom.

Type *B*.  Shallow pools (1 to 2 times average depth of stream) with a moderate amount of shelter and food production.

Type *C*.  Deep pools with little or no shelter, unprotected bottom and fast current.

Type *D*.  Shallow pools with unproductive bottoms, fast current and no shelter.

The size of the pools was designated by numbers 1, 2, 3:

1. Pools larger than twice the average width of the stream.
2. Pools up to twice the width of the stream.
3. Pools narrower than average width of the stream.

*A* grade of the Embody table includes streams in which pools are *A*–1, *A*–2, and *B*–1 and where pools constitute more than 60 per cent of the total stream area.  The *C* grade of the table includes all pools in the *C* and *D* group.  Between these two extremes falls the *B* class of Embody.  The variable nature of the stream conditions, however, has made it necessary to use a flexible designation and considerable judgment on what pool grades should be applied to the stocking table.

In using Table 21·2 Smith and Moyle (1944) made large corrections for variations in the fishing load, success of natural reproduction, and the known mortality of planted 7- to 9-inch fish.  They applied the following factors for local variations to the totals represented in the table:

1. Where fishing load was heavy and natural reproduction fair, the full calculated stocking was proposed.

2. Where fishing load was heavy and natural reproduction good or where the fishing load was moderate and natural reproduction fair, a factor of 0.50 was applied to table totals.

3. Where fishing load was light or moderate with good natural reproduction, a factor of 0.25 was used.  All stocking recommendations were conservative because the authors felt that stocking should be considered a supplement rather than a substitute for natural reproduction.

## 21·11  Lake survey

A lake is usually classified as one of three types: oligotrophic, eutrophic, or dystrophic according to its physical, chemical, and biological characters (Welch 1935).  Welch lists the important characteristics of each type as follows:

*Oligotrophic lakes:*

Relatively large amount of deep, cold water.
Water blue to green and very transparent.
Little or no organic material on the bottom in deep water.
Oxygen content high at all depths and at all seasons.
Aquatic plants rare.
Basic fertility low.
Ordinarily considered a good habitat for cold-water species.

*Eutrophic lakes:*

Lake shallow with relatively small amount of deep, cold water.
Water green to yellow and brownish green and not very transparent.
Large quantity of organic material on the bottom and suspended in
     the water.
Little or no oxygen in deep water during the summer.
Aquatic plants abundant.
Basic fertility high.
Usually not good habitat for cold-water species.

*Dystrophic lakes:*

Deep to shallow; in bog surroundings or in old mountains.
Water yellow to brown and with low transparency.
Large quantity of organic mud on bottom.
Little or no oxygen in deep water during the summer.
Aquatic plants rare.
Basic fertility low.
Usually not good habitat for cold-water species.

An examination of the above characters will indicate considerable overlapping, and in many cases it is almost impossible to classify a borderline lake.

Lakes in high latitudes undergo seasonal changes in physical, chemical and biological conditions which are of great importance to the fish fauna.  Most of these changes are dependent on two basic facts: (1) Water is at its heaviest (greatest density) at 4° C, becoming lighter (less dense) as it becomes warmer or colder.  (2) A lake receives its heat budget from contact with the air at the surface.

## 21·12   Stratification of lakes

Most of the larger, deeper lakes (particularly those that tend toward the oligotrophic characteristics) exhibit the phenomenon of stratification in which the waters are divided into three regions known as the epilimnion, thermocline, and hypolimnion.

The epilimnion contains the warm surface water and may during the summer stagnation period extend down to depths of 50 to 60 feet although an average depth of 30 feet is more general. Here you have the wind-stirred water with shifting temperatures. There is plenty of light and oxygen with abundant plankton.

The thermocline lying between the epilimnion and the lower layer or hypolimnion is the region of rapid temperature change often defined as having a drop of at least 1° C per meter of depth. At the beginning of the summer this layer may be quite thick and close to the surface but as warmer weather prevails the layer becomes thinner and is forced deeper in the lake. As much as 65 per cent of the temperature drop may occur here. The sudden drop in temperature in this region with its accompanying greater density makes the thermocline a sort of collector for weakened plankton no longer able to maintain themselves in the warmer (and therefore less dense) water of the epilimnion.

The hypolimnion, the bottommost layer, contains the cold water of the lake. The temperature drop is slight from the top to the bottom of this layer. Unaffected by the wind, no light penetrates its still depths.

During the period of summer stagnation these discrete layers of water of different density offer sufficient resistance to prevent their being mixed by the winds. However, as autumn approaches, the water of the epilimnion begins to cool and continues until it approximates the temperature and density of the lower layers, thus reducing the resistance to mixing between the layers. Eventually the fall winds are able to "turn over" the water from top to bottom, and we find the temperature rather uniform throughout the depths.

As the temperature continues to drop, the 4° water remains at the bottom of the lake. The colder, surface water (less than 4° C) being lighter remains at the surface to be frozen. Water temperature just under the ice is 0° C with the temperature increasing towards the bottom. The ice cap prevents movement of the water by the wind, and so the lake is said to have entered its period of winter stagnation.

As the air temperature warms in spring, the ice is melted from the lakes and the surface water is warmed to 4° C, at which point the wind can again mix the surface and bottom waters provided it does not warm too rapidly. This period is known as the spring overturn, and as in the fall overturn water temperatures are practically uniform throughout the lake. It is during this spring turnover period that the water of the lake destined to become part of the thermocline and hypolimnion receives its oxygen budget for the summer.

## 21·13   Biological importance of stratification

The maintenance of an extensive layer of cool, oxygenated water throughout the summer months is essential if populations of desirable, cold-water fishes are to be maintained in a lake. A lake which does not exhibit stratification may become too warm to support cold-water species. In stratified lakes oxygen in the hypolimnion may become deficient during the latter part of the summer, forcing fish into the warmer areas of the epilimnion where temperatures may prove to be too high. The $pH$ and $CO_2$ may also become undesirable in the still, unlighted waters of the hypolimnion.

## 21·14   Procedures in lake survey

As with stream surveys work will progress more efficiently if the crews are provided with ready-made forms on which to place the information. In many areas the first task (after the map has been obtained) is to determine whether the lake is natural or artificial. The shoreline should then be observed for spawning areas, aquatic plants, and extent of the littoral zones. Examination of the shoreline should indicate whether the lake is subject to drastic changes in water level. Such changes may have adverse effects on the food organisms of the littoral zone and, depending on the season of fluctuation, may destroy eggs and young of shore-spawning species such as lake trout.

Depth of a lake may be determined by sounding either with a weighted chain on which depth markers have been placed at intervals or by echo sounding with any type of fathometer designed to be carried in small boats.

Temperature readings correlated with the soundings will provide information relative to the percentage of the total lake volume in each of the three layers. Temperatures may be taken with a reversing thermometer or by one of the various types of electric thermometers. Electric thermometers are time savers since they may be lowered to the bottom and the temperatures read directly from dials in the boat as the temperature-recording element is slowly raised. The Thermistor-type thermometer now employed in Maine surveys reaches equilibrium in 10 seconds.

Color of the water is noted, and the Secchi disk is used to give a relative measure of the turbidity or the amount of suspended material in the water.

Ordinarily the temperatures are taken and the water analyzed in the latter part of the summer so that the data will record the lake at its minimum as regards habitat for cold-water species. Determinations are made of the oxygen, carbon dioxide, $pH$, and alkalinity. Extensive studies of nutrients may be undertaken as special problems.

Plankton content may be measured and the invertebrates present in bottom samples obtained as indications of the productivity of the water.

Considerable time should be spent on a careful examination of tributary streams to determine their fitness as spawning and nursery areas. This is particularly important where trout and salmon may be the desirable species. Good spawning tributaries may be the answer to a lake population of sufficient density to provide good fishing.

As much information as possible should be obtained on the exploitation of the fisheries in the lake. Such data are invaluable in determining the stocking and in formulating wise legislation.

## 21·15   Stocking tables for lakes

Davis (1938) lists the following table for the planting of 3-inch trout per acre in trout lakes:

| Fishing Intensity | Grade I—Food Abundant | | Grade II—Food Average | | Grade III—Food Poor | |
|---|---|---|---|---|---|---|
| | Good Spawning | Poor Spawning | Good Spawning | Poor Spawning | Good Spawning | Poor Spawning |
| Heavy | 180 | 240 | 90 | 120 | 50 | 60 |
| Medium | 90 | 180 | 45 | 90 | 25 | 45 |
| Light | 30 | 120 | 15 | 60 | 10 | 30 |

Survivals for other sizes are figured on the basis of the factors previously given for Table 21·3. Cooper (1939) did not feel that the above table was applicable to Maine lakes and so formulated his own (Table 21·4), taking into account the competition of the warm-water species. The competition factor was based on the estimates of abundance for the warm-water fishes in which they were given a numerical value of abundant $(AB)$–3, common $(C)$–2, and rare $(R)$–1. The following species were considered as being competitive with trout and salmon: white perch, yellow perch, smallmouth bass, chain pickerel, burbot, brown bullhead, and the American eel. The competition factor $(CF)$

was obtained for each of the lakes and ponds by adding the abundance values for each of the above species present in each pond. Sebago Lake, by the above method, is given a competition factor $(CF)$ of 12 based on abundance reports of white perch $(C-2)$, yellow perch $(C-2)$, smallmouth bass $(C-2)$, chain pickerel $(R-1)$, burbot $(AB-3)$, brown bullhead $(R-1)$, and American eel $(R-1)$. Cooper recognized the errors in this method and enumerated them in survey report no. 2.

### TABLE 21·4

A Proposed Planting Table (Highly Theoretical) for Trout and Salmon in Lakes of Southern Maine (Cooper 1939)

Number of 6-Inch * Fish per Acre †

| Fishing Intensity | CF: Competition by Warm-Water Game Fishes | Grade I—Food Abundant | | Grade II—Food Average | | Grade III—Food Rare | |
|---|---|---|---|---|---|---|---|
| | | Good Spawning | Poor Spawning | Good Spawning | Poor Spawning | Good Spawning | Poor Spawning |
| Heavy | 0 | 100 | 130 | 50 | 65 | 25 | 35 |
| | 3 | 75 | 100 | 35 | 50 | 20 | 30 |
| | 6 | 50 | 65 | 25 | 35 | 15 | 25 |
| | 9 | 34 | 45 | 20 | 25 | 12 | 20 |
| | 12 | 25 | 30 | 15 | 20 | 10 | 15 |
| Medium | 0 | 50 | 100 | 25 | 50 | 15 | 25 |
| | 3 | 35 | 75 | 20 | 35 | 12 | 20 |
| | 6 | 25 | 50 | 15 | 25 | 10 | 15 |
| | 9 | 20 | 35 | 12 | 20 | 9 | 12 |
| | 12 | 15 | 25 | 10 | 15 | 8 | 10 |
| Light | 0 | 15 | 65 | 10 | 35 | 10 | 15 |
| | 3 | 12 | 50 | 9 | 30 | 9 | 12 |
| | 6 | 10 | 35 | 8 | 25 | 8 | 10 |
| | 9 | 9 | 25 | 6 | 20 | 6 | 9 |
| | 12 | 8 | 20 | 5 | 15 | 5 | 8 |

* Figures are given here for 6-inch rather than 3-inch fish because it is believed to be highly desirable to stock these larger fish. Brook trout and landlocked salmon under natural conditions usually do not leave the stream habitat and enter lakes until they are at least about 6 inches long.

† Not based on the total area of the lake, but on the average between the total area and the area of bottom available to trout and salmon during late summer.

Lakes were graded with respect to food as follows: I—Food abundant, II—food average, and III—food rare. The abundance of plankton organisms and bottom insects and to a lesser extent the abundance of smelt and other forage fishes were used in evaluating trout food. Salmon and lake trout lakes were evaluated on the abundance of smelt and plankton and to a lesser extent on the other small fishes.

In survey report no. 3, Cooper (1940) did not consider the competition of the warm-water species and modified Davis's (1938) planting table for lakes to apply to 6-inch fish. In addition other factors were proposed if fish other than 6-inch were used. These factors were based approximately on the expected rate of mortality and were listed as:

> 8–10-inch fish multiply by 0.6
> 6–8-inch fish multiply by 0.8
> 4–6-inch fish multiply by 1.1
> 2–4-inch fish multiply by 2.0
> 1-inch fry multiply by 20.0

Thus it may be seen from an examination of Embody's original stocking table and the many modifications that a stocking table must not be considered as inflexible but rather as a general guide. Many of the factors that are considered in determining total numbers to stock, such as the carrying capacity of various types of water or the interaction of various combinations of species, have not been evaluated as yet.

Food grade, to choose one of the variables, may need modification as more information becomes available on the ratio of total food present to food utilized by the fishes.

## 21·16  Forage ratio

Food grade, as given in present stocking tables, is based on the assumption that all types of animals in the bottom fauna are available to the fish and are eaten in proportion to their abundance. However, Hess and Swartz (1941) noted a great deal of variation in the relative extent to which different animals are utilized as food. They proposed the term "forage ratio" for the ratio of the per cent that a given kind of organism constitutes of the total stomach contents of the fish sampled to the per cent that this same organism constitutes of the total population of food organisms in the bottom samples. Since the kind and amount of food eaten by a fish is a result of the interactions between the fish and its environment, both units must be studied in order to understand its food habits. The following will serve to illustrate the determination of the forage ratio:

| | Dragon-flies | Midges | Caddis-flies | Damsel-flies | Snails |
|---|---|---|---|---|---|
| % in stomach | 36 | 34 | 11 | 3 | 3 |
| % in fauna | 36 | 4 | 39 | 4 | 5 |
| Forage ratio | 1.00 | 8.50 | 0.28 | 0.75 | 0.60 |

Hess and Swartz suggest that a forage ratio of 1 means that, as the food in the stomach is in the same proportion as in the environment, it is selected at random. A ratio of less than 1 indicates that the organisms are unavailable or avoided. A ratio greater than 1 indicates that the food is easily available or actually selected. Available organisms are defined as organisms that are capable of being eaten by the fish if it so desires. Preference implies a definite choice. Availability probably is the most important factor.

The accuracy of the forage ratio depends upon the methods used in determining the number of organisms available in the habitat and the number eaten by the fish whose food habits are being studied.

## 21·17   Obtaining stomachs for analysis

Stomachs for the analysis of the food habits of fishes are usually obtained by one of the following methods:

1. Seining fish and placing them in preservative. Care should be taken to let the fish die of suffocation or by introduction into an anesthetic prior to placing them in formalin to guard against the stomach contents being regurgitated.

2. Fish may be gill-netted. Such fish may disgorge their stomach contents in their struggles to release themselves.

3. Fish may be obtained by angling although here again it frequently happens that the hooked fish will disgorge its stomach contents particularly if it has been feeding recently on large animals.

4. Chemicals may be used to obtain the sample, but in this method the smaller fish affected first by the poison are frequently easy prey for the larger fish. Later the larger fish may disgorge some of the stomach contents when they too become affected by the poison.

## 21·18   Methods of stomach analysis

There are essentially five different methods of stomach analysis each with certain applications and inherent errors which should be considered in drawing conclusions.

**Frequency of occurrence.** The frequency of occurrence method determines merely the presence or absence of a type of food. Simply, this method tabulates the different types of food present in each stomach of the series under consideration. It is usually presented as the percentage frequency of occurrence. The importance of smaller numbers of organisms and the smaller organisms is magnified. For example, if one stonefly nymph and 50 mayfly nymphs were present in the same stomach both items would be recorded as present.

**Numerical.** The numerical method or direct count records the number of each different type of food found in the individual stomachs of a series. The smaller organisms are magnified in importance. Thus a stomach with one mayfly nymph and one large forage fish would be recorded as containing one of each type with no indication as to the relative size of the food item.

**Percentage estimate of volume.** The accuracy of this method is dependent on the individual experience and ability of the technician to judge relative volumes. Each stomach is considered as 100% full, and then the various items are segregated and the volume of each is determined as a percentage of the total stomach contents. Small amounts are reported as "traces." A piece of graph paper placed under the examination container will aid in accurately determining the relative volumes.

**Volumetric.** Entire volume of the stomach contents is determined volumetrically. Then the different types of food are segregated and the volume of each is determined. Results are usually reported as percentage of the total volume. This method is very accurate but may be misleading when a single, bulky specimen, perhaps of rare occurrence, may assume an unwarranted position of dominance over smaller but commoner items. This method does not measure differential digestion or fragmentation and is not practical where a wide variety of food organisms are present. Many recent food studies combine the volumetric with the numerical method, giving a much clearer picture of the food habits of the species studied as each method supplements some deficiency in the other.

**Gravimetric.** Weight has little advantage over the volumetric method, unless the sample is incinerated so that only the inorganic weight is determined. Unfortunately the inorganic weight at present remains meaningless in the absence of physiological data on the nutritive value of the inorganic elements. If the sample is not incinerated, errors creep into the methods in various treatments of the sample prior to weighing to remove excess moisture. Total stomach contents are first weighed and then the various items segregated and weighed separately. Results are usually presented as percentages of the total.

If time is a major consideration then one of the first three methods should be chosen as either the volumetric or the gravimetric takes longer than the others. Size of fish is important since one of the first three methods would ordinarily be used with small fish. The type of food organisms must be taken into consideration since direct count with a plankton feeding fish would be extremely tedious. Aquatic insects lend themselves to all types of stomach analysis.

**References**

Cooper, Gerald P., et al.
  1939–1946. Biological surveys of Maine lakes and ponds. *Maine Dept. Inland Fish and Game, Fish Surv. Repts.* 1–7.
Davis, H. S.
  1938. Instructions for conducting stream and lake surveys. *U. S. Bur. Fish., Fish. Cir. 26:* 55 pp.
Embody, George C.
  1927. An outline of stream study and the development of a stocking policy. *Contr. Aquicultural Lab. Cornell Univ.*
  1928. Stocking policy for the streams, smaller lakes and ponds of Oswego watershed. *N. Y. Cons. Dept., Supp. to 17th Ann. Rept.* (1927):17–39.
Hazzard, A. S.
  1935. Instruction for lake and stream work. *U. S. Bur. Fish., Mimeo. Cir.:* 1–34.
Hess, A. D., and Albert H. Swartz
  1941. The forage ratio and its use in determining the food grade of streams. *5th N. Am. Wildl. Conf.:* 162–164.
Hoover, E. E., et al.
  1937–1939. Biological surveys of New Hampshire, by watersheds, 1936–1938. *Surv. Repts. 1–3, New Hampshire Fish and Game Dept.*
Leger, L.
  1910. Principes de la Methode Rationnelle du peuplement des Cours d'eau à Salmonides. *Travaux du Laboratoire de Pisciculture de L'Université de Grenoble. fas. 1:* 531.
Moore, Emmeline, et al.
  1927–1940. Biological surveys of New York, by watersheds, conducted in the years 1926–39, and published yearly as *Supps. to Ann. Rept. of State of N. Y. Cons. Dept.*
Smith, Lloyd L., Jr., and John B. Moyle
  1944. A biological survey and fishery management plan for the streams of the Lake Superior north shore watershed. *Minn. Dept. Cons., Div. Game and Fish., Tech. Bull. 1:* 228 pp.
Thorpe, Lyle M., et al.
  1942. A fishery survey of important Connecticut lakes. *Bull. Conn. Geol. and Nat. Hist. Surv. 63:* 339 pp.
Warfel, Herbert E.
  1939. Biological survey of the Connecticut watershed. *Surv. Rept. 4. New Hampshire Fish and Game Dept.*
Welch, Paul S.
  1952. *Limnology.* 2d ed. McGraw-Hill Co.: xi + 538, New York.

# PART X · MANAGING NATURAL POPULATIONS

## 22 · MANAGEMENT TECHNIQUES

### 22·1  Introduction

The techniques for management of a fish population depend on the amount of environmental control that can be applied, on the particular factors that limit the size of the population, and on the part played by man.  For valuable species in small bodies of water, it is sometimes practical to employ intensive management measures, but for marine species the available management measures are often restricted.  For purposes of discussion it is assumed in this chapter that all requisite information on the biology of the species, including ecological relationships, is at hand.  In actual practice, management quite often must operate partially on assumptions since it cannot await the acquisition of full knowledge.  It is unfortunate that fisheries often must be managed without sufficient facts, because such procedure occasionally results in unavoidable failure, which tends to discredit fishery management.  Also, once a measure has been adopted, there is often difficulty in abandoning it, should it be found wanting.

In Figure 22·1 is shown a schematic representation of the various interrelated factors that affect a fish population.  Management consists in so manipulating or controlling the action of these factors as to produce the largest available surplus to be harvested.  The continuation of this surplus depends on maintaining a delicate adjustment between annual mortality (natural and man-induced) and the annual recruitment of adults.  Because of the decrease in reproductive potential (or survival value) that invariably accompanies population increase (the curve of population growth approaches an asymptote as explained in Chapter 5), the greatest annual harvestable surplus does not occur usually at the highest levels of abundance, but at some intermediate point.  To ascertain with reasonable accuracy the range of abundance within which this optimum level lies may require data covering many years.

The techniques of fishery management consist of control of man-induced mortality by the fishery, mitigation of hazards created by man, alteration of the physical habitat, and control of the biological habitat. These main headings include a wide variety of management measures.

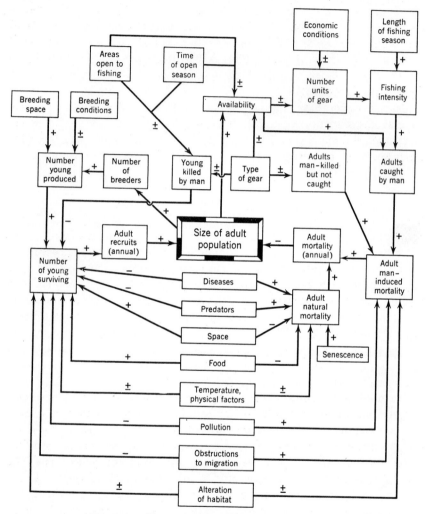

Fig. 22·1 Factors influencing population size.

## 22·2 Reduction of fishing mortality

This measure is the one most often used, perhaps because of its simplicity. Employment of this measure is postulated on the assumption that the present fishing intensity is so great as to have forced the level of the population below the point of inflection on the population growth curve so that the available harvest is lower than it would be if the total size of the population were allowed to increase. As stated above, the point of inflection of the population growth curve is hard to determine. Usually when a species is first exploited its abundance will drop. Many consider that the reattainment of this virgin level of abundance is desirable, but in reality this original level cannot be maintained if there is to be any harvestable surplus. Therefore, the level of abundance of an unexploited fishery is not a criterion of the best level to maintain.

In many fisheries, especially some of the marine fisheries, the only management measure possible is control of the amount of the catch. This measure can be very effective if the population size and the relation between the population size and the size of the annual increment of adults are known.

## 22·3   Selective mortality by the fishery

A second measure that is useful in some fisheries when certain types of gear are employed, is to make such modifications in the fishing gear as will permit the escape of the smaller fish. This method is especially applicable to the otter trawl fisheries, but can be used in most fisheries in which the fish are taken by nets or traps and there is a large size range in the individuals subject to capture. The principles governing this measure have been laid down by Herrington (1944), Nesbit (1944), and Ricker (1945). This method requires three items of information concerning a species—the rate of growth, the rate of mortality, and the size selection made by various sizes of net meshes, spaces between laths in pot traps, or other passages for escape.

In applying regulations for selective mortality it must be remembered that all of the fish to be harvested each season cannot be caught at one instant. If the minimum size limit is set therefore at the point where increase in growth exactly compensates for increased mortality, there will be some loss in weight from the death of older fish. The amount of such loss depends on the intensity of the fishery. For a fishery of light intensity the greatest catch may be made without any size limit. Even for heavy fishing intensity a larger take will be made if the minimum size is below the critical point at which growth and mortality balance. However, for fish that mature at a large size it may be necessary to set the limit at or above the critical point to assure a sufficient number of spawners. For species that live to a considerable age the employment of a high minimum size may be economically advantageous as the presence in the population of fish of several ages tends to prevent sudden fluctuations in the catch due to the poor survival of fish of one particular year class.

Where the survival of young is very high, as in many warm-water species taken in lakes, the use of a minimum size may only serve to aggravate overcrowding and thus reduce the yield. Obviously, any minimum size should be flexible so that it can be adjusted to changes in fishing intensity, in growth, and in population size.

## 22·4   Savings gear

In order to carry out in actual practice the saving of small fish discussed above, the gear must be modified to permit the escape of a

FIG. 22·2   The cod end of an otter trawl showing the shape of the stretched meshes. This is the shape they have when towed, as shown by underwater photography. (Credit: U. S. Fish and Wildlife Service)

majority of the undersized individuals. In many localities pound nets and traps are required to use meshes above a specified minimum size in the "pound" or "spiller." Oftentimes this measure is designed not so much for the escape of undersized fish of the species sought as for the escape of fish of other species. Experiments have shown that catches of undersized lobsters can be greatly reduced by using a minimum spacing between the bottom of the pot and the first lath. This measure is now being tried in the Canadian lobster fisheries.

A number of elaborate experiments carried out here and abroad

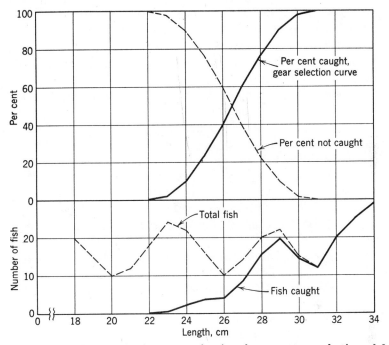

FIG. 22·3 Idealized gear selection curve, showing the percentage selection of fish at each length for a particular size of mesh.

show the sizes of fish that escape through the cod ends of otter trawls when meshes of different sizes are employed. The percentage of the fish of each available size that escape through the meshes of a cod end forms an ogive curve that has been called a "selection" curve (Figure 22·3). The steepness of the slope of the selection curve is related to the speed of towing, as the fish escape through the meshes of the cod end that are kept open by the outrushing water. Apparently if the speed becomes too great the extra strain on the net tends to keep the meshes closed.

The Danish seine or "snurrevard" is adapted to saving young fish as they are slowly driven together by the towing warps and then brought on board alive so that the small fish can be readily sorted out and released in good condition.

Fishing with line trawls takes few small fish, but in most bank fisheries the line trawl has been supplanted by the more efficient otter trawl. In the Pacific halibut fisheries it was demonstrated that by increasing the size of the hooks fewer small fish were caught.

Gill nets are highly selective for size; each size of mesh tends to capture a particular size range of fish. This fact is very often utilized for the protection of small fish.

In all of these size limitations there are certain biological principles to keep in mind. Thus most fish exhibit sexual dimorphism in regard to size. It has been shown on some salmon rivers, for instance, that use of a high minimum mesh size results in the catching of a greater number of the females and a lesser number of the smaller males, so that many more males than females reach the spawning beds—an obvious economic waste. It may have another effect. By always catching the larger fish and leaving the smaller fish to breed we may be gradually decreasing the average size that a species will attain naturally.

When the fishing intensity is very heavy so that small fish are apt to be netted several times as the fleet tries to take all of the larger individuals, savings gear is not always practical. Fortunately it hardly pays a vessel to strain a few large individuals out from thousands of undersized fish so that when large fish become scarce in an area the fishing intensity may slacken.

## 22·5  Bans on small fish

Use of savings gear poses several very practical problems. Gear with meshes small enough so as not to permit the escape of many fish of the desired minimum sizes will also take many smaller fish, especially when they are abundant. The mesh in the cod end must vary with the species sought so that mere possession of a small-mesh cod end is not evidence of wrong intent. Lastly, no fishing crew will feel that it should use savings gear so long as some vessels are selling undersized fish at a profit. One of the best measures then to prevent the capture of small fish and to make the use of savings gear attractive is to put a strict limitation on the percentage of undersized fish that any vessel may land.

## 22·6  Closure of nursery grounds

Fish of the first few age groups usually do not mingle extensively with the older fish. Often there are definite areas of the fishing banks where the undersized fish tend to congregate. Trawling on these areas, even with savings gear, destroys large numbers. Wherever it is practical of enforcement, closure of such areas is the most effective way to prevent destruction of these concentrations of young fish.

This is similar in principle to the method used in the Pacific Northwest to prevent trout fishermen from destroying the young of the sea-run rainbow or steelhead. Many tributary streams are kept closed in the spring until after the young steelhead have migrated downstream on their way to the sea.

## 22·7   Protection of spawning grounds

Only for species with fairly well-defined spawning grounds is it practical to protect fish while in a spawning area. There has been a great deal of debate concerning the protection of spawning fish, some contending that whether a fish is caught in the act of spawning or six months earlier the net result is the same. The argument for protection runs like this: Fish must run a gauntlet of enemies throughout the year so that the chances that any particular fish will spawn are much less 6 months before the spawning season than just before the spawning season. An argument in favor of the closure of spawning grounds is the fact that many fish are especially easy to capture at spawning time. Perhaps a more cogent argument is the fact that many species of fish are usually in poor market condition during the spawning season.

In sparsely populated waters, adults of black bass and other species that guard their young need protection during the spawning season. In other areas, in which overpopulation is a problem, such protection can be harmful to good fishing. This illustrates the need for full information on which to base action.

Several states are endeavoring to meet this situation by stationing regional biologists in different portions of the state where they are able to assess the needs of the local waters. This is especially beneficial in states where the laws permit the issuance of flexible local regulations as their need is determined by the biologist.

## 22·8   Removal of competing species

The effect of the removal of competitors on the survival of a species is largely undetermined. The increased yield of game fish from Bass Lake, Indiana (Ricker and Gottschalk 1941) following the removal of large numbers of carp, quillback, and buffalo is perhaps a special case, as these coarse fish were actually changing the ecology of the lake by uprooting vegetation and roiling the water.

Rawson and Elsey (1950) attempted to improve rainbow trout angling in Pyramid Lake, Alberta, by intensive netting of the large population of longnose sucker (*Catostomus catostomus*). They succeeded in reducing the average size of the suckers taken in gill nets from 5.4 to 1.6 ounces over a 5-year period. Although they reduced the numbers of large suckers, the numbers of young suckers increased. The rainbow trout did not show any increase either during the 5-year period or in the 3 years following.

On theoretical grounds the removal of a direct food competitor should increase growth and perhaps survival, but the relationship has never been adequately demonstrated.

## 22·9   Removal of predatory species

The evidence is somewhat clearer for the removal of predaceous fish. Thus Foerster and Ricker (1941) show that the reduction of predatory fish in Cultus Lake, British Columbia, increased by threefold the survival of young sockeye salmon. Here a word of caution is needed. Because of the increased numbers of young sockeye that survived, the average weight of the individual fish was reduced one half. For an anadromous species that descends to the sea to make the major share of its growth, the increased numbers probably far more than offset the decrease in individual size. However, for a species that is resident in a lake such a heightened survival might prove very disastrous. This applies especially to warm-water species in which overpopulation and stunting often result from too heavy a survival of young.

## 22·10   Stocking of barren or depleted lakes

In stocking trout or other salmonoid fishes in lakes that contain few other fish it is becoming evident that overstocking must be avoided. In such situations the survival of the first plant is high and if heavily stocked the lake soon becomes overpopulated with large fish that are too nearly of a size for cannibalism. The result may be a lake full of emaciated fish of very poor angling quality. The presence of these large fish in great quantity precludes further successful stocking of young. This danger is emphasized by Mottley (1941) and by Rawson (1947). Rawson recommends avoiding this difficulty by planting very lightly the first year, about 10 times as many the second year, and about 30 times as many the third year. The third year stocking should be about the quantity to be stocked annually thereafter. It is his belief that this procedure will develop a population with a normal type of age distribution.

## 22·11 Control of diseases and parasites

The control of diseases and parasites among natural populations of fish is usually impractical. However, in a few instances control may be feasible by reducing the numbers of an intermediate host. Whitefish from some lakes of the Canadian prairies are too heavily infested with tapeworms to be marketable. Reduction of the populations of the intermediate host fish to reduce the infestation has been attempted. The flesh of the cod of the North Atlantic banks is often heavily infested with a nematode parasite, one stage of which occurs in the harbor seal. Experiments are under way to determine the feasibility of seal reduction as a control measure. Great caution should be used in stocking hatchery fish to prevent contamination of natural populations. Never plant sick fish!

## 22·12 Habitat improvement

This subject is covered in Chapters 11 to 15. In general it is feasible only for small bodies of water and for valuable species. However, there are certain aspects that affect whole watersheds and extensive populations. Thus fishways can open a whole river to anadromous species, and erosion control may profoundly affect large areas.

The control of stream flow is too often neglected in a fishery program. Fluctuating water levels destroy bottom organisms, lowering the productivity of a stream. During floods the shifting of the bottom grinds up insect life, and during low water most of the organisms on the exposed bottom must move or perish.

Briggs (1950) studied the bottom fauna of similar sections of a stream above and below a dam built to store flood waters and permit their gradual release so they could percolate into the soil to maintain the water table. Over a period of 9 months the average weight of organisms in 114 square-foot samples from the stream above the dam was 0.35 gram. The average weight of 114 samples collected on the same dates below the dam was 0.75 gram. The portion of the stream with the steady flow produced more than twice as much food.

Long sections of stream that are of little value for fish production because of their extremely low summer flow can sometimes be converted into valuable producers by gradual release of stored water. This type of program can be aided by reforestation.

**References**

Briggs, John C.
  1950. The quantitative effects of a dam upon the bottom fauna of a small California stream. *Trans. Am. Fish. Soc. 78:* 70–81.

Foerster, R. Earle, and William E. Ricker
1941. The effect of reduction of predaceous fish on survival of young sockeye salmon at Cultus Lake. *J. Fish. Res. Bd. Canada 5* (4):315–336.
Herrington, William C.
1944. Some methods of fishery management and their usefulness in a management program. *U. S. Fish and Wildl. Serv., Spec. Sci. Rept. 18:* 3–22, 54–58.
Mottley, Charles M.
1941. The effect of increasing the stock in a lake on the size and condition of rainbow trout. *Trans. Am. Fish. Soc. 70:* 414–420.
Nesbit, Robert A.
1944. Biological and economic problems of fishery management. *U. S. Fish and Wildl. Serv., Spec. Sci. Rept. 18:* 23–53, 59–66.
Rawson, D. S.
1947. Deterioration of recently established trout populations in lakes of the Canadian Rockies. *Can. Fish Cult. 2,* Dec. 1947: 14–21.
Rawson, D. S., and C. A. Elsey
1950. Reduction in the longnose sucker population of Pyramid Lake, Alberta, in an attempt to improve angling. *Trans. Am. Fish. Soc. 78:* 13–31.
Ricker, William E.
1945. A method of estimating minimum size limits for obtaining maximum yield. *Copeia,* 1945 (2):84–94.
Ricker, William E., and John Gottschalk
1941. An experiment in removing coarse fish from a lake. *Trans. Am. Fish. Soc. 70:* 382–390.

# 23 · ARTIFICIAL PROPAGATION OF SALMONIDS AS A MANAGEMENT TOOL

## 23·1 Introduction

Artificial propagation was first developed in France during the 19th century. The early fish culturists were extremely optimistic predicting that they could "repopulate the streams, rivers and lakes of the world." Rearing of salmonids, most prized of the freshwater game fishes, receives most of the emphasis in the Federal and state hatchery programs of today. In many states the rearing of warm-water fishes is being de-emphasized with almost complete cessation of such plantings. High biotic potential and less rigid habitat requirements make it unnecessary to raise and stock such species unless they are intended for introduction to newly created waters such as farm fish ponds or artificial lakes. As more rigid restrictions are placed on the seining of bait fish from streams and lakes the artificial propagation of bait fish for sale to anglers will become more important.

For years hatcheries have been maintained to provide plantings of fish to aid the commercial fisheries. Tremendous numbers (by hatchery standards) of fry have been produced without any apparent effect on the abundance of adults. Generally the failure of plants to improve fishing is the result of low survival and the fact that the numbers planted are an infinitesimal share of those spawned naturally. The failure of extensive stocking to show any effect on the numbers of whitefish (*Coregonus clupeaformis*) in Lake Erie is shown by Van Oosten (1942). Propagation of winter flounder (*Pseudopleuronectes americanus*), of cod (*Gadus morhua*), and of the lobster (*Homarus americanus*) have also been shown to be ineffectual, and efforts for their propagation have been largely abandoned.

## 23·2 Stocking of salmonids

Today hatchery-reared salmonids are being used for:

1. Restocking such depleted waters as the trout streams in the Middle Atlantic States to provide seasonal fishing near centers of large populations.

2. Restocking waters following the abatement of pollution.

3. Restocking lakes in which winterkill has depleted or exterminated the population.

4. Restocking ponds after poisoning to remove previous fish fauna.

5. Stocking bodies of water that do not provide adequate spawning grounds.

6. Supplying fish to exchange for other desired species.

7. Supplying fish for experimental requirements.

### 23·3   Survival of hatchery-reared trout

Before the 1930's it had been generally assumed that the hatchery was a much more efficient producer than nature.  Who could doubt that the efficiency of fertilization in the hatchery was higher or that the survival of newly hatched fry or of hatchery-reared fingerlings was higher than the natural rate.  Embody (1927) and Davis (1938) based their stocking tables on extremely optimistic survival rates for liberated fish.  Critical analyses of the survival of hatchery trout have since been made and the results of these investigations have modified much of the thinking in respect to the survival of hatchery-reared fish.

Various reasons (Schuck 1948) advanced for the lack of survival of hatchery-reared trout after being liberated are:

1. High percentage of fats and carbohydrates in the artificial diets.  Diet is probably the most important item in the rearing of fish today.  At Cortland, New York, the U. S. Fish and Wildlife Service in cooperation with the New York State Conservation Commission and Cornell University has established a program of nutritional studies which will undoubtedly improve the hatchery diets of the future.

2. Overfeeding of hatchery fish in an effort to raise legal-sized fish in shorter periods.  Research in other fields has shown that overfeeding can shorten the life span of an animal as much as one half.

3. Lack of exercise in the hatchery.

4. Relatively uniform habitat of the hatchery pool.

5. Artificial conditions in which there is little or no foraging for their food.  Work on feeding habits of trout planted as fry indicates that in most cases they begin to feed almost immediately.

6. Freedom from predators in hatchery.

7. Domestication of the brood stock so that a race or variety of fish is developed for its abilities to produce eggs and withstand hatchery conditions.

Fig. 23·1  Dipnetting Atlantic salmon from the Machias River fishway in Maine to obtain eggs for hatching.

8. Planting of fish in the fall as a convenience to the fish culturist.

9. Fish often planted in undesirable habitats.

### 23·4  Survival rate of salmonid fry

The survival to maturity of fish planted as fry has been negligible in streams and in most lakes. Foerster (1936) indicates that a mortality of 94 to 97 per cent took place in sockeye salmon planted after the fry stage was reached. Natural fertilization and subsequent hatching were close to 100 per cent. Natural fertilization of over 90 per cent for the eggs of cutthroat trout (*Salmo clarki*) and brown trout (*Salmo trutta*) and of over 80 per cent for eastern brook trout (*Salvelinus fontinalis*) and rainbow trout (*Salmo gairdneri*) preclude the possibility that present hatchery methods can show any significant improvement over natural propagation before hatching.

Hobbs (1948) gives interesting figures on survival to the fry stage in a comparison between natural and artificial propagation of trout in New Zealand (Table 23·1). In all fairness it should be noted that the 33 per cent loss of eggs shed below the trap is evidence of poor fish culture and would not occur in a modern hatchery. Hobbs (op. cit.) reaches a general conclusion on losses to the angler when trout become available at 7 inches. If a hypothetical planting of 1 million unfed

TABLE 23.1

| Item | Artificial Propagation | Natural Propagation Ova Dislodged, Superimposition | No Ova Dislodged |
|---|---|---|---|
| Total ova | 100% | 100% | 100% |
| Eggs shed below trap | 33 | . . . | . . . |
| Loss in imperfect stripping | 7 | . . . | . . . |
| Loss of pre-eyed ova | 6 | . . . | . . . |
| Loss of eyed ova and alevins | 6 | . . . | . . . |
| Loss in distribution of fry | 2 | . . . | . . . |
| Loss of ova retained or not lodged | . . | 2.5 | 2.5 |
| Loss through superimposition | . . | 31.0 | . . . |
| Other losses in redds (as ova 10%, as alevins, say 1%) 11% of balance | . . | 7.4 | 10.7 |
| Total losses | 54 | 41.0 | 13.0 |
| Surviving to fry stage | 46 | 59.0 | 87.0 |

fry is used, the loss by the time a length of 6 to 8 inches is attained is about 99.5 per cent.

## 23·5 Survival rate of trout fingerlings

Survival in lakes is higher than in streams. In California lakes characterized by insufficient or no spawning facilities, Curtis (1951) reports that fingerling plants of rainbow, eastern brook trout, and brown trout in three lakes over 800 acres in extent yielded an average of 1 per cent to the angler with a range of 0.2 to 1.5 per cent. Three small lakes (33 to 68 acres) yielded an average recovery to the angler of 8.7 per cent with a range of 2.7 to 25.3. Combined fingerling plants yielded an average of 5.4 per cent survival.

Schuck (1943) reports the following survival of wild brown trout from the fingerling stage (group 1) to older age groups in fenced areas of a stream.

| Age Group | Percentage Survival |
|---|---|
| 1 to 2 | 24.10 |
| 1 to 3 | 11.00 |
| 1 to 4 | 5.49 |
| 1 to 5 | 1.25 |
| 1 to 6 | 0.48 |

Chamberlain (1943) recovered 1.11 per cent of 61,400 brook trout fingerlings stocked in the Pisgah National Forest stream management program. Westerman and Hazzard (1945) reported the following returns to the angler's creel from marked fingerlings planted in Michigan streams (legal limit of 7 inches): 1.2 per cent recovery in 19 plantings with eastern brook trout, 2.0 per cent recovery in 12 plantings of rainbow trout, and 3.4 per cent recovery from 5 plantings of brown trout. A recovery of 2.4 per cent resulted from a planting of 11,000 fingerlings in the St. Mary River, Virginia (Surber 1940). Table 23·2 summarizes data on return to angler from fingerling (3.0 to 6.0 inches) trout-stocking experiments in streams during fall, spring, and summer months:

TABLE 23·2

| State and Authority | Species | Percentage Return to Angler |
|---|---|---|
| North Carolina | Rainbow | 1.0 |
| (Chamberlain 1943) | Eastern brook trout | 1.1 |
| Michigan | Rainbow | 1.1 |
| (Shetter 1939) | Eastern brook trout | 0.4 |
| Virginia | Rainbow | 2.0 |
| (Surber 1940) | Eastern brook trout | 2.6 |
| California | Rainbow | 0.9 |
| (Randle and Cramer 1941) | | |
| Average | | 1.26 |

## 23·6    Survival and recovery of legal-sized trout

"A perusal of the official publications of Federal agencies and state departments leads one to believe that 'the proper use of large fish in stocking managed waters' is the aim of most responsible administrative agencies even though in most instances the primary objective is to rear as many legal-sized fish as budgets allow" (Simon 1949). The above quotation is taken from the report of the division of fish culture to the American Fisheries Society in 1947. What are the deciding factors and ramifications of a program of legal-sized plantings of hatchery fish?

As evidence from experiments designed to test the survival and recovery of trout to the angler is obtained, it becomes increasingly apparent that in general, "the bigger the fish stocked and the closer to the fishing season the higher would be the return to the angler." A glance at Table 23·3, if we keep in mind the low recovery of fry and fingerlings, will show the increased recovery from the plantings of larger (legal-sized) fish, particularly if they are introduced into the streams just before or during the fishing season. Although yielding a

TABLE 23·3

| State and Authority | Species | Percentage Return to Angler from Plantings Made in Either Spring or Summer | Fall |
|---|---|---|---|
| North Carolina (Chamberlain, 1943) | Rainbow | 58.8 | 9.2 |
|  | Eastern brook trout | 44.5 | 6.4 |
|  | Brown | 15.6 | 14.3 |
| Michigan (Shetter and Hazzard, 1941) | Rainbow | 24.4 | 4.9 |
|  | Eastern brook trout | 25.4 | 4.4 |
|  | Brown | 12.0 | 5.8 |
| Wisconsin (Williamson and Schneberger, 1943) | Rainbow | 30.5 | 48.4 |
|  | Eastern brook trout | 82.0 | 28.2 |
| Michigan (Smith, 1941) | Eastern brook trout | 16.8 | 0.5 |
| Average |  | 34.4 | 13.7 |

much larger recovery to the angler, the planting of legal-sized fish presents several problems. As a result of the higher recoveries from legal-sized fish, many states, such as the Middle Atlantic group, have embarked on a program of "put and take" in which the hatchery truck proceeding to the brook incites the surrounding anglers with the urge to fish. Small legal-sized fish are dumped into the waters and about as quickly removed by the hordes of anglers "fishing" the water.

Data from Shetter (1947) will serve to emphasize another important aspect of the legal-sized plantings: namely, that plantings of legal-sized fish are removed very quickly after stocking of the waters (Table 23·4). Results from creel censuses and marking experiments on lakes suitable for trout have proved that from 13 to 81 per cent of fall-planted brook and rainbow were removed by angling in the following season. This is of course considerably better than can be expected from streams. However, *90 per cent* of the season's catch was removed during the first 2 weeks by a very small per cent of the total number of anglers. Three quarters of the 4757 marked trout planted in the Blackledge River, Connecticut, were removed within 4 days after planting (Thorpe, Raynor and Webster 1947). One third of the anglers fishing the experimental area of 1.7 miles accounted for three fourths of the catch during the first few days of fishing. Data from Shetter (1947) indicate that, even when legal-sized trout are stocked, the carryover to the second season is so slight as to be of little value in improving the

Fɪɢ. 23·2   Stocking a stream properly cannot be done by dumping a load of fish in one hole. This handy livecar is used in Connecticut to distribute fish along the streams.

TABLE 23·4

Rᴇᴄᴏᴠᴇʀʏ ᴏꜰ Lᴇɢᴀʟ-Sɪᴢᴇᴅ Bʀᴏᴏᴋ Tʀᴏᴜᴛ ɪɴ Mɪᴄʜɪɢᴀɴ Lᴀᴋᴇs ᴅᴜʀɪɴɢ ᴛʜᴇ Tʀᴏᴜᴛ Sᴇᴀsᴏɴ ᴏꜰ 1941 ᴀɴᴅ 1942 ꜰʀᴏᴍ Pʟᴀɴᴛɪɴɢs Mᴀᴅᴇ ɪɴ ᴛʜᴇ Pʀᴇᴄᴇᴅɪɴɢ Fᴀʟʟ

| Lake | Number Planted | Number Re-covered | Percent-age of Recovery | Total Marked Trout Captured Opening Day | Percentage of Total Recovery on Open-ing Day |
|---|---|---|---|---|---|
| South Twin Lake * | 590 | 427 | 72.3 | 340 | 79.6 |
| North Twin Lake * | 456 | 402 | 88.1 | 368 | 91.5 |
| Holland Lake † | 200 | 136 | 68.0 | 129 | .... |
| Kimes Lake ‡ | 1000 | 422 | 42.2 | 422 | .... |
| East Fish Lake, 1941 | 243 | 34 | 13.9 | 32 | 94.1 |
| East Fish Lake, 1942 | 250 | 133 | 53.5 | 123 | 92.4 |

* To July 1 only. An unmarked midseason planting interfered with further calculations.

† Creel census for first two days of 1942.

‡ Creel census records for opening day only, 1942. Shows total taken on opening day.

fishing (Table 23·5). Information taken from heavily fished streams, where the legal-sized trout were depleted quickly, shows the importance of naturally spawned fish in maintaining fishing. The percentages given in Table 23·6 show quite conclusively that even though "put and take" programs are already straining the budgets in many states natural propagation is still bearing the brunt of the fishing pressure.

TABLE 23·5

A COMPARISON OF RESULTS FROM SPRING AND FALL PLANTINGS OF LEGAL-SIZED BROOK, BROWN, AND RAINBOW TROUT IN MICHIGAN STREAMS

| Species | Number Planted | | Number Recovered First Season | | Number Recovered Second Season | | Number Recovered Third Season | |
|---|---|---|---|---|---|---|---|---|
| | Spring | Fall | Spring | Fall | Spring | Fall | Spring | Fall |
| Rainbow | 2352 | 1869 | 429 | 132 | 14 | 2 | ... | ... |
| | | | (18.2) * | (7.1) | (0.6) | (0.1) | | |
| Brown | 2693 | 1550 | 334 | 107 | 23 | 4 | 3 | 2 |
| | | | (12.4) | (6.9) | (0.9) | (0.3) | (0.1) | (0.1) |
| Brook | 250 | 150 | 40 | 12 | 2 | ... | 1 | ... |
| | | | (16.0) | (8.0) | (0.8) | | (0.4) | |
| All species | 5295 | 3569 | 803 | 251 | 39 | 6 | 4 | 2 |
| | | | (15.2) | (7.0) | (0.7) | (0.2) | (0.1−) | (0.1−) |

* Percentage recovery to angler.

Table 23·6

| State and Authority | Percentage of Naturally Spawned Trout in Angler's Captures |
|---|---|
| North Carolina (Chamberlain, 1943) | 63.0 |
| Michigan (Shetter and Hazzard, 1942) | 88.5 |
| Michigan (Smith, 1941) | 61.4 |
| Virginia (Surber, 1940) | 72.5 |
| California (Randle and Cramer, 1941) | 97.9 |
| Wisconsin (Williamson and Schneberger, 1943) | 71.0 |

## 23·7   Cost of trout rearing

What of the cost of raising and planting legal-sized trout? Smith (1948) includes the following cost figures: *"If capitalization costs on* the hatchery plant are ignored, the cost of each 7- to 10-inch fish placed in the stream is 25 to 50 cents. On the basis of known percentage returns from planted fish, this means that each fish in the angler's creel will cost from 30 cents to $2.50 each, or $1.50 to $12.50 per pound. In most states the resident angler's license does not exceed $2.00 and is usually less. About half of this fee will go for law en-

Fig. 23·3 Circular pools for rearing trout at the Leetown, West Virginia, experimental station of the U. S. Fish and Wildlife Service, for studying diseases, diets, and hatchery techniques. (Credit: H. B. Carr, U. S. Fish and Wildlife Service)

forcement, education, and general overhead, leaving about a dollar or less for planting, steam improvement, noxious fish control, etc. This means that, when an angler has caught one to four hatchery fish, he has exhausted his contribution to trout stream maintenance. Careful checks have also shown that one fourth to one third of the anglers may take as much as three fourths of all planted fish which are eventually returned." Eicher (1949) in his article on Current Trends in State Fishery Programs had this to say about costs: "In costs per pound for food alone and cost per pound for all expenses there seems to be an unwarranted divergence. It seems likely that some replies (data based on questionnaire sent to states) were guesses or misinterpretations of the questions. Many did not report at all; however, of 18 reporting on costs per pound for food alone, the answers ranged from 3 cents to 3 dollars, averaging 14.6 cents. Total costs ranged from 24 cents to $4.50 per pound and averaged 66 cents." Considering the time that fish culturists have been pursuing their trade it seems impossible that the costs show such discrepancies or impossible that anyone would have to guess as to the costs. If we take the average of $0.66 (an absolute minimum not including new construction) per pound of trout and divide it into the average fishing license fee of $2.00, the angler is then entitled to about 3 pounds of hatchery-reared fish. Having examined the survival figures it seems likely that about 10 per cent of the angler's 3 pounds will be recovered or nearly 5 ounces of fish. Since there are on the average 11.6 six-inch trout to the pound, about 4 six-inch fish is all the angler has paid for. If he depends on planted legal-sized fish that he has paid for, his fishing season may be very short.

Kingsbury (1951) writes:

For many years, there has been a great divergence of opinion as to the cost of producing trout. Fish-culturists realize that variation in costs can be attributed to many factors which vary widely in different hatcheries. However, the greatest cause for deviation is the lack of a standard method of keeping hatchery records which would insure uniform production statistics and permit direct comparison of costs.

Kingsbury (op. cit.) lists the total cost per pound of trout as $0.8774 (does not include general administrative overhead). Cost and production statistics as listed by Kingsbury are included in Table 23·7. Statistics and records of this nature will do much toward increasing the efficiency of the hatchery as a necessary tool of fish management.

## 23·8  "Put and take fishing"

Two courses in planting programs face state departments today. The first is the planting of legal-sized fish just prior to or during the fishing season. The larger the fish and the closer to the rod they are planted the greater the recovery. In many parts of the country good trout streams are becoming scarce and the number of anglers is increasing. Consequently many states under fisherman pressure have embarked on "put and take" fishing programs which in the end will prove to be an uneconomical way of providing sport for the angler.

There are a few advantages to such a program. Because the planted fish are quickly removed in the beginning of the season trout streams inferior during the summer may be used for a short period in the early spring. No growth or survival to another season is expected in such

TABLE 23·7

Cost and Production Statistics for a Trout Hatchery for Period
April 1, 1949, to March 31, 1950

| Item | |
| --- | --- |
| Personal service, cost per pound | $0.3639 |
| Maintenance and operation, cost per pound | 0.1053 |
| Fish food, cost per pound | 0.3567 |
| Investment and interest, cost per pound | 0.0515 |
| Total cost per pound | $0.8774 * |
| Pounds produced per gallon per minute flow | 48.50 |
| Pounds produced per cubic foot of space | 2.25 |
| Rate of change per hour,† total | 0.37 |
| Rate of change per hour, series of 4 ponds | 0.46 |
| Rate of change per hour, single pond | 1.85 |
| Rate of change per hour, series of 3 rearing troughs | 5.33 |
| Rate of change per hour, single rearing trough | 16.00 |

* Does not include general administrative overhead.

† Rate of change per hour equals flow per hour in cubic feet divided by pond volume in cubic feet.

waters. This type of program does provide fishing for the angler who would in most instances be unable to creel the naturally spawned wild trout. The disadvantages to such a program are many and have been discussed in the previous section, 23·7. The high cost of the legal-sized fish and difficulty in spreading the catch through the season are the chief disadvantages. Reduction of legal limit and periodic stocking of rotated streams throughout the open season (Chamberlain 1943) may serve to provide a more equal distribution and sustain the fishing.

## 23·9  Long-range planting programs

The second type of planting involves stocking a considerable time before the fish are expected to be caught. This includes legal-sized fish planted in the fall for the next season and fingerlings or fry planted to survive and grow large enough to enter the fishery.

This type of program to be successful must provide the proper habitat for good growth and survival; in other words, trout must be planted in good trout waters. If the waters provide an ideal habitat for hatchery fish then it is likely that they are already producing a population of wild fish which represents the stream's total capacity.

Introductions of hatchery fish to such water merely serve to handicap the naturally reared population and increase the burden on the productivity of the habitat. Research workers have proved that more than enough brood stock survive to repopulate good, natural trout waters. Westerman and Hazzard (1945) came to the conclusion that stocking is unnecessary, uneconomical, or even harmful if the species suited to the environment are already present.

## 23·10   Status of the hatchery

Survival rates and costs suggest that much of our thinking regarding the hatchery and its products needs revision. Needham (1949) writes:

In spite of extremely heavy expenditures for rearing of hatchery fish, the angling continues to decline. Millions of fish are wasted each year because of lack of facts on how best to utilize properly the product of hatcheries.

The conclusion is reached that the angling public must be made aware of the basic economics of hatchery operation, its costs, successes, and failures, in order that the field of fishery management again may move ahead.

The compilation of facts now available leaves no justification for any attempt to use the products of the hatchery as the miracle drug for the curing of all fishery problems.

"The principal barrier to further progress is the unreasoning and abiding faith of our customers in the planting of fish under all conditions, at all times, and in every water." (Taft 1947.) However, there is convincing evidence that sportsmen and conservation-minded individuals are beginning to question the results of stocking programs. Anglers, aware of the numbers of hatchery-reared fish placed in the waters, are beginning to question the results in terms of fish creeled.

Sportsmen must be convinced that natural propagation is the answer to continued "good fishing" and that artificial propagation like habitat improvement is just another tool of fish management.

**References**

Chamberlain, Thomas K.
  1943. Research in stream management in the Pisgah National Forest. *Trans. Am. Fish. Soc. 72:* 150–176.
Curtis, Brian
  1951. Yield of hatchery trout in California lakes. *Calif. Fish and Game 37* (2):197–215.
Eicher, George J., Jr.
  1949. Current trends in state fishery programs. *Trans. Am. Fish. Soc. 76:* 13–22.
Foerster, R. Earle
  1936. Sockeye salmon propagation in British Columbia. *Bull. Biol. Bd. Canada 53:* 1–16.

Hobbs, Derisley F.
1948. Trout fisheries in New Zealand: their development and management. *New Zealand Mar. Dept., Fish. Bull. 9:* 1–175.

Kingsbury, O. R.
1951. Production statistics and costs in relation to fish hatcheries. *Trans. Am. Fish. Soc. 80:* 148–153.

Needham, Paul R.
1949. Survival of trout in streams. *Trans. Am. Fish. Soc. 77:* 26–31.

Randle, A. C., and F. K. Cramer
1941. The Squaw Creek test stream. *Calif. Fish and Game 27:* 172–184.

Schuck, Howard A.
1943. Survival, population density, growth, and movement of wild brown trout in Crystal Creek. *Trans. Am. Fish. Soc. 73:* 209–230.
1948. Survival of hatchery trout in streams and possible methods of improving the quality of hatchery trout. *Prog. Fish-Cult. 10:* 3–14.

Shetter, D. S.
1939. Success of planting fingerling trout in Michigan waters as demonstrated by marking experiments and creel census. *4th N. Am. Wildl. Conf.:* 318–325.
1947. Further results from spring and fall plantings of legal-sized hatchery-reared trout in streams and lakes of Michigan. *Trans. Am. Fish. Soc. 74:* 35–58.

Shetter, D. S., and A. S. Hazzard
1941. Results from planting marked trout of legal size in streams and lakes of Michigan. *Trans. Am. Fish. Soc. 70:* 446–467.
1942. Planting keeper trout. *Mich. Conservationist 11* (4).

Simon, J. R.
1949. Report of the division of fish culture. *Trans. Am. Fish. Soc. 76:* 398–399.

Smith, Lloyd L., Jr.
1941. The results of planting brook trout of legal length in the Salmon Trout River—Northern Michigan. *Trans. Am. Fish. Soc. 70:* 249–259.
1948. Effectiveness of modern fish management practices: Planting. *Proc. 38th Conv. Int. Assoc. Game, Fish and Cons. Comm.:* 42–48.

Surber, Eugene W.
1940. Lost: 10,839 fingerling trout! An appraisal of the results of planting fingerling trout in the St. Mary River, Virginia. *Prog. Fish-Cult. 49:* 1–13.

Taft, Alan C.
1947. Maintenance of angling in California. *12th N. Am. Wildl. Conf.:* 254–257.

Thorpe, Lyle M., A. J. Raynor, and D. A. Webster
1947. Population depletion in brook, brown and rainbow trout stocked in the Blackledge River, Connecticut, in 1942. *Trans. Am. Fish. Soc. 74:* 166–187.

Van Oosten, John
1942. Relationship between the plantings of fry and production of whitefish in Lake Erie. *Trans. Am. Fish. Soc. 71:* 118–121.

Westerman, F. A., and A. S. Hazzard
1945. For better fishing. *Mich. Conservationist 14:* 7–10.

Williamson, L. O., and E. Schneberger
1943. The results of planting legal-sized trout in the Deerskin River, Vilas County, Wisconsin. *Trans. Am. Fish. Soc. 72:* 92–96.

# 24 REGULATIONS AND THEIR EFFECT

## 24·1 Introduction

A disgruntled angler, throwing back a short fish after hours of effort, had an inspiration before tossing in the pole too. "Let's pass a law," he said. The attempt to manage fisheries by means of legislation has been going on for a long, long time. A few laws have been helpful, but probably the majority have had an adverse effect.

The difficulties are many and varied. Whenever a fishery reaches a low ebb or perhaps merely a low point in its natural variation there is apt to be a clamor for legislation. But in order to pass an intelligent law one must correctly diagnose the difficulty. Too often fishery laws are passed with utter disregard for the biology of the species, or even for the economics of the fishery. The fact that nothing tangible is known concerning a situation does not always deter legislators when a sufficient number of voters desire a law.

The purpose of this chapter is to discuss the various ways in which fisheries can be affected by legislation and the effects produced by different types of legislation. Fishery laws and fishery regulations are made by a number of agencies from the Federal Government and international commissions down to the selectmen of a New England village.

## 24·2 Purpose of fishery regulations

It is important to discuss the why of fishery regulations because they are often little understood. Many a fishery regulation masquerading as a conservation act is in reality merely another milepost in the internecine warfare between operators of different types of fishing gear, or between manufacturers who wish different sizes or time of harvesting for the raw product.

The purpose of any fishery regulation from a strictly conservation point of view is to provide for a more bountiful harvest of fish, in either volume or net value. However, the recent social and economic trends have so impinged upon the fisheries that conservation often plays a subordinate role. This discussion will be largely confined to

382

those types of regulations that may have an actual effect on the numbers of fish.

### 24·3   General types of regulations

Most regulations are based on the theory that the fewer the fish that are caught now, the more will be available for future fishing. This is not always true, but it has been so generally accepted for such a long time that it is engraved on the public mind.

The general theories on which most regulations have been based can be classified about as follows:

1. It is necessary to have a fairly large number of older fish for a spawning stock.

2. All smaller fish must be fully protected as the majority will grow into big fish.

3. It is very essential to protect fish during the spawning season.

It can easily be shown that none of these three theories is always correct. Thus number 1 may be true for a few species, such as salmon, in which the small number of eggs is fairly well protected so that a connection between spawners and progeny can be established. However, for many species that are extremely prolific but whose eggs are at the mercy of environmental conditions it has not been possible to establish such a connection, so that maintenance of a large stock of older fish may well represent a loss. We do not imply that there is no connection. However, there may be an upper limit beyond which additional spawning stock is of no advantage. At lower levels the connection may be so obscured by the varying effect of environmental factors that it cannot be shown without a long series of data encompassing both spawning stock and ecological factors. By means of multiple regression the concomitant effects of spawners and these other forces may be shown and the effect of the variation in number of spawners perhaps may be assessed.

Theory 2 is also under grave suspicion, especially in the sport fisheries. Many lakes suffer from overpopulation by sunfish or perch that are so stunted from competition for insufficient food that they never reach a respectable size. This often happens to trout in small cold ponds or cold spring-fed brooks.

Theory 3 may or may not be true according to circumstances. Thus, if the stock of mature fish is extremely low and the fish are (as is sometimes the case) particularly vulnerable to capture during the spawning period, protection may be justified. If the fish are not more vulnerable while spawning, little is gained usually by protection during the spawning season that could not be gained by reducing the catch during the remainder of the year.

How can regulations affect a species? Obviously only by causing some change in the predation practiced upon it by man, unless one includes the indirect consequences of man preying also upon a competitor or predator of the species.

In what manner can man's exploitation of a species be modified? According to circumstances it can be modified as follows:

1. The total quantity taken can be reduced or limited.

2. The catch can be taken from selected portions of the population (or certain portions can be protected against capture).

## 24·4  Classification of types of regulations

There are a circumscribed number of ways to achieve a limitation or reduction in the total catch of a species:

1. A limitation on the efficiency of the individual fishing unit.

2. A limitation on the number of fishing units permitted to operate.

3. A limitation (quota) on the total quantity of fish that can be captured.

Regulations designed to protect selected portions of the population may or may not result in any over-all reduction in catch. The regulations used to achieve this are:

4. Restrictions or modifications on the gear used in order to lessen catches of sizes or groups that it is desired to protect.

5. Closure of certain fishing areas.

6. Restriction of fishing to selected seasons.

7. Restrictions on the sizes, condition, or quantities that can be marketed.

8. Protection of individual fish based on sex or condition.

## 24·5  Limitations on efficiency of the fishing unit

This type of regulation always has been very popular. Part of its popularity emanates from its comparative ease of enforcement. Typical examples are the following:

**Restriction on the size or type of the fishing vessel.** Size may be based on over-all length, on keel length, or on net or gross tonnage. Thus, in Alaska salmon purse seiners have been restricted at times and places to a 50-foot keel length, and herring vessels fishing for bait during the winter have been restricted to 20 net tons. Salmon seiners have been built with a long overhang on the stern in order to gain size without exceeding a 50-foot keel.

Type of vessel may be governed by motor power, decking, etc. Thus the salmon gill netters in Bristol Bay have been restricted until very recently to the use of open vessels propelled only by oars or sail. On many lakes fishermen are restricted to rowboats. However, this last is as often from an aesthetic standpoint as from a desire to protect fish.

Regulating the size or type of fishing vessels is highly artificial and, like most gear regulations, increases costs of operation. When the product enters into competition with that from other regions or with other proteins, such restrictions may reduce the margin of profit.

**Restrictions on the type of gear used.** This is perhaps the most universal type of control. Its adoption does not always spring from true conservation principles but has its roots in social and economic trends. Very often it is based on the desire of a group using one type of gear to eliminate competition, either by reducing competition for the market or by increasing the quantity of fish available to themselves. The users of a less efficient form of gear often achieve their aims by pointing out the great destructiveness of the gear they wish to restrain. Although there are exceptions, such assertions are based usually merely on the efficiency of the gear and the fact (purely social in its implications) that ownership of the more efficient gear is not so widespread. Such assertions of restricted ownership are especially potent when used against fixed gear, where the operation of the gear depends on the ownership or exclusive use of the fishing site.

Examples of this sort of restriction are numerous. Thus the fish wheels on the Columbia River were eliminated by popular referendum. Established by the early pioneers, they have in recent years taken but a very small fraction of the total catch. However, because they were farther up the river than the other gear the argument was used that they were taking salmon that should be allowed to spawn. Obviously the major share of these salmon, on the same migration, were being taken down river by other gear. However, the popular conception of protecting a spawning fish (even though still a great many miles from the spawning grounds) was brought to bear against them. The real basis of the antagonism from other gear users was the vested right in fishing sites that were limited in number. They were also a convenient whipping boy for the reduction in the runs from other causes, one of which was overfishing in the lower river.

Owners of mobile gear used the same social arguments of high efficiency and restricted fishing sites to eliminate the salmon traps in

Puget Sound. There was some justice in the argument, because, although the law permitted only 3 traps per owner, this clause was largely avoided by dummy holding companies. Also the law obliged the licensee to actually construct and operate a trap at least once in every 4 years on any fishing site held (to permit taking advantage of the formerly dominant 4-year cycle in the abundance of the Fraser River sockeye salmon). Legally this was often complied with merely by constructing a dummy trap every 4 years, hanging it with wornout gear, and then lifting it once or twice during the season, with a total catch of perhaps a score or so of salmon. By these tactics the ownership of the trap sites actually, if not legally, was kept in the hands of a few companies. The chief popular argument used was the protection of the king and silver salmon (*Oncorhynchus tshawytscha* and *O. kisutch*) which were intensively sought by thousands of sport fishermen. Actually, the traps took only a very minor share of these two species, and then only on certain sites. The traps fished chiefly for the sockeye and pink salmon (*Oncorhynchus nerka* and *O. gorbuscha*) which are not sport species. Nevertheless the users of mobile gear, which take most of the sport species of salmon, enlisted the support of the sportsmen in eliminating the traps.

Restrictions on the type of gear permitted usually result in less efficiency in taking fish, thus increasing their cost. The arguments favoring regulations are largely social, although a highly efficient gear in a localized area may take too large a proportion of the population unless restraints are imposed.

**Restriction on the areas open to some types of gear.** Opening of a fishing area to one form of gear while banning another is usually based either on the high efficiency or on the actual or alleged destructiveness of the gear banned. On this basis, for example, purse seiners or otter trawlers are often banned from specified inshore areas that are fished by local fishermen or by sportsmen. Similarly, some streams and lakes are closed to all but fly fishing.

When the quantity of fish is strictly limited and the number of fishermen high, then prohibition of an efficient gear may result in more fish per unit to the less efficient gear. For a sport fishery in which the fisherman does not need to earn a livelihood such restrictions are sometimes desirable. For situations in which the fish are part of a large population the closing of a small area will merely be a nuisance to the gear banned. The fish will be caught outside the restricted area at greater cost to the fisherman. There is, however, the argument that the local abundance of the species will be temporarily higher, favoring the operations of less efficient gear.

**Bag limits.** A favorite regulation to restrict gear efficiency is the bag limit. This sets an arbitrary upper limit to the efficiency of an individual fishing unit. However, it has another effect; many a sport fisherman, pleasure-bound, has spent hours of fishing after he was tired and wet, because he wanted to take the limit. Because of human greed the bag limit on many species is here to stay, but it should be set low enough to be often attainable if it is to achieve any actual results.

Commercial fisheries are not usually subject to bag limits, but there are a few exceptions. In Rhode Island quahog dredges have been restricted to 30 bushels per day, and in Delaware commercial diggers have been allowed a daily bag of 1000 clams. Indirect limitations are more common. Thus, during the height of the run in the sardine and herring fisheries, the companies themselves must sometimes impose a limit on the take of the vessels since they can process only a given quantity of fish per day. Fishermen's unions have also at times restricted the pounds of fish or scallops per man that a vessel can land after each trip. The reasons may be twofold: to keep the price level high and to spread the work among the members of the union.

**Restriction on size of units of gear.** Aside from restrictions on fishing-vessel size, discussed above, the gear itself is often the subject of size regulation. Thus a purse seine may be limited in total length and sometimes in depth. Alaska herring seines for instance are limited to 180 fathoms in length and 1400 meshes in depth. Trolling boats that once used 6 to 8 lines are now limited usually to 4. Fixed gear is sometimes limited to a maximum depth of water; usually a minimum distance is required between successive units, and there may be a limitation on the length of trap leaders.

At times a minimum size of gear may be required. Thus, in Alaska salmon purse seines have a minimum size limit because a smaller-sized net would be too handy for use in robbing creeks of spawning salmon.

**Restriction on fishing time.** One purpose of fishing-time restrictions is to impair the efficiency of the individual units of fishing gear by cutting their time of operation. The other purposes of closed seasons will be discussed in a later section. The efficacy of this measure in actually reducing the catching power of an individual unit of fishing gear depends almost wholly on the relation between the closed season and the normal curve of seasonal availability of a species. If the season is closed for 6 months of the year during which only 10 per cent of the catch of a species is normally taken, then it can be expected to cut down the catch of each unit by not more than 10 per cent. In actual practice the maximum indicated cut is seldom obtained as during a long closed season the fishermen overhaul vessels and repair gear, starting the open season at peak efficiency. Also a closed season tends to be somewhat counterbalanced by fishing longer hours during the open season.

When a closed season does cover a substantial portion of the true fishing season the catch per unit of gear may be drastically cut, but even this does not always result in achieving the smaller total catch that it is intended to produce. The usual reaction of the operators is to increase the number of units of gear. The individual operator who runs a fish-processing plant may require a certain minimum volume of raw material. If the closed season reduces the volume that can be produced by the existing gear below this minimum economic requirement, his only recourse is to employ more units of gear. Thus a closed season may result in as great a catch as before, made at a higher cost to the producer.

For anadromous species of fish, such as salmon and alewives, the total fishing season is so short that a difference of only one or two weeks in the time of occurrence of the peak of the run will make a tremendous difference in the proportion of the run that will pass through the fishery before or after any fixed date set for a closed season. For this reason it has been found more practical in such fisheries to have many short closed seasons during the fishing season. These closed periods usually vary in length from 24 hours in some localities to 2 or 3 days in places where the fishery is very intense. Since the fish are migrating through the fishery and up the streams such periods guarantee the escape of a number of fish for spawning. In some long rivers in which fishing is permitted in the estuary, the weekly closed season is even staggered, commencing and ending earlier in the lower estuary than in the upper portion so that the migrating salmon will not escape the lower river nets only to be caught a few miles upstream.

Another ramification of the closed season occurs in parts of Alaska where the Fish and Wildlife Service maintains weirs to count the number of salmon that escape through the fishery and continue up the rivers to spawn. The White Act of 1924 provides that 50 per cent of the run shall be permitted to escape through the fishery to spawn. Therefore whenever the catch gets too far ahead of the weir counts, fishing is suspended until more salmon reach the weir. In practice this somewhat resembles the fixed quota system discussed in a later section.

## 24·6    Limitations on the number of fishing units

Another way to limit the catch without necessarily restricting the efficiency of each unit of gear is to limit the number of fishing units. Such a limitation on the number of persons permitted to fish has grave economic and political implications, but in some instances it has been achieved. For instance, the use of fixed gear gives the owner of a fishing site one of a limited number of such sites, and in some localities the practical exclusion of other forms of gear, either because of unfavorable conditions for their use or by regulation, has resulted virtually in the creation of a limited fishery.

In the salmon fisheries of Bristol Bay the number of units of gear, although under no legal restriction, has nevertheless been limited by the fact that the length of the weekly season closed to salmon fishing has been governed by the number of units of gear in operation. The salmon packers therefore gain nothing in quantity of fish landed but are under additional expense if they add more units of gear.

In Maine the number of lobster fishermen is kept in bounds by the requirement that a licensee must have been a resident of the state for at least 3 years (formerly 10 years). Because of the already intense fishery for lobsters and the great increase in licensees that would otherwise result each time the lobsters approached the peak of a cycle of abundance, this regulation serves as a protection to those who gain a permanent livelihood from the fishery. Without this restriction it might be necessary to limit the gear each individual could run to a point below that necessary to earn a living.

Another form of limited license is exemplified by many of the New England alewife fisheries. Most of these fisheries are the property of one or more towns bordering the stream. In a few instances residents of the town are permitted to fish, but more usually the alewives are sold in advance by auction and all fishing is conducted either by the town or by the successful bidder.

The most ambitious use of this form of restricted fishing has been by the state of Maryland and for this reason it is often called the Maryland plan. The arguments concering the merits and demerits of this plan are too lengthy to include here but are rather fully set forth by Herrington and Nesbit (1944).

One problem seldom mentioned in discussions of limited licensing is the fact that under such a system there is a tendency for each unit of gear to be fished over longer hours. In the Fraser River gill net fisheries the Japanese fishermen used to be limited to a specified total

number of licenses.  Each licensed vessel fished day and night with
the result that these limited licensees caught nearly twice as much
fish per license as the other fishermen.  If limited licensing results in
a greater abundance of fish the time must come when there will be
public clamor to issue more licenses.  Does the state then have to
decide what the income of a fisherman should be?

### 24·7    Limiting the total catch by the quota system

A third way to restrict the total catch without limiting either the
efficiency of the individual unit of fishing gear or the number of fishermen is to impose a limit on the total quantity that can be taken.

This method is suitable only for species about which enough biological knowledge has been accumulated to permit making a forecast
of their expected abundance sufficiently in advance of the fishing
season.

Such a forecast must be made within fairly narrow limits for the
method to be practical.  The reliability of the forecast depends on
several factors, including adequate annual sampling of the population.
If the sampling is adequate, then the variability in the forecast will
depend on the amount of variation in the annual mortality rates and
in the variations that may occur in the number of annual recruits to
the population.  Thus, if the adult population comprises fish of many
age groups the annual recruitment usually makes up a lesser proportion of the total population.  For species in which the annual success
of spawning exhibits wide variation the forecasts will usually be less
reliable.

A quota has been applied for several years to the fishery for Pacific
halibut (*Hippoglossus stenolepis*) in the eastern Pacific.  Each major
fishing area is assigned a quota in advance of the season, and when
the quota is nearly reached a closing date is set so that the catch will
come close to the quota set.

A similar system is employed under the International Whaling
Treaty whereby an annual quota of 16,000 blue whale units has been
set for the Antarctic whaling.  A blue whale is used as a unit and two
finner whales are counted as one blue whale unit.

The imposition of these catch quotas has indeed resulted in an increased abundance of halibut, but there have been other disquieting
consequences.  As the abundance of halibut increased the regular
halibut fleet was able to catch the quota in less time.  Also, as the
abundance increased, more and more vessels from other fisheries were
attracted into the halibut fishery, further shortening the season.
Whereas, at one time a fleet of halibut vessels fished throughout all

or most of the year, the total season in some areas is now about six weeks.

Ironically, in spite of the increased abundance of halibut, no fisherman can now make a living by halibut fishing. A further consequence has been to reduce greatly the season for fresh halibut on the market. The bulk of the catch must be frozen.

The quota system has been applied also to the Alaska herring fisheries but because of the biological differences between halibut and herring the forecasts of abundance are far less reliable so that the system is not yet a proved success.

A form of quota system (although not described as such) has long been in operation in the California sardine fisheries. This came about from the system of permitting only a portion of the catch to be used for reduction into oil and meal, the remainder having to be canned. Ostensibly aimed at preventing the reduction of valuable foodstuffs the actual purpose was to restrict the total sardine catch. In spite of these restrictions the catch grew. By using modern methods of handling, tremendous quantities were canned, sometimes at a slight loss, in order to obtain permits for the profitable reduction into oil and meal.

## 24·8   Protection of certain portions of a population by restrictions on gear

In many fisheries it has been deemed advisable to protect certain portions of the population. There is ample biological justification in some cases, whereas in others the facts are not so clear. Public sympathy for the protection of small-sized fish makes such regulations easy to pass, even when unsupported by biological evidence.

The advantage or disadvantage of protecting small fish must be weighed wholly by what happens to such fish and what losses may be incurred in extending such protection. If the group of young fish under consideration are growing with sufficient rapidity so that their continuous loss in total weight from natural causes of mortality is much more than compensated for by gain in their total weight on account of the increased size of the remaining individuals, protection assuredly pays, provided that they are subject to recapture at some time in the future. This is fully explained in Section 22·3.

The chief types of gear restrictions that are used to protect young fish (see Section 22·4) are:

1. Minimum-sized meshes in the cod ends of otter trawls.
2. Minimum-sized meshes in the "pots" or "spillers" of traps and

pound nets. This measure is also used in a mixed fishery to permit the escape of smaller-sized species.

3. Minimum spacing between the bottom and the first lath in lobster pots.

4. Use of minimum-sized hooks in hook-and-line fisheries.

5. Minimum-sized meshes in gill nets.

The protection of small fish should always be supported by evidence showing its advantage and the sizes that need protection. In a fishery of low intensity the protection should be removed at a smaller size than in one of high intensity because it takes a certain period of time to harvest a group of fish. The lower the rate of capture the longer the period of time that will elapse between the time when protection is removed and the time when the small fish are recaptured. There should then be an adjustment between the maximum size protected and the period of time required to recapture them so that they will be recaptured before they reach a size where their total gain in weight from growth is overbalanced by their total loss in weight from natural causes of mortality.

If fishing intensity is sufficiently low, no protection may be warranted. For example, the fishing pressure on sunfish, bluegills, perch, and other panfish in lakes is often too low to keep pace with their high reproductive capacity, and their abundance may be further augmented by the fishery removing large bass, pickerel, and other natural predators. As a result the numerous young fish outgrow their food supply. The solution in such cases is removal of as many of the small fish of these species as can be captured by any means, until a balance is again achieved between the fish and the available food.

### 24·9  Closure of certain fishing areas

Certain areas are often closed to fishing to achieve one or more of the following results:

1. To limit the total catch.

2. To protect fish on their spawning grounds.

3. To protect fish while migrating through areas of restricted extent where they are very vulnerable to capture.

4. To protect young fish on nursery grounds or areas.

5. To prevent harvesting and sale of shellfish contaminated by sewage pollution.

6. To prevent poisoning from mussels or other mollusks at times when routine tests show them to be dangerously toxic through the ingestion of certain plankton organisms.

The closure of certain areas to limit the total catch is not practiced to any degree. The closure of spawning grounds to fishing is almost universal for anadromous species. In the same way areas of lake shore are often closed to protect bass while spawning and guarding their nests.

The closure of limited areas to protect migrating fish is well illustrated in the salmon fisheries of Alaska, where no fixed gear is permitted within a mile of the mouth of most salmon streams, and none is permitted in most narrow passages either between islands or at the entrances to bays.

The closing of nursery areas to protect young fish is justified for species in which the young leave the protected areas as they grow larger (see Section 22·6). This is exemplified in the Pacific halibut fisheries by closure of an area off Cape Addington which has a heavy population of young halibut. In closing areas populated by small fish, first make certain that the small fish are young fish, not merely an overcrowded population of slow-growing older fish.

The unwitting protection of stunted fish may occur in lakes overcrowded with panfish, or in cold spring-fed brooks in which trout may be spawning at 3 or 4 inches in length and may seldom attain the usual legal size.

The necessary closing of shellfish areas because of sewage pollution represents a tremendous loss to the fisheries. As the public insists on more sewage treatment and clean bathing beaches these areas may eventually shrink.

## 24·10   Restriction of fishing to certain seasons

The closed season is a widely employed device with several purposes. Those already discussed above are:

1. To end fishing on attainment of a fixed quota.

2. To permit anadromous fish to escape through a zone of intense fishing.

3. To restrict the efficiency of the individual unit of gear by curtailing the time of operation.

Other purposes of closed seasons are:

4. To enhance the quality and value of the product by permitting fishing only when the fish are in prime condition. This is important to fisheries that produce oil and meal as the yield of oil is vastly greater during certain seasons. When official regulations are absent, operators of reduction plants have often themselves agreed on an

opening date for fishing to avoid fish of poor quality. The same reason, quality, is often the chief reason for the closing of fishing during spawning seasons.

5. To permit the taking of the major share of the catch after or toward the end of the growing season in order to gain considerable more poundage from the same group of fish than if the fishing season opened before the growing season.

6. To protect fish during the spawning season. Since fish are usually of poor quality at this time the closed season often serves a double purpose.

7. To prevent fishing during periods when the smaller fish are more vulnerable to the gear.

## 24·11   Regulations concerning sale

At times attempts are made to influence the catches by regulations concerning the sizes that can be legally marketed. Usually both catching and sale are regulated in such instances, but sometimes only the sale is prohibited. Regulations against the sale of undersized fish are a great incentive to the use of savings gear. Also the task of enforcing the use of savings gear is lightened when the sale of small fish is discouraged.

## 24·12   Protection based on sex or condition

Situations unique to some fisheries have caused restrictions based on the sex or condition of the individual. Thus the Dungeness crab (*Cancer magister*) of the Pacific Coast is usually protected during molting by regulations against taking "softshell" crabs. The female crab is also protected against possession and when taken must be released.

The female lobster (*Homarus americanus*) is usually protected when carrying eggs ("berried") and, as a rule, can either be returned immediately to the water or brought in unharmed and sold to the state. The state then returns the berried females to the water or retains them for propagation.

## 24·13   Effect of regulations on a mixed fishery

The above discussion has all been based on the effect of regulations on a simple one-species fishery. At one time each fishery depended primarily on a few species. As market demand increased beyond the limits of production attainable from varieties already exploited, more effort was expended in taking species hitherto largely ignored. The expanded markets stimulated the development of methods for utilizing species formerly not readily salable, either because of their ugly appearance, i.e., ocean pout; because of their rapid deterioration when shipped fresh, i.e., hake; or because of the difficulty of handling by the housewife, i.e., ocean perch. The production of frozen fillets by quick freezing methods has placed these species on the desirable list. Formerly most fishing vessels were built to engage in only one type of fishing, but recently vessels have been designed for speedy conversion from one type of gear to another.

Thus Pacific halibut long-line vessels once had a small cabin aft of amidships, hatches forward, and a high stern. Today they are built along the same lines as a purse seiner with a larger cabin forward, larger hatches for seine brailing, and lower stern to permit easier hauling of seines and installation of power-operated turntables. The loss in seaworthiness once given by the high stern and smaller cabin aft is partially regained by higher flaring bows. Such vessels purse-seine for salmon or herring, and long-line for halibut in the summers, purse-seine for sardines in the winter, with perhaps a few long-line trips for sablefish. The larger offshore salmon trolling vessels are adapted to gill netting for soupfin shark, and to long lining for halibut.

On the North Atlantic Coast the larger otter-trawl vessels once fished almost exclusively for haddock, taking other species only incidentally. Now they also fish for ocean perch (*Sebastes marinus*) and yellowtail flounder (*Limanda ferruginea*). The smaller vessels also fish extensively for whiting (*Merluccius bilinearis*) and pollock (*Pollachius virens*). Many of the otter-trawl vessels occasionally dredge for sea scallops. In the winter many of the northern vessels visit the New Jersey shore and the Virginia capes for scup and butterfish, and at times they make large catches of mackerel. Small inshore vessels that formerly dragged chiefly for winter flounders or blackbacks (*Pseudo-pleuronectes americanus*) now often fish for so-called "trash" species such as red hake (*Urophycis chuss*) and ocean pout (*Macrozoarces americanus*), and may dredge for black quahogs.

This continuing trend toward versatility in fishing vessels poses an increasing problem for the fishery administrator. Whenever protection is afforded one species, there is a tendency for the bulk of the released fishing effort to be thrown upon another species. Such trends have been long observed. For instance the Alaska herring purse seiners usually leave for the South earlier on the odd-numbered years to engage in the Puget Sound fishery for pink salmon. This intense odd-year purse-seine fishery for pink salmon also imposes a heavier strain on the late-running sockeye salmon passing through the same waters. Because of this versatility in the use to which fishing vessels may be put, all regulations should be made with a broad view of the fisheries as a whole, so that protection of one species does not put an undue strain on another.

# PART XI · PROBLEMS

# 25 · PROBLEMS

## 25·1  Abundance predictions

The problems that confront the fishery manager vary from region to region and from species to species, but some are rather general in their occurrence.  Perhaps the most valuable achievement of fishery research—and one of the more difficult to accomplish—is the ability to predict the abundance of fish populations.  For only a few species are predictions now sufficiently accurate for management purposes. For most species such forecasts must await a clearer knowledge of the relation of various environmental factors to the success of reproduction and survival.  Unfortunately most fishery investigators have lacked sufficient facilities to study adequately both the fish and its environment.

The evaluation of the effect of environmental factors is often difficult; occasionally one may be dominant, but usually several exert an influence, and there may be interaction among them.  When several factors are involved, such as temperature, space, and salinity, multiple regression is a powerful tool in determining the net effect of each independent variable.

All variables, however, do not exert an effect throughout their range of variation.  A typical example is afforded by the effect of the runs of pink salmon (*Oncorhynchus gorbuscha*) on the abundance of the runs of red salmon (*O. nerka*) of the Karluk River, Alaska.  Ordinarily, all of the Karluk River pink salmon spawn in the 20-mile stretch between Karluk Lake and a point where the river empties into a shallow lagoon that connects with Shelikof Strait (Barnaby 1944). However, on an occasional year when the pink-salmon cycle is approaching a peak, population pressure in the river becomes so great that hordes of pink salmon press on through Karluk Lake and invade the tributary streams.  Here they dig their redds in the same gravels in which the spring-running red salmon have already spawned, causing the death of millions of red-salmon eggs.  The quantitative evaluation

397

of the effect of such a variable with its discontinuous effect and its erratic appearance at an effective level poses no mean problem. Certainly no short-term program can cope with such erratic variables; yet, without their correct appraisal, what appears to be a safe prediction may go suddenly awry.

The above example points up the dangers inherent in reaching conclusions based on a short series of observations. The very existence of many important factors may be overlooked entirely unless a sufficiently long period of time is covered to permit most of the factors involved to fluctuate widely within their ranges of possible variation. Thus after several years of investigation it was decided that the annual abundance of mackerel (*Scomber scombrus*) of the Atlantic Coast could be forecast within fairly narrow limits, and several predictions did indeed satisfy this requirement (Sette 1931–1934). Then without warning the estimates fell far from their mark. The predictions had been based on the numbers of each year class of young mackerel in relation to the numbers of older mackerel (that comprised the bulk of the catch). The rather violent short-term fluctuations in the abundance of the older mackerel were found to depend on the relative size of the group of young mackerel that each year entered the catch for the first time. When a dominant year class of young mackerel from a very successful spawning became sufficiently old to be taken by the fishing gear, the over-all abundance would rise and remain high until this dominant group had diminished in numbers. Unfortunately, after the behavior of these dominant groups had been studied for several years and found to afford a basis for prediction, their behavior suddenly changed. Dominant groups expected to swell the catch of older fish at a future date would often fail to appear in following years. This destroyed the whole basis for prediction until such time as we can discover and evaluate the factor or factors responsible for these "transient" dominant year classes.

## 25·2  Natural balance

Reams of manuscript have been devoted to discussions of the balance of nature. Does this balance exist in fact or is it merely another chimerical hypothesis useful in explaining the inexplicable? If such a balance exists the classical concept surely must undergo drastic revision, for as our observations span increasing periods of time we are finding that biological conditions are far from stable. If one wishes to define "balance of nature" one must perforce define the time period involved. Climatic and hydrographic conditions exhibit long-term trends that exert tremendous influence on biological populations, so that a definition of balance would need to include a whole meteorological cycle, postulating that whenever the cycle returned to any particular starting point the populations would return to their preexisting balance.

The existence of such long-term cycles or trends in hydrographic conditions has become apparent. Europeans have discovered cycles of approximately 25 years in their cod fisheries, and 50 to 80 years in their herring fisheries (Ahlmann 1949, Lee 1949, Rollefsen 1949). Within the past few decades the waters of the Barents Sea between Norway and Spitzbergen have warmed several degrees. This warming of the Arctic has had a profound effect, especially in increasing the yield of the Arctic cod fisheries. It has also greatly extended the range of the cod along the shores of Greenland. Such hydrographic cycles may also account for the disappearance and reappearance, often for many years at a time, of the menhaden along the coast of Maine. Tully (1950) found a long-term increase in the mean annual sea temperature—between 1917 and 1940—in the Gulf of Georgia on the coast of British Columbia, an increase of about $3\frac{1}{2}°$ F. In Alaska, Muir Glacier in Glacier Bay retreated about 16 miles between 1892 and 1947, leaving behind a deep fjord.

Since, in reality, the balance of nature is undergoing constant change, one must be alert to the implications. Neither declines nor increases in abundance can be ascribed to man's activity without weighing these gradual natural changes. It is not necessarily true that populations return to their previous condition at the termination of a long climatic cycle. All reactions are not reversible. Once a predator, for instance, has extended its range we can only speculate whether a return to former climatic conditions will cause it to decline. If it can become adapted by evolutionary process to its new habitat it may well survive and become a permanent feature of the environment.

## 25·3  Environmental measurements

One workaday problem of fishery management is the obtaining of objective quantitative measurements of environmental factors, both physical and biological. As physical factors are usually the easiest to measure, much more information has been accumulated concerning them. Most lake surveys contain detailed information of the area, volume, temperature, and water chemistry of each depth layer, but the biological information is seldom as complete. Likewise, oceanographers chart the chemistry and the currents of the open seas but experience difficulty in obtaining accurate measurements of the living forms.

The measurement of the environment of moving waters is many times more difficult than that of waters in lakes or on the high seas. Because the hydrography of coastal and estuarine waters is so complex it has not received the attention it deserves as the most productive area for fisheries. Streams are even more difficult to study than the littoral waters, and the knowledge of stream limnology lags far behind that of lakes.

## 25·4  Genetics

How can we increase the annual harvest of fish from any body of water? In the preceding chapters we have outlined the progress in fertilization of waters to aid the supply of fish food, the control of undesirable species, and the methods of exploitation that will give the highest yields from a population. We have not touched upon changing the composition of the population itself through the development of superior strains of fish. Breeding has long been recognized as fundamental in horticulture, agronomy, and animal husbandry, but in fisheries it has been neglected. Even worse, fish of one species from whatever source have been planted indiscriminately, without thought or regard to their genetic characteristics. In agriculture different strains are developed for different soils and for different climates. Failure to observe the difference between varieties of fish of the same species has resulted in many failures of fish plantings. In the Fraser River watershed the planting in headwater streams of red-salmon fry derived from eggs of the lower-river races was a failure because the lower-river fish come of a race that develops only small quantities of fat for the short upstream migration required of the adults. When these lower-river fry were stocked in the upper river the young developed normally and migrated to the sea. The returning adults were caught in the commercial fishery at the mouth of the river, but none had enough stored energy to reach the headwaters. Transfers of headwater strains of red salmon to the lower-river tributaries, on the other hand, were successful.

Evidence is also accumulating that strains of wild trout are best adapted to their particular environment, especially in regard to temperature and $pH$, and do not thrive when transferred to radically different conditions. Fish genetics is a practically unexplored field, meriting intensive research.

## 25·5  Role of nutrients

The growth of phytoplankton can be increased by the addition of nutrient materials to water, but the effect of an increased abundance of phytoplankton on the ultimate productivity of the fisheries is not sufficiently understood. Nor is there sufficient knowledge of the kinds and amounts of nutrients necessary to produce different kinds and amounts of phytoplankton. That fertilization may not be an unmixed blessing is well illustrated by the fertilization of Moriches Bay and Great South Bay on Long Island, New York, by the effluent from millions of domestic ducks. These effluents, rich in phosphates, have resulted in tremendous abundance of a green Chlorella-like organism. Since this organism has become abundant the oysters in the area have become so thin and watery that they are unmarketable, resulting in tremendous losses.

The fertilization of shallow lakes in northern areas, which increases the growth of phytoplankton and other aquatic vegetation, has often contributed to winter depletion of dissolved oxygen, resulting in winter-kill of fish. Except for its use in the small farm pond, fertilization of water for fish production is still in an experimental stage and requires a great deal of basic research before becoming a standardized operational procedure.

## 25·6   Estuarine ecology

Where the seas meet the land, they are productive. Here the nutrients carried by the rivers and washed in by heavy rains enrich the euphotic zone (Riley 1937). The fishes of this zone are often subjected to wide fluctuations in temperature and salinity. The most striking example is afforded by the long narrow bays that fringe the northern and western shores of the Gulf of Mexico behind low barrier islands. Only a few narrow passes connect these shallow bays with the Gulf of Mexico. Because of the few passes and the small tidal range there is poor interchange of bay and gulf waters. (Hedgpeth 1947). When the rivers are in flood the salinities fall until many of the bays are sometimes practically fresh for months at a time. Many of these bays have an average salinity of 15 to 20‰ compared to about 34‰ or higher in the Gulf. Flood-control dams under construction and planned will aid in narrowing this range of fluctuation in salinity.

By contrast the Laguna Madre, extending for 115 miles along the southern coast of Texas, is bothered by high salinities. No rivers enter the Laguna, and the only remaining connection with the gulf is through Corpus Christi Bay to the north. Strong winds occasionally raise the high tides sufficiently to aid in keeping up a nominal exchange of bay and gulf water, but every few years the salinities rise to 60‰ and above, occasionally reaching as high as 100‰. Above the critical point (about 72‰, Gunter 1945) fish die by the thousands. The Laguna only averages about 9 inches to 4 feet in depth with occasional deep holes, and the other bays are not much deeper. When a cold "norther" springs up suddenly in winter, great numbers of cold-sensitive fish often succumb before they can reach deep water.

## 25·7 Interspecific relations

Although the relations between a fish population and the populations of other fishes in its environment are of great importance, information on the subject is fragmentary. Responsibility for this lack of knowledge is traceable to the manner in which most fishery investigations have been organized. Appropriations usually have been made for the study of individual species rather than for the study of whole fisheries or the study of the fisheries of regions. As a result we have a great deal of detailed information on many individual species, but not sufficient information on their biological environment. Attempts are being made to remedy this situation by determining simultaneously the abundance of the various species of an area. An illustration of the importance of this knowledge is furnished on Georges Bank off the New England coast. Certain areas of the southwest portion of the bank once furnished good haddock fishing, but haddock have been practically absent from these areas since about 1928. Later these same areas were heavily populated by yellowtail flounder (*Limanda ferruginea*). More recently the yellowtail flounder have become scarce, and the area is heavily populated with red hake (*Urophycis chuss*). This poses several questions. Do these changes represent an ecological succession? Do they represent the shifts that take place in accordance with long period changes in hydrographic conditions? Are these changes more or less permanent or are they reversible?

Perhaps the most important question relates to the total productivity of the bank. Does an area like Georges Bank tend to produce annually the same poundage of fish, making up for a decline in one species by an increase in another? These questions are fundamental to fishery management, and the answers can be obtained only from the over-all studies of the bank now being pursued.

More information on this subject is available for smaller bodies of water. Thus in Cultus Lake, British Columbia, the survival of salmon (*Oncorhynchus nerka*) to the smolt stage was approximately doubled by reducing the numbers of predator and competitor species (Foerster and Ricker 1941). However the total weight of the salmon smolts in each annual migration appears to approach an asymptote so that when the numbers are larger the weight of the individual smolt is smaller (Foerster 1944, Rounsefell 1946). This supports the hypothesis that the total fish production of any body of water is limited under any particular set of conditions.

Despite the excellent progress in fishery management over the past few decades we have only begun to grapple with many of the most important problems. This is largely because fishery investigations, to be fruitful, must be carried on consistently over a long period of time. Few organizations are able to conduct or have conducted uninterrupted studies with sufficient detail to obtain the basic data required to solve some of the more difficult problems.

## References

Ahlmann, H. W.
    1949. Introductory address. I. Climatic changes in the Arctic in relation to plants and animals. *Rapp. et Proc.-Verb. 125*, Sec. I: 9–16.

Barnaby, Joseph T.
    1944. Fluctuations in abundance of red salmon, *Oncorhynchus nerka* (Walbaum) of the Karluk River, Alaska. *U. S. Fish and Wildl. Serv., Fish. Bull. 50* (39):237–295.

Foerster, R. Earle
    1944. The relation of lake population density to size of young sockeye salmon (*Oncorhynchus nerka*). *J. Fish. Res. Bd. Canada 6* (3):267–280.

Foerster, R. Earle, and William E. Ricker
    1941. The effect of reduction of predaceous fish on survival of young sockeye salmon at Cultus Lake. *J. Fish. Res. Bd. Canada 5* (4):315–336.

Gunter, Gordon
    1945. Some characteristics of ocean waters and Laguna Madre. *Texas Game and Fish 3* (11):7, 9, 21–22, October.

Hedgpeth, Joel W.
    1947. What happens in the Laguna Madre. *Texas Game and Fish 5* (4):14–15, 30, March.

Lee, A. J.
    1949. The forecasting of climatic fluctuations and its importance to the Arctic fishery (with an extensive bibliography). *Rapp. et Proc.-Verb. 125*, Sec. IB (5):40–52.

Riley, Gordon A.
    1937. The significance of the Mississippi River drainage for biological conditions in the northern Gulf of Mexico. *J. Mar. Res. 1* (5):60–74.

Rollefsen, Gunnar
    1949. Fluctuations in two of the most important stocks of fish in northern waters, the cod and the herring. *Rapp. et Proc.-Verb. 125*, Sec. IB (3): 33–35.

Rounsefell, George A.
    1946. Fish production in lakes as a guide for estimating production in proposed reservoirs. *Copeia*, 1946 (1):29–40.

Sette, Oscar E.
    1931–34. Outlook for the mackerel fishery. *U. S. Bur. Fish., Fish. Circ. 4, 10, 14* and *17*.

Tully, John P.
    1950. Seasonal cycles in the sea. *Fish Res. Bd. Canada, Prog. Rept. Pacific 85:* 88–90.

# APPENDIX

## FISHERY JOURNALS

The appended list of organizations and the journals they publish is not intended to be complete, but it contains the majority of the regular serials in which articles on fishery research occupy a large portion of the space. It is given to aid students and others in library browsing:

*American Fisheries Society*
Transactions, Annual (Chiefly freshwater management)

*American Society of Ichthyologists and Herpetologists*
Copeia, Quarterly (Taxonomic, occasional research paper)

*Australia*
Commonwealth Scientific and Industrial Research Organization, Division of Fisheries
Australian Journal of Marine and Freshwater Research

*British Columbia*
Department of Fisheries
Report, Annual (Marine, anadromous and shellfish)

*California*
Department of Fish and Game
California Fish and Game, Quarterly (Wide range, excellent quality)
Bureau of Marine Fisheries, Bulletin (Marine and shellfish)

*Canada*
Department of Fisheries
Canadian Fish Culturist, Quarterly (Freshwater management)
Fisheries Research Board
Bulletin (Wide range, technical presentation)
Journal, Annual (Wide range, shorter articles)
Progress Reports: Pacific Coast Stations and Ibid., Atlantic Coast Stations, Quarterly (Current work)

*Denmark*
Danish Biological Station, Reports (Marine, excellent ecological work)
Medd. Komm. Danmarks Fisk. og Havunders., Ser. Fiskeri (Marine and anadromous)

*Eire*

Department of Agriculture, Fisheries Branch
  Reports (Chiefly salmon fisheries)

*Food and Agricultural Organization of the United Nations*
  Fishery Bulletin

*France*

Office Scientifique et Technique des Pêches Maritimes
  Revue des Travaux
  Memoires

*Germany*

  Archiv für Hydrobiologie. Stuttgart.
  Deutsche Wissenschaftliche Kommission für Meeresforschung. Berichte.
    Stuttgart.
  Helgoländer Wiss. Meeresuntersuchungen. Helgoland.
  Internationale Revue der gesamten Hydrobiologie und Hydrographie.
    Liepzig.
  Mitt. Inst. Seefischerei. Hamburg.

*Great Britain*

Marine Biological Association of the United Kingdom
  Journal (Basic life history material)
Ministry of Agriculture and Fisheries.  Fishery Investigations
  Series I—Freshwater (Largely salmon and sea trout)
  Series II—Marine (Quantitative approach)
Colonial Office
  Fishery Publications

*Illinois*

Natural History Survey
  Biological Notes
  Bulletin (Stream and lake management)
  Circular

*Indiana*

Department of Conservation.  Division of Fish and Game.
  Investigations of Indiana lakes and streams.

*International Council for the Study of the Sea*
  Journal du Conseil, Quarterly (Excellent, wide range)
  Rapports et Procès-Verbaux
  Annales Biologiques

*International Fisheries Commission (U. S. and Canada)*
  Report (Halibut investigations in the Pacific)

*International Pacific Salmon Fisheries Commission*
  Report (Fraser River salmon investigations)
  Bulletin

*Maryland*

Chesapeake Biological Laboratory, Solomons Island
  Publications

*Miami, University of*

Marine Laboratory
  Proceedings of the Gulf and Caribbean Fishery Institute

*Michigan*

Department of Conservation, Institute for Fisheries Research.
  Bulletin (Excellent for freshwater fishery management)
  Miscellaneous Publications

*Minnesota*

Department of Conservation, Fisheries Research Laboratory
  Technical Bulletin (Especially good for stream improvement)

*New York*

Conservation Department
  Fishery Research Bulletin
  New York State Biological Survey.  Bulletin (Stream Surveys)

*New Zealand*

Marine Department
  Fisheries Bulletin

*North American Wildlife Conference*

  Transactions (Wide range, short articles, not too technical)

*Norway*

Norwegian Fishery and Marine Investigations
  Report (Excellent basic material on populations)

*Ohio*

Department of Conservation
  Bulletin
Ohio State University Bulletin.  Ohio Biological Survey
  Bulletin

*Oregon*

Oregon Fish Commission
  Contributions (Chiefly anadromous)

*Quebec*

Department of Fisheries
  Contributions (Marine fish and mammals, salmon, etc.)
  Station Biologique Saint-Laurent.  Reports

*Scotland*

Fishery Board for Scotland
  Salmon Fisheries
  Scientific Investigations

*Sears Foundation*
Journal of Marine Research, Quarterly

*South Africa*
Fisheries and Marine Biological Survey
Investigational Reports

*Spain*
Institute Español de Oceanografia
Bulletin (Sardine life history)

*Stanford University*
Ichthyological Bulletin (Chiefly, but not exclusively, taxonomic)

*Sweden*
Fishery Board
Institute of Freshwater Research. Drottningholm (Freshwater management)
Institute of Marine Research. **Lysekil**

*Texas, University of*
Institute of Marine Science
Publications

*Toronto, University of*
University of Toronto Studies. Fisheries Research Laboratory
Publications (Basic life history material)

*United States*
Department of the Interior, Fish and Wildlife Service
Fishery Bulletin (Results of research)
Research Report (Shorter or less technical research)
Progressive Fish-Culturist (Freshwater management)
Special Scientific Reports: Fisheries (Processed for speed of publication, or bulk, or ephemeral quality)
Fishery Leaflets (Processed, used especially for answering correspondence)

*Washington*
Department of Fisheries
Report
Biological Bulletin (Shellfish, salmon, marine research)

*Washington, University of*
Fisheries Research Institute
Publications (Salmon research)

*Wildlife Society*
Journal of Wildlife Management (Wide range, well edited)

*Yale University*
Peabody Museum of Natural History. Bingham Oceanographic Foundation
Bulletin (Quantitative marine fisheries)

# GLOSSARY

*Abdominal vertebrae.* The anterior vertebrae without haemal spines.

*Abundance.* This word is used in fisheries to denote the relative numbers. Thus the level of abundance may be high or low.

*Abyssal.* Refers to the great ocean depths; also the fish inhabiting them.

*Acre-foot.* Volume of water required to cover an acre one foot in depth, or 43,560 cubic feet.

*Anadromous.* Up running; refers to fishes that leave seas and ascend streams to spawn.

*Annulus.* The annual mark or zone on the scales, vertebrae, or other hard portion of a fish, which is formed once each year.

*Anoxemia.* Pathological condition resulting from a lack of sufficient oxygen.

*Archibenthic.* Refers to forms inhabiting the sea bottom below the edge of the continental shelf.

*Asymptote.* A line that a curve approaches without ever attaining, as one function of the curve approaches infinity. The line approached, as the tangent to a curve receding indefinitely from the origin approaches a limiting position.

*Adfluvial.* To the streams: refers to lake-dwelling fishes that ascend streams to spawn.

*Basal metabolism.* The amount of metabolism necessary to sustain life without growth.

*Bathypelagic.* Refers to intermediate ocean depths, also the fish inhabiting them.

*Benthic.* Refers to bottom-living forms on the continental shelf.

*Benthopelagic.* Refers to fishes that seasonally inhabit both the bottom and the surface layers.

*Bioassay.* The determination of the effect of any material on living organisms by testing it against living organisms under standardized conditions.

*Biological indicators.* Organisms that by their presence (or absence) tend to indicate environmental conditions.

*Biomass.* The total quantity of living material in any particular body of water.

*Biometry.* The use of statistical methods to solve biological problems.

*Carrying capacity.* Usually considered to be the maximum quantity of fish that any particular body of water can support over a long period. Temporary carrying capacity may be much higher, and this is taken advantage of in stocking waters subject to heavy fishing.

*Catadromous.* Down running; refers to fishes, of which the true eel (*Anguilla*) is the classic example, that spawn in the sea, but live a large portion of their existence in fresh waters.

*Caudal vertebrae.* Posterior vertebrae bearing haemal spines.

*Coastal.* Refers to fishes that never stray far from shore.

*Competition.* The indirect effect (excluding predation) that one species may have on another through utilization of food, space, dissolved gases, spawning beds, etc.

*Competition between units of fishing effort.* Effect on the catch of the individual unit of fishing effort caused by changes in the total number of units operating.

*Continental shelf.* Shallow waters that surround the continents. The shallow shelf usually ends and the bottom slopes steeply toward the deeper ocean bottoms at about 100 to 150 fathoms, but the depth varies somewhat in different regions.

*Controls.* In making a bioassay or other experiment, the controls are fish subjected to all of the experimental conditions except the toxic substance, or condition, being tested.

*Correlation.* The degree of interdependence of two variables.

*Creel census.* A canvass of anglers to gather data on their catches, time spent in fishing, etc.

*Ctenoid scale.* A teleost scale possessing small sharp spines or ctenii.

*Cultch.* Shells or other material, spread on oyster grounds, on which the oyster larvae can attach and develop into spat.

*Cycloid scale.* A teleost scale without spines or ctenii.

*Demersal.* On the bottom; also applied to fish eggs that are spawned on or sink to the bottom where they hatch.

*Dromous.* Running; a term applied to fish that are compelled by their life histories to spend a portion of their existence in a marine environment and a portion in fresh waters.

*Ecology.* The interrelations between living organisms and their environment.

*Efficient comparison (method, statistic).* Use of a method which utilizes most of the information contained in the data.

*Egg pit.* One of the small holes within a redd in which spawn is deposited. A redd often contains several egg pits.

*Endemic.* Native to the locality.

*Epilimnion.* The layer of water above the thermocline in stratified lakes. Sometimes used to denote the total volume of lakes without a thermocline.

*Escapement.* For runs of anadromous or adfluvial species, the portion of the population that escapes past the fishing gear to migrate upstream toward the spawning grounds.

*Estuarine.* Refers to estuaries, also to fishes very tolerant of salinity changes that live chiefly in estuaries.

*Euphotic zone.* The upper layers of water in which the light is sufficient for photosynthesis.

*Eutrophic.* Refers to a type of lake characterized by a high ratio of volume of epilimnion to hypolimnion, a high rate of sedimentation, and high productivity.

*Eutrophication.* The process whereby deep clear lakes of low productivity gradually become shallower and more productive, eventually filling up completely and becoming dry land.

*Extrapolate.* To project a curve (function) beyond the range of the observed co-ordinates.

*Fluvial.* Pertaining to streams; also to fishes that live their entire life in moving fresh waters.

*Fluvial anadromous.* Referring to anadromous fishes whose life histories are not normally dependent on the presence of lakes in the streams that they ascend to spawn.

*Food chain.* The successive stages from the bacteria and phytoplankton that can utilize inorganic dissolved nutrients (the base of the food chain or pyramid), to the zooplankton, insect larvae, and some fishes that devour them, up to the larger fish that may exist principally by preying on other fishes.

*Forage fish.* Fish, usually smaller species, that are important as food for other species.

*Forebay.* The impounded waters just above a dam.

*Gillraker.* One of a number of hard projections on the anterior edge of each gill arch.

*Gonad.* A general term including both ovaries and testes.

*Gravid fish.* Fish with mature gonads.

*Grilse.* A precocious salmon or anadromous trout that has matured at a much smaller size (and usually younger age) than that of the fully grown adult fish.

*Groundfish.* Marine fishes living on or near the bottom; a term applied especially in New England to fish usually taken by otter trawls or line trawls.

*Haemal arch.* The passage ventral to the vertebral column carrying the dorsal aorta that is formed by the haemapophyses.

*Hypolimnion.* The water mass below the thermocline. In lakes of sufficient depth the water tends to become stratified in summer, with a lower layer or hypolimnion.

*Hypural.* A flattened plate to support the rays of the caudal fin, that may be formed from one or more vertebrae.

*Interorbital width.* The measurement between adjacent edges of the eye sockets.

*Kelt.* A mature salmon that has spawned and has not yet recovered its weight or silvery color.

*Lacustrine.* Pertaining to lakes; also to fishes that live their entire life in quiet waters (lake dwelling).

*Lacustrine anadromous.* Refers to anadromous fishes that normally ascend streams with lakes to spawn, as the young dwell in lakes.

*Linear relation.* When changes in a variable that are associated with changes in another variable do not differ significantly from a straight line.

*Littoral zone.* The shallow area near the shore.

*Mean lethal dose.* The dose of a toxic substance under which, on the average, 50 per cent of the test animals succumb. Also given as $LD_{50}$.

*Meristic.* Pertaining to the segmentation of the body (metameres).

*Mesotrophic (dystrophic).* Descriptive of a type of lake more or less intermediate in characteristics between oligotrophic and eutrophic.

*Microhabitat.* A subhabitat within a major habitat. Thus the pools may be classed as microhabitats within the streams.

*Morphometric.* Pertaining to measurements of body proportions.

*Oceanic.* Pertaining to oceans; also to fishes that inhabit the surface waters of the oceans far from land.

*Oligotrophic.* Descriptive of a type of lake characterized by a low ratio of volume of epilimnion to hypolimnion, by low rate of sedimentation, and by low productivity.

*Overfishing.* Fishing with a sufficiently high intensity, or sufficiently high on certain portions of a population, to reduce the continuous annual surplus that it should be capable of producing. Any fishing whatsoever reduces the numbers of a population, but all populations exhibit a greater or lesser degree of resistance through such means as increased rates of growth and greater survival of young to the adult stage. Only when fishing reduces a population below the point where the forces of resistance balance fishing intensity can there be said to be overfishing.

*Overpopulation.* A level of abundance so high as to militate against future abundance, or actually to invite self-destruction.

*Overturn.* The mixing of the waters of a lake in the temperate zone when the summer thermal stratification ends. As water reaches its greatest density at 4° C, the water sinks as it cools until the lake is practically all at or about 4° C before the surface commences to freeze. Most northern lakes also experience a spring overturn. As the water warms to 4° C, the wind tends to mix the surface with the deeper waters. This is the time at which these lakes normally obtain their summer oxygen. When the water warms rapidly in the absence of sufficient wind there may be little or no spring overturn.

*Oviparous.* Refers to fishes that reproduce by eggs that are hatched externally.

*Ovoviviparous.* Refers to fishes, reproducing by eggs hatched internally, that receive no nourishment from the parent.

*pH.* Hydrogen-ion concentration. It is expressed as the reciprocal of the common logarithm of the hydrogen-ion concentration in gram equivalents per liter. Thus $pH$ equals 7 means that the hydrogen-ion concentration is $10^{-7}$ or $1/10^7$ or $1/10,000,000$ or $0.000\,000\,1$ normal. $pH$ equals 7 is approximately neutral, a lower value of the $pH$ means increasing acidity, a higher value increasing alkalinity.

*Parameter.* A quantity that specifies a certain characteristic of the hypothetical (or true) population from which samples are drawn. Thus the arithmetic mean and the standard deviation are two statistics of a sample from which one may estimate the ranges in which the mean and standard deviation of the true population lie. The latter two values are parameters.

*Parr.* Young freshwater-living salmon or anadromous trout that have not yet begun their migration to the sea. Usually distinguishable by bright colors and darker bars or "parr" marks that are later hidden by the scales as they become silvery.

*Pelagic.* Pertaining to the ocean; also to fishes inhabiting surface layers that are not confined to the offshore waters.

*Penstock.* The tube or tunnel carrying water to a turbine.

*Phytoplankton.* The plant constituents of plankton, such as diatoms.

*Piscivorous.* Fish-eating.

*Plankton.* Organisms that float more or less passively in the water, such as jellyfishes, diatoms, eggs and larvae of fishes and invertebrates, many protozoans and small invertebrates, and bacteria.

*Population pressure.* The condition of excessive numbers in relation to the space occupied. This may cause migration (presumably to readjust the numbers of individuals per unit of space).

*Population.* A stock or race of fish that exists as a biological unit.

*Production (Yield).* The annual harvest of desirable species from any particular body of water.

*Productivity.* Yield, either in the general sense of fish harvest, or in the more specialized usage of the limnologists, denoting the annual production of the basic food substance, plankton, in any particular body of water.

*Race.* A term used by taxonomists to denote a subspecific difference between two populations.

*Random.* Without choice. Thus random samples are taken in such a manner that every fish in a group being sampled has an equal chance of being included in the sample.

*Recruits.* The younger fish that each year are added to the portion of the population vulnerable to the fishery.

*Redd.* (See also Egg pit.) The spawning nest which is excavated in the gravel or stones of the stream bed, filled with the eggs, and then partially refilled with coarse stones. Applied especially to the nests of the Salmonidae.

*Regression.* The degree in which one variate, termed the dependent variate (usually designated as $y$), changes with changes in another variate, termed the independent variate (usually designated as $x$).

*Replication.* The repetition of each independent unit of an experiment two or more times in order to determine the experimental and random errors, which are needed in order to judge the significance of the results of a test.

*Reproductive potential.* The potential number of fish that will attain maturity from the spawning of each adult. Obviously, the long-term average cannot exceed 1.0, but it varies both with environmental conditions and with the size of the population itself, tending to increase as the size of the population decreases. It is this fact that permits the taking of large numbers of fish without inevitably causing depletion.

*Residual variation.* The amount of variation in a dependent variate that is unaccounted for after the variation caused by one or more independent variates has been removed.

*Secchi disk.* A disk 20 cm in diameter with two white and two black quadrants. It is lowered into the water, and the average of the distance below the surface at which it disappears from sight and the distance at which it reappears while being hauled back is used as a rough index of turbidity.

*Sigmoid curve.* An S-shaped curve.

*Significance.* This term is reserved for the statement of a rigorous statistical test. When the probability of the occurrence of a particular event is 1 in 20 or less ($P = 0.05$) the probability is termed significant. When the probability is 1 in 100 or less ($P = 0.01$) it is termed highly significant.

*Standing crop.* The total quantity of fish (or plankton) present in any body of water at any particular moment.

*Tailrace.* The portion of a stream just below a dam; specifically, the water flowing from the draft tubes of a turbine.

*Teleost.* Any one of the bony fishes or Teleostomi.

*Test animals.* Animals selected for making bioassays.

*Thermocline.* The thin layer of water lying between the warmer surface layer or epilimnion, and the cooler bottom layer or hypolimnion in a stratified lake. It is characterized by a rapid change in temperature of 1° C or more per meter of depth. A somewhat similar change in temperature occasionally found in the sea is sometimes called a thermocline.

*Viviparous.* Pertaining to fishes that extrude living young as opposed to those that extrude eggs.

*Yield.* (See Production.)

*Zooplankton.* The animal constituents of plankton, such as the small crustaceans.

# INDEX